ALL THE MOONLIGHT ON EARTH

JESSE
MUEHLBAUER

ALL THE
MOONLIGHT
ON
EARTH

A Novel

www.JesseMuehlbauer.com

Published by Allaire Publishing, LLC.
Milwaukee, Wisconsin
www.AllairePublishing.com

ISBN: 979-8-9854935-2-8 (Softcover)

Edited by Christine Vassos
Cover design and interior layout by MiblArt

Printed in the United States of America

For Poe, John, and Lindsey.
Heroes in this world.

"We shall not cease from exploration,
and the end of all our exploring,
will be to arrive where we started,
and know the place for the first time."

— T.S. Eliot

CHAPTER 1

ORTELIUS

Cate jumped, you fool.

Gillen Rainer bristled as the memory struck him. The thought clouded his vision as he stood at the crowded intersection while awaiting his turn to cross, seemingly oblivious to the droplets of rain which were pelting away at his overcoat. Dusk had been rapidly gaining ascendancy over the skyline, leaving the city below it in a rush to conclude the day. Those shackled to unrelenting deadlines or unexpected projects were easily spotted in their fluorescent offices throughout the downtown skyscrapers. The lights emitting from their windows beaconed as a public declaration of either their pride in working too hard or else their punishment for not working hard enough.

Incongruous to the rain falling from above, the last remaining remnants of the sun could still be seen off in the sky, melting into a parapet of clouds along the horizon and leaving behind fiery streaks of amber. Gillen shifted his focus across the visual panoramic until his eyes locked onto a totemic image. It was the emblem of the city in which he lived. Pinnacled high above the nestled streets, was a structure massive enough to be seen from across the city, its orange stanchions ablaze in the sun's leftover light. The Golden Gate Bridge stood motionless, impervious to either the wind or the swells, breathtaking in its scope, hypnotic in its allure.

There's nothing worse than loss...

A raindrop smacked Gillen's forehead and zigzagged its way down his face as he approached another intersection. Rows of vehicles lined the streets, moving at sporadic intervals, much like a malfunctioning assembly line. At the crosswalk, a man standing next to Gillen was mumbling, to no one in particular, within the cluster of pedestrians awaiting their turn to cross. A transistor radio in his hand was set to its highest volume, yet the noise emitting from the device took concentration to perceive. It was the sound of telemetry coming from the first manmade satellite to ever orbit the planet, and its steady, insistent beep was rapidly unnerving a nation.

"Are you feeling all right?" he recalled himself once asking Cate, the words manifesting from a memory unfiltered by time. He had stepped out of the town car and offered his wife his hand. Cate's heel made contact with the sidewalk, and for a moment, she hesitated, seeming to adjust to the environment of the city. She had reached for Gillen's extended hand and gave it a significant pull as she stood upright and breathed in the brisk evening air. As the town car slowly pulled away she had responded, "Don't worry about me."

From a streetlamp, a sphere of halogen flickered to life above his head, dissipating both the darkness and the memory. In the present, a woman standing next to him held an evening edition with large bold letters declaring the headline, "U.S. Stunned - A Startling Weekend as Sputnik Orbits the Globe", which he did not register, and in much smaller font, the date, which he did.

It was October 7th, 1957.

Gillen gave a firm tug at his collar as the crosswalk signal changed. He quickly moved forward, passing the windows of small shops, the glass portraits offering a momentary glimpse of merchant life within. On the sidewalk, he witnessed people weaving around each other, their faces etched with the sort of malcontent expressed when either trying to leave a place or else when dreading the destination.

It had been a waxing crescent moon the evening Gillen and Cate had walked along the city streets together, her hand gently enveloped by his. The act of lifting his head had brought a relief to his mind.

"It's going to be a good night," he had said to Cate. "You're going to be amazed."

"I'm sure I will be," she had said.

Cate had crossed her arms against her torso and silently winced as the next intersection signal changed. She started forward with Gillen, but hesitated in the middle of the crosswalk taking a glance backward at an analog street clock which also displayed the date.

It had been October 7th, 1956.

Once again pulled from his reverie, a familiar bell rung out across the street and another fixture of the city approached. Gillen stepped from off the curb and skillfully leapt onto the cable car's running boards as it passed, his left hand gripping tightly the passenger bar, his right clutching the handle of his briefcase.

He drew in a quick breath and closed his eyes as the breeze caressed his cheeks and hair. These motions had become second nature to him, a familiarity for which he was grateful. Seated adjacent to where he was standing, a man he had seen on this car with some frequency sat cross-armed within the layers of his jacket, appearing as if he wanted to vanish within the folds. The woman next to him was also a regular on this route, a jovial, chatty sort of persona, having suddenly been replaced by her mute doppelgänger, the rim of her hat slanted downward toward her face protecting her thoughts.

Gillen looked away from the passengers and out at the neighborhoods they were sailing past. Blocks of diners, markets, and dime stores, interspersed with multi-story Victorian row houses lined each street, giving the city a recognizable distinction within the sections of town. Bay windows on the upper and lower floors pushed out the left side of the homes, while the flight of stairs leading to the front entry doors on the right gave the buildings a balanced aesthetic.

Inside the panes of glass Gillen would regularly witness people living their lives. Families, couples, singles, all existing from day-to-day, many of them riders of the very cable cars and yet oblivious to them the moment they entered the worlds they had created for themselves within their quiet homes. As the cable car moved up the graded street, Gillen gazed into the bay windows and found a subdued existence, little movement, and silhouettes crackling with the kind of trepidation that came from absorbing televised light.

"This is going to change the world," Walter Iselin thundered the evening Gillen and Cate had entered the private observation tower. The room had been circular, with window walls the only partition between the guests and the city of San Francisco. On the ride up to the top, Gillen and Cate watched as their reflections in the elevator glass gazed back at them. The man was nearly forty, with dark brown hair and the kind of gray eyes that appeared to see through people, and the woman was close in age, with platinum blonde hair and sea-green eyes, the kind which always appeared fatigued yet not in the way that would be helped by a good night's rest.

"Is that your investor pitch, Walter?" Gillen had joked, foregoing a handshake in lieu of a hug.

"I thought it was less cliché than 'let's put a man on the moon.'"

"I assure you, it's not."

Walter had turned to embrace Cate as the silver of his hair reflected the lights. "Hello, darling. Thanks for joining us. I trust you're doing well?"

Cate returned the embrace with abandon. "Hello, Walter. I'll be all right. Just feeling the buildup to this day."

The cable car bell struck the intersection like a gong as the brakeman stopped along a level part of the street, and Gillen and several other riders jumped off. The sound of leather shoes and heels clicking against the pavement reminded him that he was now walking.

Although several blocks from home, he periodically made pit stops on the corner with the red delicatessen, as that was his landmark to head east, toward the white oval dome up the hill. Upon entering the massive domed complex, the evening light from the door gave way to a darkened corridor. At the end of the corridor was not so much light as white. In the center of the whiteness stood an angel.

The blade from her skate sliced across the ice as she moved, her body one with the motion and with the music. Arms outstretched, she shifted her weight onto one leg, leaned her body forward, and using her other leg as a counterbalance, soared into the vast open space of the rink. Loose strands of auburn hair wisped from her ponytail as she sailed, her intelligent eyes gazing straight ahead, as if focusing on her own movements from some higher vantage point.

The arena, nearly empty, looked like an ice palace, standing as a monument to the human ability to replace vast emptiness with stark beauty. Gillen had long been witness to this beauty, to failure and triumph, to heartbreak and resilience. He had been taking his daughter to this rink since just after she had learned to walk, her tenacity a testament to both her character and her grace.

Allaire Rainer glided past him without notice, her mind preoccupied with a hundred subtle gestures. The flick of her wrist, the tilt of her neck, and her hand pressing out against the void as if to use it as momentum for her next spin, all encompassed the thirteen-year-old as she rotated her body in accordance with the symphonic aria.

Gillen smiled as he watched and listened. Allaire had always loved this piece of music. She skated to it often during practice sessions and it was sometimes difficult to ascertain whether the orchestra was driving her or if she was driving the orchestra. As the intensity of the music grew, Allaire's routine changed. She broke from the edge of the oval and sliced violently across the rink toward the center, swinging her head downward and her left leg upward. The motion carried with it the low chords of stringed and woodwind instruments, and Gillen could feel the vibrations in his ears.

Allaire then swung upright and quickly glanced behind her, as if avoiding some predator, all while the symphony moved toward a crescendo. Gillen squared his jaw as he stood witness, the devastating beauty of the aria overwhelming his senses. Allaire gazed forward again, her body coasting across the ice in reverse, and prepared for her double axel. With a movement that appeared to be all one motion, she turned her body forward and sprung into the jump, her muscular legs twisting against each other like propellers, her arms tight against her torso, her head a pinnacle high in the air.

Then, accompanied by the crash of cymbals, her blades struck the ice, sending minuscule pieces flying into a vapor. With finesse Allaire curved her skate sideways and pulled herself into a rotation, and as the final triumphant notes from the operetta echoed into the rafters of the arena, Allaire slowed her spin, slammed her blade into the ice, threw back her arms and head, and gazed out into the void that had just been hers.

Gillen leaned against the wall in silence, unable to decide whether he was energized or spent. Allaire held her pose for a moment, her chest and abdomen rising and falling in waves. When she finally did break free, she instinctively turned her face toward the bleachers where her father was standing.

"Hey, Dad," she said, her cheeks flushed.

"Hey, champ," he responded.

The surge of pride he felt for Allaire brought to memory the pride he had felt for Walter Iselin a year prior. Walter had rallied the attendees which had comprised mostly of his own employees and a few investors sanctimoniously selected by Walter himself for the next round of funding. Gillen had smiled as they all took their seats and watched as his boss began the presentation, a giant draped object standing just off center of the dais where he stood. With showmanship, Walter commanded the story of the meager origins of Iselin Amalgamate and the scrappy, can-do attitude of its staff. He took pause to recognize several of his employees, namely, Jack DaLette — Director of Engineering, Samantha Leung — Vice President of Operations, and Gillen Rainer — Vice President of Research and Development and the man who had uncovered the mathematical equation which made the mysterious object under the sheet possible. For that distinction, Walter had added a few extra claps.

"The time has come," Walter had stated, "for mankind to take his rightful place among the stars, and that first step of course, is the moon." In that moment, Gillen remembered squeezing Cate's hand.

"The problem is how to get there," Walter had continued. "Rocketry is unstable. Earth's gravity is formidable. And the moon, nearly a quarter of a million miles away, is surrounded by a vacuum that will kill you in seconds. So how do we propel a man 239,000 miles to another celestial body and then retrieve him in one piece?"

Gillen had held his breath and mouthed out Walter's next sentence with him.

"We don't. Instead, we take a shortcut."

With precision timing, the giant red drape had slowly levitated from off the object, revealing a ten foot tall metallic hexagon. The face of the device had reflective platinum panels with a centralized opening large enough to accommodate a human, or even a forklift. Running along the length of the observation deck floor was a single serpentine tube, corralling countless cables, cords, and wires, vanishing off into another room. Standing next to the Hexagon was an operator at a small switchboard, whose sole attention was focused on only a few dials and meters. The simplicity of the device was astounding, and that was Walter's way.

"Ladies and gentlemen, this is the Hexagon, and it is currently connected to a duplicate Hexagon on the moon via a naturally occurring phenomenon in spacetime that our team discovered, and that we call, an Alignment."

Gillen felt a shiver as the memory ebbed. The sequence of events from leaving the ice rink, to riding the cable car home with Allaire, to shuffling up the walkway seemed like one continuous motion to him as he entered their foyer and felt an immediate burst of warm air rushing to greet him. Passing the cherry mahogany bannisters and stairwell on the left, Gillen and Allaire hung their coats on the rack above the wainscoting which ran parallel along the wall on the right. The decorative paneling connected the foyer to the main hallway, living room, kitchen, and den where Gillen instinctively found himself pouring some scotch into a tumbler.

Burning embers flickered inside of the fireplace, casting an ochre hue against the shadows in the den. Among those silhouettes was that of Gillen, whose movements were imperceptible, albeit seeming to exist with the same crackling energy that was coming from the flames. His shadow seemed to be forever stalking him, trying to overtake him, yet the towering dark mass was somehow dwarfed by the true image of the man seated on the arm of the chaise lounge.

From the stereo atop the olive wood cabinet, an announcer's voice filled the room, its qualities both warm and authoritative. "...launched into an elliptical low earth orbit, circling the globe every ninety-six minutes and passing over the United States seven times a day. The beeping, its radio signal, which we have played for you multiple times on this station, is being transmitted on 20.005 and 40.002 megahertz, and is being monitored by radio amateurs, professionals, and governments around the world."

Gillen yanked at his tie and pulled the fabric from around his neck like he was removing a noose. He held his drink for a moment, letting the sensation of the tumbler envelope his hand: thin rim, heavy bottom, and the perfect amount of ice jangling inside.

By that time, Allaire had returned from showering and was seated on the davenport in the den, across from the radio, her sketchbook spread across her lap, her eyes one with the pencil in her hand.

"Why is everyone so afraid?" she asked, without so much as missing a stroke.

Despite the wafts of heat drifting out from the fireplace, the metallic dial on the stereo felt cool as Gillen gently lowered the volume. "There's a lot about this that we don't know. People are afraid of what they don't know."

Allaire nodded, still immersed by her drawing. "Some of the kids at school said that Sputnik can listen to our phone calls. Maybe even read our thoughts as it passes overhead."

"Where did they hear that?"

"From one of the substitute teachers."

Gillen grimaced and walked over to the sofa. He sat down opposite Allaire and watched her mind remove the unnecessary white spaces on the paper. "What do you think?" he asked her.

The pencil stopped moving for an instant before she responded, "I think probably not."

Gillen smiled. After another moment, he said, "Your skating today was tremendous. I've never seen you in better form."

The pencil stopped moving again, only this time, it stayed inert. "I love that song," she said softly.

Gillen tightened his grip ever so slightly. Taking the final portion of scotch by gulp, he set the glass down on a coaster and stood up from the davenport. "Dinner out tonight sound like a good idea?"

Allaire nodded and smiled, fully aware of her father's attempt to derail her train of thought and fully aware that he knew it too. "I'm starving. Can we go to that place along the Embarcadero?"

The pall that hung over the humans encompassing the city of San Francisco had not been lifted as Gillen and Allaire ventured out into the void. Shell-shocked faces walked past them on the sidewalks, in the streetcar, and at the restaurant. Gillen and Allaire had made no agreement to be mindful of their countenance, no discussion of pre-approved topics of conversation, and had made no pacts to cheer up those with whom they interacted.

They simply decided to live like they were alive.

"Imagine," Walter Iselin had said to the small crowd, "being able to step off the earth and onto the moon in one motion. Instantaneously."

At that moment, Walter and Gillen's eyes both turned toward the Hexagon burning with a lust not seen before by any lover. "This machine," Walter had said, "in tandem and in harmony with the laws of general relativity, is about to move the human race forward. Not just to the moon, not just to Mars, but to becoming a multi-planet dwelling species. And it's all possible, because of the Alignment."

Walter had called Gillen up to the podium to assist in answering the volley of questions being raised by the investors, primarily — how this had been done, and could they step through the Alignment themselves.

"Why has no one on earth detected your presence on the moon yet?"

"For security reasons, all communications are being sent directly through the Alignment itself.

Once we announce this to the world, we will transmit from a secure antenna array."

"So aside from this portal here, you have another portal on the moon right now?"

Gillen nodded. "We have more than that. There's a building on the moon, a giant space telescope, an observatory, and even a makeshift cruiser so that we can explore the vicinity."

"Is the opening stable?"

"Very. Once we figured out the mathematical equation to maintaining the Alignment, the rest was academic."

"What happens if the Alignment closes? What if someone gets marooned?"

"We can open and close the Alignment at will using the Hexagons. There have been zero instances of Alignment failure between the earth and moon."

"But what if it did?" one wide-eyed investor had asked, visibly shaken.

Walter returned to the podium. "Then we simply open up a parallel Alignment to use as a rescue channel."

The room fell silent.

"Look, we've consulted with the best physicists and scientific minds available. I'm not asking any of you to take my word for it." Walter then added, "Now, who's coming with me on a quick trip to the moon?"

Gillen had been awash in the moment as he kissed Cate on the cheek, took her by the hand, and led her over to Walter to be first in line through the

Hexagon. She had been a member of the team since the beginning, helping with administrative tasks, bringing late night meals to the office, and being an anchor during pivotal brainstorming sessions. Gillen had gazed at her that evening, so proud of her contributions to the project, amazed at her stamina during it all, and inspired by her resilience in light of the phantom illness that, without warning or trigger and at random intervals, would send sudden and excruciating muscle pain radiating throughout her slender frame, often rendering her bedridden.

"Are you all right, darling?" he had asked Cate, sensing her lassitude.

Her smile was labored. "Don't worry about me."

Walter Iselin stepped in front of the Hexagon. Impervious to fear, he took a step forward and his image reflected back at him from the amniotic field. His reflection merged with his person and he vanished into the void.

"Shall we?" Gillen said to Cate, her eyes filled with the width of the Hexagon.

Hand in hand, Gillen and Cate approached their reflections and within the span of one motion, stepped off of the earth and onto the moon. The action was swift, painless, and something that always left them in a state of wonder.

More of the small group had filed through, following Walter and Samantha as they showcased the building, its self-sustaining features, its artificial gravity, and also allowing the guests to come to terms with where they were standing.

"Come on," Gillen had whispered to Cate. "Let's go be the first inside."

He gently led her away from the group, down a narrow corridor, and into a massive round space not unlike the observation tower on earth from which they had just left. Cate's eyes followed the flow of the room, with two thirds of the circle being comprised of mahogany wood panels and recessed lighting, the walls bedecked by evenly spaced international flags leaning far enough forward so as to allow the fabric to drape. At the center of the room was a circular conference table with leather executive chairs, and beyond that, the final third of the space's wall was made up entirely of glass from floor to ceiling, which showcased in all of its glory miles of flat lunar surface, the horizon off in the distance, the almost tactile blackness of space, and finally, nestled within that blackness, a small blue sphere.

"This is phase one of what will be the first lunar embassy," Walter's voice bellowed from the entrance, his entourage shuffling from behind. "We've aptly named it, Ortelius, in honor of the eminent cartographer and creator of the first modern atlas. Ortelius will be an international zone, safe from the eyes and ears of the world below, where diplomats and ambassadors will have autonomy to work out solutions together, at this table, overlooking the planet we all share."

Walter had paced up to the window wall and outstretched his arm in the direction of earth.

Turning back to his audience he said, "It's a sobering thing to look all of humanity in the face."

Gillen had turned to Cate and was unsurprised to see tears running down her cheeks. Yet something about her countenance betrayed the overwhelming wonder in her eyes, and for a moment, Gillen surmised that she was in pain.

"I can take you back..." he had whispered, caressing her wrist.

"Gillen..." she had responded, her eyes locked onto his, "don't do this—"

"Gillen?" Walter restated. The absence of chatter lassoed Gillen's attention over to where Walter was standing, next to a number of investors seemingly ready to pounce if made to wait any longer. "I think we've piqued their interest."

Gillen hesitated as Cate's lips made an attempt at elocution, her eyes shifting between him and Walter.

"If you would..." Walter began.

"Sure," Gillen responded, joining Walter, Samantha, and Jack over by the window wall and helping them field a series of return on investment inquiries. Before the night was finished, Iselin Amalgamate had every dime they wanted.

Back through the Alignment and into the town car on earth, Gillen held Cate as the city lights dotted the rear seat like bioluminescence. Outside the windshield the crescent moon hung in the sky seeming not quite as distant as it should. It existed no longer as a deity to be acquiesced, but as a monument to the human mind.

"So beautiful," Allaire said as she gazed up at the sky. Gillen stood next to her, lost in his thoughts. Following dinner, they walked along the boulevard that connected the bay's many piers, each dotted by street lamps atop a stylish pole. They strolled in silence, each painfully aware of the towering reminder coming up ahead upon which they longed to gaze but dreaded to see.

Allaire glanced first. The towers evenly spaced across the bay, the sections demarcated by strobe lights, the cantilevers seeming to rise out of the water and suspend the bridge by sheer will, all filled the girl with a sense of wonder and sorrow. Gillen looked afterward. Reality dictated that he acknowledge everything his daughter was seeing, yet he had been the only other person, aside from the police, who had also witnessed the condition of his wife's mangled vehicle in the photos.

"Her car hit an embankment along the interstate," the officer had told Gillen, citing the police report. "Crushed the hood and shattered the windshield. The driver's side door was open too."

Upon finding her body in the bay below, two theories had emerged. One was that the force of the crash had jettisoned her out through the windshield and over the guardrail. The other was that immediately following the accident, Cate Rainer had committed suicide by jumping off the Bay Bridge.

Adamant was Gillen's refusal to accept the second scenario. The open door, the lack of shard wounds on her body, even the proximity of the vehicle to the guardrail, none of it had swayed him. His wife had died from a brutal car accident on the Bay Bridge, on the evening of October 8th, one year prior.

"Oh... no..." Allaire had said in a voice so broken that it nearly broke Gillen's heart. The look on his daughter's face was hauntingly indescribable. It was the horror not of someone learning of a murder, but of witnessing it. Gillen was rendered mute as he gazed at Allaire. She was not moving or breathing, seemingly trapped in a suspension of disbelief. The crushing nature of the event left the girl's existence spiraling, as if some tormentor had her dangling over insanity by a thread. Her mother, who had taught her resilience, cheered her on and off the ice, and had been a sounding board for countless adolescent diatribes about life, now could not express anything more than the black sepulcher of a bodybag declaring her lifelessness.

After the minutes had passed within what felt like an hour, the statue that had been Allaire Rainer shattered into a human being once again, and the girl began to weep. Muffled sobs of pain demanded to be heard through the hands guarding her face from the world. Her shoulders arched in response to the waves of uncontrollable tears cascading down her cheeks. The cry coming from within her was not a wail, but the most heartbreaking whimper Gillen had ever heard. The utter hopelessness of the sound caused Gillen's eyes to moisten, and if he was certain of anything at all, he was certain that he never wanted to hear that sound again on earth.

Allaire collapsed onto the floor, curled up into a fetal position, and tried to shut down the torrent of emotion. After weeping for nearly an hour, she stopped. Rather without warning the tears evaporated from her torrid cheeks leaving Allaire in a monolithic daze. Then, with the weariness of someone trying to gain strength by forcing themselves to move, the girl slowly pushed herself up from the floor and stumbled into the bathroom. When she exited a moment later, she stood in front of Gillen with the frightening expression of death indwelling life. She was able to move, but unable to react. Her mouth formulated words, yet it seemed like she never actually said anything. Even her breathing patterns were disturbingly sporadic, acting more like an obligatory movement necessary to quell any suspicions rather than an involuntary action for survival.

Allaire Rainer had become the conscious manifestation of anti-living. Gillen swallowed the stale air from his agape mouth and attempted to collect his thoughts. Allaire's eyes stared through the monochromatic world which seemed to engulf her and into the face of her father who appeared to encompass the colors of life itself.

Gillen struggled to maintain control over his voice as he said, "We're going to get through this. I know that seems impossible in this moment, but I promise you, this pain won't last forever."

Allaire stood and listened to her father speak. She offered no counter-argument and gave little indication that she was either in agreement with or vehemently against his statements. She just stood and watched him talk as if words had shapes. The slightest shift in Allaire's eye position indicated to Gillen that she was at least hearing him, and the outcome of his speech would determine if she started marching left or right.

Gillen stood idle, lost in a sea of well-meaning words. Words which, in any other circumstance, might offer support. Yet he also knew what was to come. The awkward condolences of those too daft to recognize that grief was a process, and that their words of comfort, inappropriately timed, served only as a levy, transferring the duty of solace into the burden of gratitude. Extending his hand toward her, he whispered, "Let's just sit in the den for a while."

Allaire had nodded indifferently. "All right."

He blinked as the images of that day were absorbed into the mist surrounding the Bay Bridge, its massive structure seeming to stretch out into the distant fog and into an invisible world. Gillen and Allaire observed without comment, and for the first time that day, they didn't even think about Sputnik as it orbited the sky above them for the seventh time.

NINE NOTES

"Why did she leave?"

Emerging from the deepest recesses of Allaire Rainer's mind, the words formed their own existence, as if the effort to speak them had been unnecessary. Her lips felt violated. They tensed in rebellion from having been coerced. The utterance was barely audible, spoken in the hollow tones of confessing a sin for which the guilt was obligatory.

The dream sequence always started the same way, with serenity. There was a sound far off in the distance. The unmistakable notes of a freight train's whistle drifted through her subconscious. She listened intently to the sound, wishing for it to never leave, or if it must, for the sound to take her with it. Then, in a flash of light, she was transported to a prairie.

The tender chirp of a cardinal.

The morning dew dripping from the daffodil leaves.

Stalks of wheat swaying in the wind.

Then a human voice. The first few notes of that song...

Why do I know that...?

Allaire's body involuntarily jerked as if her muscles were unwilling to be passive during the dream and her mind was taming their insubordination. The minutes seemed to pass by the span of an hour at a time. No longer could she differentiate between the seconds behind her and the seconds yet to come. It all merged into a waveform pattern of equilibrium.

Allaire heard a familiar voice. It had the tonal quality of a quiet strength. Yet the voice was not really speaking, it was humming, it was calling, it was wooing. At first, Allaire could not recognize it, for it seemed eternally distant, yet the melody which she was humming drifted into her soul with the fierce emotion of a song teetering on the edge of recollection.

"I know this song," Allaire whispered, whether verbally or in her head she could not discern. The beautiful instrumental floated over her like an illusive dream, daring her to grab hold. She then noticed that the scenery surrounding her had changed.

Like a series of slides they transitioned from one into the other, accompanied by the notes from the mysterious melody. It began with a rising sun, bursting forth from the horizon with a brightness and a power that superseded all else. The fireball ascended into the sky before melting into the clouds. The clouds then rolled over and into each other, racing across the azure firmament toward destinations never to be known. Day quickly turned into night and the world became a dais underneath a dome of stars. The sky rotated around the point to which Allaire seemed to be fixed, as the lights above swirled in varying sizes and luminosity.

Then she saw the moon. An entity all its own, the metallic sphere was a forced perspective enlargement of reality, filling up the expanse of sky, seemingly suspended by nothing, dangling from space over her head. The vision was overwhelming, as terrifying as it was sensational. Allaire could make out the pockmarks across the lunar surface, a subtle glow of light reflecting from the regolith, Shackleton crater an ethereal touchstone.

The song became more pronounced.

I know this... Yet her mind strained to form even one syllable of the melody which she believed she knew so well. The voice spoke the sounds with intentional delicacy, as if the words could break if stated with any force. Allaire heard them, but could not understand them. They tugged at a portion of her heart which protected the most precious of childhood memories, and by doing so, revealed the singer to be that of her mother.

Allaire gazed at her in awe as she made the motions of walking toward her yet remained in a state of inertia. She was thirteen, then fourteen, then fifteen, and then, within the span of an instant, had grown into a woman.

"Mom..." she tried to speak, but her words had been muted. The blissful atmosphere in which she found herself was rapidly deteriorating. Her delight, steadily building throughout the dream, now felt like the onset of some sickening virus.

"Mom," she tried to say again, but she had vanished along with the world around her.

Why did she leave?

"Mom!" she yelled out from her restless sleep.

Cate... thought Gillen, as across the hallway, his eyes opened only partially from the nightmare in which he was engulfed. His bedroom door was closed, yet the sound of Allaire's call brought a lucidity to the events playing out in his mind. As his eyelids fell forward again, he found himself plunged back onto the front porch steps of his home, dressed as if heading to work, feeling a rapidly surging sense of unease welling up within his chest.

It was daytime, yet the sunlight seemed filtered, bathing the neighborhood in an unnaturally rust-colored tint. The street before him was empty, so were the sidewalks, which left Gillen to wonder why his eyes were being continuously drawn to the curb.

"Cate?" he said in his dream, his voice sounding not so much his own, but instead, more a recreation of what someone would perceive his voice to be.

The street remained empty as his focus drifted upward toward the sky. To his surprise, a dark mass was slowly moving overhead. The object was round and seemed to have spokes protruding from it at various angles. Startled, Gillen took a step back while his heart rate began to gallop. The metallic device was floating through the air, perhaps only a couple hundred feet above his head, and with it, producing an unnerving sound that traveled from Gillen's eardrums into his teeth.

What the hell is that?

He took a few steps forward onto the sidewalk and tried to determine where the apparatus was going. As it crossed over the sun, he shielded his eyes from the blinding haze. Only then did he notice that the shadow below him had ceased movement. His eyes widened along with the circumference of the shadow as the object began descending. Gillen looked up and saw it rotate in midair, reorienting its antenna toward him with terrifying accuracy.

Sputnik... he thought to himself, as the deafening ping grew with intensity. *It can see me...*

He neither remembered turning nor having initiated the motions of running, yet cutting across his lawn and toward a parked vehicle down the street was suddenly his mind's primary objective. Gillen bolted while feeling the piloerection of hairs on his arms seeming to align themselves with whatever malevolent force was being projected from the rapidly approaching satellite.

Up ahead, the car sizzled in the sunlight.

"Cate!" he heard himself exclaim, somehow becoming aware that she was sitting behind the steering wheel. When he reached her window, his hands pressed against the glass in a desperate attempt to garner her attention.

"Get out of the car!" he pleaded.

Gone was the motive for his frenzied state, for suddenly seeing Cate again had transformed the meaning and the outcome of his nightmare. The satellite vanished from the sky. The rest of the street faded into the background. Finding no door handle to latch onto, he stared through the pane at his wife, who sat despondently in the driver's seat with both hands on the wheel and with eyes unable to look away from whatever existed beyond the windshield.

"Cate! Please... get out of the car! Let me help you!"

This isn't real... he said to himself. *I'm dreaming...*

The words proved true as he felt himself levitating off the ground. A swell of emotions washed over his body as the soft sensation of his bedsheets enveloped his hands and feet. The sound of his own breathing preceded the shifting of his eyes beneath his eyelids, and before he had another chance to capture the outline of her facial features, Cate dissipated into the woodwork of his nightstand.

◄ ◆ ● ● ● ● ● ◆ ►

"Allaire?" Gillen whispered, knocking on her door as he opened it.

She was already sitting up, her arms wrapped around her knees, her knees nestled under her chin, her torso rocking her small frame back and forth.

"Hi, Dad," she said. "Sorry to wake you."

"You didn't," he said with a weary smile.

"Did you have a nightmare too?"

Gillen shrugged as he sat down on the edge of her bed. "For me, insomnia is the nightmare." With a gentle caress of her face he asked, "Was this the same dream you've been having?"

Allaire nodded as she rocked. Gillen had been witness to this act of self-soothing more often recently. Her face was somewhat difficult to see, but he could make out contours from the ebbing light outside her window. She wasn't crying. She was simply staring. A framed photograph facing her bed on the desk next to her armoire was indistinguishable from any other photo in the dark room. Yet Gillen knew what image the photo contained.

It was of Gillen and Cate, arms wrapped around Allaire wearing a dazzling blue leotard dress, moments after winning a junior figure skating championship. Below the frame, and the desk on which it stood, Allaire's white skates lay against the frame of her closet door, the door upon which dozens of certificates, ribbons, and medallions were affixed. A testament to her work, a shrine to her mother's affirmation.

Gillen's eyes shifted away from the awards and along the carpeted floor back to his daughter, who had soothed herself down to only minor trembling. "I was trying to remember this song Mom used to sing to me when I was little. But I can never remember it when I wake up."

How she's grown up, Gillen thought to himself. *In just a year... Cate's missed so much.* "That sounds like a sweet memory, Allaire. Can you recall the tune?"

Allaire continued gazing at the photo, but her mind's eye drifted into childhood memories. "Only the first few notes."

Her father smiled. "That's as good a start as any."

Drawing in a breath, Allaire began to hum. Five seconds later, Gillen sat motionless, stunned at how absolutely beautiful nine notes could be. Like a string of chosen sounds flawlessly woven through the fabric of sensation, the beginning of the song had left Gillen tingling with feelings he had both forgotten and repressed.

Allaire turned to him. "Do you remember how the rest of it goes?"

Feeling uneasy, Gillen rubbed his thumb and forefinger against his temples and wondered why he felt so adrift. Numerous were the sleepless nights he had spent with Cate, caring for her during particularly painful instances of phantom pain so debilitating that it literally took her breath away. When she wasn't suffering she was overdoing it in an effort to compensate for her downtime, and therefore, setting herself up for yet another physical episode.

I miss you, Cate...

Gillen caressed Allaire's face. "How about some chamomile tea?"

She offered a gentle smile as a reply.

The kitchen seemed more desolate than the rest of the house. It flooded Gillen's mind with scenes: meals and meetings, homework and holidays, conversations with friends, hangovers and cleanup.

"You're going to be a father," Cate had once told him standing next to the icebox, her hands resting on her abdomen.

"I didn't think we were that drunk!" he had exclaimed, twirling Cate in his arms, the mahogany cabinets spinning in their periphery.

Cate had laughed in her special way when she was as terrified as she was ecstatic. "When I think about it, I just have trouble imagining it."

"In what way?"

Cate said, "A child, a small version of me... existing, outside of me. With their own thoughts and experiences and ambitions. Their own way of viewing the world. Their own hopes and dreams. Their own fears and regrets. It's... hard for me to picture."

Nine months later the picture came into focus. Allaire had changed everything and had also changed nothing, a dichotomy which had fascinated Gillen for the next thirteen years.

I love you, Cate...

The steam from the carafe pulled Gillen back to the present moment as he finished preparing the tea for Allaire. It was only upon reentering her bedroom that the idea dawned. Setting the tea kettle, cup, and saucer on her nightstand, he said, "Allaire, this afternoon, I was talking with the rest of the team at work and we finally decided that we're ready to hold a press conference and announce to the world what me, and Grandpa Walt, and the team at Iselin Amalgamate, and even your mom, have been working on all these years."

"You mean the space telescope?"

That had been the simplest way of explaining it without risking too many follow-up questions and jeopardizing the project. Gillen could only imagine what kind of inquiries would have been raised by the school had Allaire started broadcasting that her parents were building a magic portal to the moon.

"Yes—the space telescope." Gillen nodded. "Only, it isn't exactly a telescope. It's a bit more complicated than that, and I assure you, far more amazing. Since I think you're old enough to be trusted with keeping this quiet for a few more days, I thought it might be fun to give you your own private tour. Shall we go now?"

Allaire sat still for a moment, her eyes working out something that her mind already knew. Then, without rush, she sat up on her knees and drew Gillen into an embrace, burying her face in his shoulder, gently nodding.

◄ ◆ ● ● ● ● ● ◆ ►

The Iselin Amalgamate building was a forgettable structure set atop a hill with an unforgettable view. The nighttime lights from the bay below twinkled, dotting the landscape like the pinpoints of an archipelago. Above the bay, the stanchions of the Golden Gate Bridge towered over the earth, periodically vanishing into the darkened mist. During moments of contemplation, Gillen had often gazed through the office windows at the massive monument waiting for it to reappear in the same way a freighter's apparition enters a midnight harbor.

Gillen led Allaire through the building showcasing the views, the interior conference rooms, and the corridors connecting places where minds had struggled, given up, revived, and ultimately triumphed.

"This isn't what I had pictured at all, Dad," Allaire said as they wandered.

"What had you pictured?"

"More like an observatory."

"In a way, you were exactly right."

They reached the main hallway which led to a pair of double doors, reinforced by steel paneling, and a backlit keypad off to the side. Gillen held his hand in front of the numbers for an instant, seeming to compose himself as one would upon entering a house of worship.

"Ready?"

Allaire nodded enthusiastically.

The latch unlocked with the sound of wanting to either keep what was exterior out, or what was interior contained. Allaire drew in a quick breath as they entered the giant laboratory. Her eyes first followed the metal catwalks along what would have been the second floor of the wing, its vaulted ceiling a skylit dome above their heads. The catwalks made angled turns at a landing before descending down to where Allaire was, her already small frame further dwarfed by the rows of machines and workstations hugging the walls.

Her eyes then focused on what was standing directly in the center of the lab. She blinked in an effort to comprehend what she was seeing and also in wonder that it had not captured her attention sooner. "Wow," she said, sotto voce, but in a manner amplified by the enormous space. "What is that?"

Gillen offered her his hand and led her closer to his second child, an object without pulse yet containing the heartbeat of the universe. So out of place it seemed in this room that their individual perceptions revealed themselves differently in their own countenances — Allaire's, that this was an idol to be obeyed; Gillen's, that this was a deity who obeyed them.

"Allaire," he said, "don't be afraid. This is what your mother and I, Grandpa Walt, and many others over the last several years have been working on. This is the first of three components, and it's called the Hexagon. There's another one identical to it, that's the second component. The third is a tunnel that connects the two, allowing safe and immediate passage of any individual crossing over."

The sheen of the lights reflecting off the metallic coating on the Hexagon found a home in the mocha eyes gazing back at it. Allaire stood motionless, transfixed by the wonder of what she knew and paralyzed by the question yet to be asked. Mounting the courage, she whispered, "Where does the person go?"

Had Gillen not pointed upward, Allaire would not have been able to tear her focus away from the unorthodoxy commanding her attention. As she slowly shifted her eyes back toward the domed skylight, her vision swam from not blinking, not breathing, from the weight of anticipation. When she steadied her focus on the single source of light emitting through the pane, the dawning of the answer made sense of all that was confounding in the world and caused everything she thought she understood to crumble.

"We're going to the moon," Allaire said, whether as a statement or an inquiry Gillen couldn't tell.

"Yes, Allaire. We're going to the moon."

‹ ♦ ● ● ● ● ● ♦ ›

The last thing Allaire Rainer saw before stepping through the Alignment was her own reflection in the opaque field of the Hexagon. When the heel of her shoe made contact with the floor of the lunar complex, she involuntarily gasped. The laboratory in which the second Hexagon stood hummed quietly, as if even the machinery knew to pay proper tribute to the hallowed ground.

Allaire walked cautiously at first, wondering if the artificial gravity would suddenly give out. A series of successful steps forward proved otherwise. The equilibrium she felt jumping instantaneously from one world to another left her with a suspicion that perhaps she had not. Only the credibility of her father's words settled the matter in her mind.

"Dad?" she asked, looking back toward the Hexagon, surprised that his presence with her had been an afterthought.

Gillen was there, just a few steps behind, staring at her with a beaming smile. Reassured, Allaire motioned toward the workstations. Indicator lights flashed intermittently next to dials attuned to precise frequencies. A level higher on the electronics rack, the delicate needles within the VU meters pulsed left and right past unity, and Allaire hesitated upon seeing them.

"Do you hear that?" she asked.

Gillen nodded as he approached, reaching for a smooth titanium dial built into the panel. As his wrist turned, the audio drifted out of a pair of speakers housed at eye level. The fabric encasing them was dark and taut.

"Music," she said, turning to Gillen. "Where is it coming from?"

"Earth. It tunes to various radio stations depending on the positioning of the earth and the moon. That way we can get the lunar weather reports." Allaire's belly laugh was an instant reminder that there was still some kid left in the blossoming teenager. *Cate... you're missing it.*

As Allaire wandered about the laboratory, her hand made contact with one of the beige panels lining the exterior wall of the complex. A dull vibration moved from the panel and into her hand as the entirety of the enclosure emitted a faint gurgling sound.

"It sounds like there's water in there?" she questioned, pressing her ear up to the panel.

"An osmotic pressure concentration of mineral infused hydro-particles, but I'll spare you the jargon. It's a water wall. We run it along much of the exterior of the habitat as a method of radiation shielding. The gurgling sound you're hearing happens automatically every few hours when the tanks are stirred."

The tour continued with Gillen leading Allaire down the main corridor and into another wing of the complex. As they entered the observation room, Gillen could sense Allaire slowing her pace, trying to absorb a dozen remarkable images simultaneously. The draped flags, the intense cherry mahogany of the conference table, the recessed lighting, and the galactic enormity of the window wall with a blue sphere beyond the panes of glass. With widened eyes, Allaire looked up at Gillen who said, "This is the first lunar embassy, on the first lunar habitat, on the first city on the moon. Welcome to Ortelius, Allaire."

She parted her lips to speak, but when she saw the earth off in the distance just over the lunar horizon cradled in the rich blackness of space, her words lost all sound. In slow meaningful steps, the teenager worked one foot in front of the other on her way to the window wall. As she approached the desolate view, the planet in the center of the pane came into focus. The oceans, the continents, the palette of color against the starkness of its surroundings, it was all there, minus two of its inhabitants.

Allaire pressed her hand against the glass and felt an artificial warmth combatting the intense cold. For several minutes she gazed, hardly moving, rarely breathing, searching for something, trying to bring to mind a feeling she used to know.

"It's all right," Gillen finally whispered, resting his hand on her shoulder.

She nodded from a trance, gazing through her own reflection in the window which was gazing back at her. The earth, up in the sky, observable in the same manner in which humans down below were observing the moon. Both looking up and battling to remain with their heads held high.

The portrait before her welled up from within her emotions and seeped out through a single tear that trickled down her cheek. With her lips still parted, Allaire mouthed something and failed, and after swallowing the stale air in her throat, gave it another try. "You know what I see, Dad?"

Gillen shut his eyes slowly, his hand gripping his daughter's shoulder, half in support for her, half in support for himself. "What's that?"

The words emerged from her body in a mixed tonal quality, partially from the voice of a little girl who had lost her mother and partially from the voice of a young woman who had just learned the meaning of life. "I see something that looks more alive than anything else in the universe... and that makes me happy."

◂ ◆ ● ● ● ● ● ◆ ▸

The walk back through the complex toward the Hexagon was brief, but had Allaire and Gillen holding hands and smiling through their shared experience. As Gillen stood at the main console double checking the coordinates of the Alignment, Allaire meandered back over to the workstation fascinated by the knobs and switchboard.

Faint whispers of audio were escaping from the speakers, having been turned down but not off. Allaire scanned the panel for the titanium stereo dial and began to rotate it counterclockwise. She then hesitated. The frequency had changed, and with it, the style of music. The instruments were orchestral yet reserved, as if the musicians feared playing over one another. A flautist skillfully breathed across the mouthpiece of the woodwind, gently lifting the melody from the strings and piano. What resulted was an introduction soothing and meek, emerging from the pathos of a musician acquainted with sentimentality.

Then a male voice began to hum, nine notes, in the most beautiful arrangement imaginable. Allaire blinked and from her hypnotic reverie felt her hand reaching out toward the dial, moving it clockwise.

"Dad," she whispered, "this is the—"

It vanished, awash in a jarring cacophony of static. Allaire's eyes darted up to the board, and in horror, she pulled her hand away from the frequency tuner — the dial housed right next to the volume.

"What did you say, Allaire?" Gillen asked.

The static hissed through the speakers, a desecration of the sacred sounds heard only seconds earlier. Allaire frantically moved the tuner back, sending it cycling through signals. "No, no, no..." she muttered, twisting the dial the opposite direction and overcompensating again. Allaire could feel the pulse of each signal in her ears as it emerged and vanished from the speakers. The sound for which she was looking was unmistakable and she was positive it was gone.

"Everything all right?" Gillen asked, approaching the panel.

Allaire stared blankly at the speakers for a moment, unable to move, uncertain it had been real, and unwilling to admit that it wasn't. Gillen rested his hand on her shoulder and smiled. Allaire found composure as she sighed heavily and felt her fingers slip from the dial. "Yes," she nodded, avoiding eye contact with Gillen. "I'm ready to go."

CHAPTER 3

PERENNIAL MOONRISE

"And would you also call the ice rink and let them know I'll be a few minutes late picking up Allaire?"

"Yes, Mr. Rainer. Anything else?"

"No, we'll draft that letter tomorrow. Thanks, Lisa."

The secretary finished jotting on her notepad before leaving Gillen's office and passing Samantha Leung in the anteroom. Gillen was still cleaning his desk as Samantha entered the modest office space.

"Friday then?"

Gillen glanced up at her, hesitated, and nodded with caution. "Friday it is."

Samantha stood with confidence, her white blouse and black capri pants seeming to direct attention to the fact that even if she had not been wearing heels she would still appear tall. Her hair was black with natural burnt umber highlights and had a stylish wave as it curved past her ears and up into a clip. She was the striking combination of her Hong Kongese mother and German-born father, resulting in a face many wondered if they had ever witnessed on the silver screen. "Our first press conference. Announcing the most incredible achievement of humankind to date."

"Maybe we'll make the evening news," Gillen added with a smirk.

"Walter is upset about Sputnik."

"I'm sure of that."

"Don't worry about it," Samantha said. "I've already reminded him that three days from now, that little satellite will be a footnote in comparison to what we'll have to share. I only mention it because he tends to get lost in the minutia. It will be important for us to help him think big picture leading up to the press conference."

"Good thinking."

"Oh, Miss Leung," Lisa said, reentering the office. "Dr. Iselin asked if the final shipment of the microwave relay antenna arrived today?"

"All four pallets of it. Transported onto Ortelius this afternoon."

"Thank you."

Gillen slapped shut the lid of his briefcase and pressed the bronze latches simultaneously.

"Heading out?" Samantha asked.

"I need to go pick up Allaire from skating practice."

"I'm heading out as well. Would you like a ride?"

Gillen fumbled the start of his sentence before saying, "Taking the cable car has been nice, actually. Gives me time to clear my head."

Samantha nodded thoughtfully. "I'll walk you out then."

The parking lot of the Iselin Amalgamate building was mostly vacant, and the few vehicles that remained had the subtle shimmer of sunlight hitting chrome. Samantha's platinum overcoat was open, the hem of which was bobbing in the breeze as they walked to her car. Stopping at her vehicle, she lit a cigarette and said, "Walter has narrowed the shortlist down to just a few candidates."

Gillen stood silently holding his briefcase. "Ambassador to Ortelius, embassy on the moon. That's a once in a lifetime position."

"Which is why I find it concerning that he's already cutting the list."

"Because of the press conference?"

Samantha exhaled, the puff dissipating into the wind. "Likely."

"Why?"

"Isn't it obvious?"

Gillen sighed. "Sputnik."

"What else?"

"So Walter is moving up the selection of the lunar ambassador by four weeks in order to present him at the press conference?"

Samantha shook her head. "Eight weeks. The press conference was moved up eight weeks."

"Thanks to Sputnik."

"Correct."

Gillen furled his brows ever so slightly and caught a momentary glimpse of the amber flame within Samantha's cigarette, crackling with heat. "That's unlike him. Walter's not usually one for knee-jerk reactions."

"He doesn't want any of us caught in front of this. The Soviets have Sputnik. We now have the Alignment. If positioned properly, this could effectively end the space race before it's even begun."

"During the International Geophysical Year, no less."

"There's your headline."

The wind was beginning to pick up and Gillen's hand instinctively moved to secure his hat. His lips parted effortlessly yet the words struggled to form. "I saw him yesterday."

"Jack," she responded, as a statement and not a question. "I stopped by the hospital this morning for a few minutes."

Gillen nodded distantly. "They said... it might be a while... before..."

"Just as well," Samantha said. "We're all pulling for him, but we can't have him around right now. Not with the press conference. Not with the ambassadorship. Not with access to Ortelius."

"Yeah," Gillen whispered, fighting off the images of a few days prior when he had been the first to see Jack lying on the floor of his office having written on the wall — in his own crimson blood, the words *There's nothing worse than loss*. "I've known him for a long time. I suppose I should have seen this coming."

Samantha tilted her head. "How do you mean?"

"I mean, that he's never been the same since Danielle asked him for a divorce. Two years is a long time to grieve, but apparently it wasn't long enough for Jack. Past six months he's been growing more despondent. Then a bit obsessive. I saw what was happening to him, but I guess not to what extent. Danielle..."

Samantha took a long draw from her cigarette. "She seems to have been on his mind. But I was asking why you feel you should have seen this coming." Gillen shrugged and gazed off at the green slope of grass that dipped toward the road below. Samantha added, "Losing your wife won't turn you into Jack. You know that, right, Gillen?"

The wind died down enough so that he felt that his hat was secure. He slowly lowered his arm and smiled. "I do. But thanks for the reminder."

"And as for the ambassadorship, you should talk to Walter."

"Did I tell you I took Allaire up to see the moon last night?"

"Aren't you curious as to who the final candidates are?"

Gillen exhaled. "Should I be?"

Samantha flicked the cigarette to the ground. "I suppose not. Only, the embassy was your idea. A forum for the men of values, of purpose, of mind. A place where delegates can gaze out over the people whom they represent and say: 'It's a sobering thing to look all of humanity in the face.' Those were your words first."

"And now those words are Walter's responsibility."

"That's true. But I think he wants your input on this."

Gillen scoffed. "You and I don't lie to each other, Samantha."

"That is also true."

The two stood inert in silent acknowledgment of each other as their shadows on the pavement shifted in accordance to the cumulonimbus clouds rolling past the sun. Breaking her stance, Samantha then reached for her car door and said, "You've known Walter almost as long as I have. He's practically family to you all. Allaire adores him. He was there for you when Cate... when... well..."

Gillen blinked. "Died."

Samantha hesitated, either unwilling or else unable to go down that road with him. The road of alternate possibilities. The road of facts and likelihood. The road of reality. The demise of Cate Rainer was not up for debate. Her death had been a tragedy, not a suicide. Pivoting topics, she said, "We all have an interesting relationship with Walter. He is our boss and our friend. We're free to voice any concern or objection if done so respectfully, and yet quite often we choose not to because we believe our compliance will bind him closer to us. That sort of codependency is not healthy for a relationship and it's malignant to an organization."

"You're my friend, and in certain instances, my boss," Gillen said.

"And yet here we are having this conversation."

"And avoiding another."

Samantha nodded slowly and dropped her purse into the vehicle. She then walked around the open door and drew Gillen into a soft embrace. "Was she amazed?"

"I'm sorry?"

Samantha pulled away. "Allaire. Was she amazed by Ortelius?"

Gillen's countenance broke into a wide smile. "Immensely."

Stepping backward toward her vehicle, she added, "Tell her I said hello, and tell Walter you should have a voice in the choosing of the lunar ambassador."

"Are you speaking as a boss or as a friend?"

Samantha chuckled. "Can't it be both?"

As her vehicle pulled out of the parking lot, Gillen tied his overcoat tight and carefully readjusted his hat onto his head, its wool lining coming to a stop along the same hairline it had covered for many years. Hand atop his head, he rushed along the city street retracing familiar steps and rehashing familiar memories.

"Have you ever played two shakers and a dinnerware set?" Walter had asked one night at their favorite restaurant. Gillen and Cate were sitting across from him at a rectangular table nestled up against a giant window overlooking the bay. The sommelier had just left their table with an appassimento style wine to compliment their tiramisu. The desserts remained untouched as Walter began his antic.

"So you've never played this?"

Gillen and Cate were trying to subdue their uncouth level of laughter. "I can't say that I have," Gillen choked back.

"Neither have I," added Cate, in tears. "Please, demonstrate."

What ensued were the nonsensical instructions to a game consisting of a salt and pepper shaker, three pairs of silverware, and a napkin ring.

"I don't get it," said Gillen, taking slightly more than a sip of wine.

"I do," chimed Cate, reaching for the salt. "This is a game of—" She then chortled, pressing her napkin up to her lips. "This is a game of skill more than luck, you know, like poker." The table then erupted into raucous laughter, generating more than a few leering glances from nearby patrons.

An hour later the dessert was gone and spread out on the linen tablecloth were three sheets of paper with rough sketches of a semicircular addition to what was already well underway on Ortelius. Gillen was holding the pencil.

"An embassy on the moon," he whispered to Walter and Cate who were leaning into the table. "A place where world leaders, philosophers, and maybe even a political refugee, can go for a day or even a month if need be. For some, a forum to discuss solutions. For others, a brief haven to secure asylum. For most, a place to regain a proper perspective of this wonderful planet and the individuals who inhabit it, or perhaps more accurately stated, to discover it."

Walter's eyes danced across the pages. "This is sensational, Gillen. Who would we have manage it?"

"The first ever lunar ambassador, divested of any domestic or foreign government obligations. A person of values, of empathy, of reason."

"This," Walter punctuated, "gives Ortelius a level of credibility we didn't have before. With this, we've lassoed the interests of both the industrialists and the philanthropists. With this... we haven't just started a habitat on the moon."

Cate added, looking at Walter, "We've started a city."

Her words and the sound of her voice faded softly as Gillen stood impatiently at the vermilion streetlight next to a throng of people awaiting the crosswalk signal. Next to the crowd on the corner, the same man with the transistor radio leaned against a pedestrian signpost seeming to offer unsolicited news reports at random intervals.

"Are you hearing this?" he blurted to no one in particular. "That satellite is orbiting the earth every 96 minutes... 560 miles above our heads... 18,000 miles an hour! I betcha those bastards are watching every move we make!"

Gillen glanced away. Standing next to him was a woman reading the evening edition. Its headline was irrelevant, but the date seared itself into his mind.

It was October 8th.

Finding himself bathed in a green hue as the crosswalk signal changed, Gillen squinted and marshaled on. Weaving around people and objects he kept his eyes straight ahead, watching for the cable car to appear at the next intersection. Faces, billboards, street signs — all seemed to be clamoring for his attention and the sensory overload fueled his quickening pace. He was keenly aware of the thumping in his neck and of the heightened sense of perception it provided as he neared the still vacant corner. He wondered if he had missed his usual cable car, yet knew that if anything, his rapid pacing had made his arrival time earlier.

The heaviness of his jaw reminded him that his mouth was agape as he stood at the intersection, panting, unsettled by the increasing chill of the air in his lungs.

In through the nose, out through the mouth.

His eyes shifted up and down the graded street. The cable car was nowhere in sight. His wristwatch confirmed that he was minutes early, as did the giant clock atop the bank which normally was a welcomed feature of this section of town, but now, felt to him like some frustrating reminder that he was already late for a meeting he hadn't set.

The leather handle of his briefcase adhered to his sweaty palm as the gong of the brakeman's bell tolled out into the street, striking his nerves and jading his unwarranted irritation. It was crowded with riders, and only a few of them had stepped off at this stop. He hopped onto a vacant spot on the running board and tried to hold his positioning between the arms, knees, coats, and shopping bags of those in his immediate realm as the cable car began to move up the street.

The woman seated adjacent to where Gillen was standing shot a glance up at him. He met her gaze for no more than a moment before his gaze was too heavy for her to hold. A man standing in front of him appeared to be silently whispering the words to some monologue, the cracks in his face suggesting occasional humor. Behind Gillen, the thick paper of a supermarket bag brushed against his overcoat, the paper not thick enough to hide the outline or feeling or noise of dozens of clanging bottles.

Tightening his grip on the passenger bar, Gillen shut his eyes and tried to focus on breathing. While he had learned to cope with a perpetual and sickening sense of lifelessness since Cate's death, he was unaccustomed to dealing with anxiety, especially tethered to a lack of impending danger. Fear without reason was unfamiliar to him, and compounded his already taxed awareness as the red delicatessen appeared in the distance.

"Pardon me," he said as the cable car screeched to a halt and a flood of exiting bodies tried to occupy the same space.

Ahead was the white dome. The length of the walk up to the arena seemed directly proportional to the dwindling energy supply he had left to exert. His panting became more pronounced as the incline increased, and despite his internal body temperature rising, the chill in the air left him wishing for an extra layer.

The double glass doors of the skating rink's entrance led to the lobby of the arena. The space was uninhabited and dimly lit. Pacing quickly down the main corridor, Gillen could hear the unique sounds of skates coasting across ice. The overwhelmingly large area was filled with skaters, their coaches along the periphery of the rink watching their pupils with intense, unblinking eyes.

"Mr. Rainer," a voice said from the side office.

Gillen turned to see the senior instructor walking briskly toward him, her approach not to be mistaken for congeniality.

"Hello, Mrs. McNamara," he said, leaning forward ever so slightly. "Hope you're well."

"I am," she said, her gaze suspicious. "Is there a problem?"

Gillen blinked. "Not at all. Just here to pick up Allaire."

Mrs. McNamara didn't immediately respond. Then her eyes shifted away from Gillen toward the rink, seeming to watch for someone. "Natasha!" the woman yelled out. "Would you come here please?"

Gillen turned to see Allaire's coach marching up from the rink with a smile, her goldenrod hair braided and curled around her head like a crown. "Mr. Rainer," she said, offering her hand. "You didn't need to come all the way here just to return a phone call," and with that remark, tossed in a hearty laugh.

A confused smile etched his mouth. "Hello, Natasha. Just here to pick up Allaire."

Natasha's smile evaporated. She exchanged glances with the senior instructor and then back at Gillen. "Allaire's not here."

"Where is she?" Mrs. McNamara asked, usurping the urgency from Gillen's lips.

"Mr. Rainer, please forgive me, but I just got off the phone with your office. I spoke with a young lady who said she would tell you."

"Tell me what?"

"That Allaire never showed up for practice today."

Gillen felt the muscles in his face contract as the vast space surrounding him no longer felt measured in distance but measured in time. His eyes scanned the blinding white of the rink, every young girl on the ice appearing as a replica of his daughter.

"Even though Allaire has never been late to practice," Natasha stammered, "I thought she might—might still... show up. So I only just dialed your office... not even... twenty minutes ago—"

"May I use your phone?" Gillen interrupted, doing his best to remain collected.

"Please," said Mrs. McNamara, pointing toward her office.

The telephone handset was torn from off the cradle as Gillen dialed for the operator. Within minutes, he was speaking to the school principal.

"Our apologies for the delay in notifying you, Mr. Rainer," the man said, "but the matter was only just relayed to me an hour ago. That's when we tried contacting you at your home."

"I've been at work," Gillen snapped. "So you're saying Allaire was last seen leaving the premises after the lunch break and never returned for afternoon classes?"

"Correct, according to one of our teachers. We thought it odd as Allaire has never been one to ditch school in order to meet with friends."

"All of Allaire's friends attend your school. Are any students unaccounted for?"

The principal paused. "In this particular instance, regrettably not."

"Then she probably didn't leave to go meet a friend, now did she?"

"Mr. Rainer, I'm sorry we had difficulty in reaching you. After trying your residence several times, we just left a message with your secretary at your office."

"When?"

"Oh, perhaps thirty minutes ago."

Gillen sighed and loosened his grip of the handset. "Of all the days not to be able to reach me, it had to be this one."

The principal grunted, seeming to sympathize with the plight of this parent. "Naturally."

The skating instructors appeared to watch him as he left Mrs. McNamara's office. Gillen turned and felt the impact of his shoes smacking against the linoleum as he marched back outside and breathed in the serene, damp air.

Air which made him feel like choking.

"Allaire!" he exclaimed, his voice echoing off of the building and vaporizing into a vacuum. A pair of headlamps caught his periphery as a car sped purposefully along the curved entryway of the arena. The earth below him felt wobbly and unstable as he watched.

Go to the school. Someone must know what happened. Maybe they're wrong and she's still there... studying... playing with a friend... necking with a boy for all I care!

The revving of an engine captured Gillen's attention as he spun on his heels toward the front curb of the arena. The vehicle had completed a full circle around the giant dome and was now attempting to make a right turn back onto the main street.

I'll find her... don't panic... there's no reason to panic...

To his surprise, the vehicle slowed to a stop next to the curb of the front entrance sidewalk, the driver seeming to anticipate his approach. A keen sense of awareness that this confrontation could lead to recovering Allaire, losing his life, or something in between, pushed back all other thoughts in his mind as he closed in on the vehicle, and using his hands as buffers, slammed to a stop against the passenger door.

"Gillen!" the woman behind the wheel said, not so much as a statement, but as a command.

"Samantha!" Gillen gasped, his knees trembling. "What are you doing here?"

"Get in," she ordered.

Sliding onto the passenger seat, Gillen reached for the inner handle to shut the door but the sudden acceleration of the vehicle did the work for him. The car careened onto the graded street from which he had just walked, filling the windshield with blurred neighborhood imagery as if it were an impressionistic portrait.

Samantha said, "I was walking into my apartment when Lisa called from the office. She's been trying to reach you. Apparently, Allaire never showed up to practice."

"I know, I just spoke to her instructor."

"Lisa said the school called too. Allaire was spotted leaving the premises during lunch and never returned for afternoon classes."

"Let's go check anyway."

Samantha's death grip on the steering wheel frightened Gillen as the car neared an intersection. The traffic light had been yellow for far too many seconds as she floored the gas pedal. Sailing through the red light, the vehicle bounced as it hit the level road and then continued the descent down the graded street.

"Has she ever done anything like this before?" Samantha asked.

"Never," Gillen stated, with a finality that knew Allaire would not be found roaming the schoolyard. "But let's... let's not get worked up about this. She probably just..." Silence filled the cabin as his mind faltered on formulating a plausible scenario. Unless there had been some inexplicable emergency, this behavior was completely outside of his daughter's character. A reason had to exist, yet the ones that did offered him little comfort.

Gillen struggled to discern one individual from another as they flew through another city block and down the next. "I really appreciate your help," he said, exchanging glances between the road and Samantha, "but perhaps we should slow down just a bit."

"Damn it, I think we're going the wrong way," she said.

The car leveled out at an intersection and then proceeded to wheel around the circumference of the intersecting streets. Gillen clenched his teeth as the neighborhood surrounding them spun dangerously against his vision, and as they neared completion of the maneuver, he finally felt the cruel jostling effect of the brakes as Samantha slammed the vehicle to a stop at a red light.

"Would Allaire have ditched school to meet up with some friends?" she asked.

"They all attend the same school. There's no reason for her to leave early. And she loathes missing skating practice, even when she's ill."

The cabin again fell silent as they drove, the Bay Bridge in the distance a monument piercing through the mist. The motion of the car had been making Gillen's nausea worse. Now, it offered something else: a reminder that at least they were moving, looking, searching. Only when he attempted to lean his cheek against his clenched fist did he notice the tremors in his hands. Outstretched, the trembling in his hands betrayed the composure of his face. A slow, simmering panic was steadily welling up within him, one he was desperately trying to suppress. A stark, horrific realization that in his present reality, he had lost both his wife and his daughter.

The woman behind the wheel didn't flinch, but operated the vehicle with the sort of precision that believed the slightest inching of the car left or right could alter history. Her face, absorbing the orange light of the setting sun, showed no sign of fatigue, but instead held both the light and her own countenance with the same kind of self-assurance as a steelworker on a girder.

The oxygen in Gillen's lungs felt like it had been syphoned from his body, leaving his chest flat and arrested. When he did finally remember how to inhale, there was no air left in the vehicle, leaving only the suffocating grip of asphyxiation. Feeling like a trapeze artist dangling over hysteria by a thread, he wheezed in his seat before working the window crank with his shaking hands. A sudden burst of wind came whistling through the opening, and Gillen found himself leaning forward in his seat, head in his hands, unable to cease from trembling. The rumble of acceleration below his feet jostled his palms against his face, and for an instant, he wondered if the earth was about to swallow him whole.

There's nothing worse than loss, he thought.

Then he shivered when he remembered that there was.

Gazing upward toward the sky, he felt the same light that was radiating Samantha's face, yet without the warmth, the same brightness; without the illumination, the same visual panoramic, minus the wonder. Gillen's eyes then shifted away from the setting sun and onto the rising moon.

"Samantha," Gillen said, more calmly, yet with the kind of vocal tension necessary to make sounds. "What time did you say that antenna shipment arrived today?"

"Around one in the afternoon."

"Was someone there to receive it?"

"Yes."

"No, I mean, who moved the pallets from the loading dock through the Alignment?"

Samantha hesitated. "Two of the engineers."

"How many pallets?"

"Four."

"So the Hexagon was open for a while then? Unmonitored?"

Samantha swerved the wheel to the right, and dragging a tail of dust from behind, the vehicle slowed to a stop along the gravel next to the interstate. After placing the car in park she turned to address him and said, "Why would Allaire ditch school and skating practice in order to sneak onto the moon?"

CHAPTER 4

OFFWORLD

A series of glimpses was all Gillen could recall from the minutes spent driving back to the Iselin Amalgamate building, racing through the corridor, and entering the laboratory with Samantha. Like some heinous growth clawing for liberation, the pulse in his neck pounded against his skin, reminding Gillen with each beat that this moment was not a dream. With eyes darting across the onslaught of indicator switches, dials, monitors, and the panel boards in which they were housed, he suddenly felt lightheaded as he stood in the center of the circular room.

Samantha touched Gillen's arm and pointed toward the Hexagon. "There," she said, directing his attention toward a sizable, red bulb protected by a steel wire guard. "The Hexagon is locked. The engineers followed protocol and closed it after transporting the pallets through the Alignment."

Gillen felt his frame decompress, but only momentarily.

Then where is she?

Moving slowly toward the Hexagon's control board, he punched in a command on the thick black keys and watched the data populate line by line on the screen. The Hexagon had indeed been closed before midafternoon, according to the timestamp. It had not been opened since. Gillen stared at the command line longer than necessary, prompting Samantha to join him at the board. With no more than an essence of a worried glance, she shifted her eyes toward Gillen whose intense gaze had not yet left the screen.

"This tells us nothing," he said, finally blinking.

Samantha watched as Gillen marched over to the workstation nearest the Hexagon and began flipping indicator switches. "Because of the timestamp," she said, mouthing the words as her mind processed the reason. "It only tells us when it was closed, not what happened during the window of opportunity when it was open."

"Correct."

She swiftly motioned toward him. "We've been having issues with the closed-circuit camera on one. Try two."

A high-pitched whine dissipated into the air as the analog monitor flashed a single line of static across the screen before the image came into focus. The colorless picture was at once grainy and then clear, with fluctuating instances of textured richness and noir shadows. The image was smaller than the parameters of the monitor, and although the quality was improving, it seemed to be broadcasting from the parallel environment of another world.

It was the embassy on Ortelius and it was vacant.

"Check the laboratory," urged Samantha.

Gillen's fingers danced across the keyboard, each keystroke a command to alter reality. The picture on the screen jumped out of frame as a single line of static replaced it with a hovering view of the laboratory on Ortelius. The second Hexagon stood off center within the frame, along with a similar setup to the surroundings in which Gillen and Samantha found themselves. The nerve center on the moon was mostly still, save for a few blinking panel lights and the indefatigable second hands of several large wall clocks displaying terrestrial and lunar time zones.

Gillen and Samantha moved their focus across the length of the laboratory over to the other row of workstations. Like a statue positioned by the sculptor to be forever seated, leaning with her head down against the desk, her auburn hair cascading across her shoulder and arm, her other arm a pillow on which her head rested, eyes shut to both the observer and the sculptor, was Allaire.

"Oh, God," Gillen gasped in relief and horror. "She's there. She looks all right. How the hell did she get up there? She's up there all by herself."

Samantha rested a hand on his wrist in acknowledgement that the search was over. "She's resourceful. Just like her father."

An anxious, tearful laugh escaped Gillen's lips as he flipped a switch along the indicator panel and adjusted the gooseneck of a microphone. Speaking softly into the diaphragm he whispered, "Allaire? Can you hear me?"

The audio from Gillen's voice drifted through the speakers in the lunar laboratory. From their vantage point, they could see the VU meter needles moving back and forth like a metronome, but their movement was incongruent with the number of words Gillen had spoken.

"Is there another audio source coming through?" Samantha asked, turning a dial clockwise.

Through their own speakers, Gillen and Samantha could hear sounds originating from a station on earth, being broadcast onto Ortelius, and then picked up and relayed back to San Francisco via the small open microphone on Allaire's workstation. The harmonics were tinny with an occasional hiss, but it was also the ear of his daughter.

"Allaire?" Gillen said again. "Can you hear me?"

Allaire's eyes opened slowly. It was not the action of one who had just awoken, but of one trying desperately to sleep. "Dad?" she said wearily, shifting her head from off the desk and gazing up at the instrumentation panel before her.

"Hey, champ," came Gillen's voice, interpreted by the moving needles.

"Where are you?" she asked, her voice sounding unused.

Gillen wondered at the moment at how technology could both bring people together and cause them vertigo. "I'm on earth."

"Oh," Allaire said, sounding in equal parts disappointed and relieved. She lowered the attenuation on the radio tuner and gave her father's audio a boost. Where one may have thought an explanation would be forthcoming, Allaire simply sat there, leaning against the workstation's desk, staring at the meters, awaiting her father's next statement.

Gillen paused, chuckled to himself, and said, "What are you doing up there?"

From their closed circuit view, Allaire remained mostly inert. Either her inability or else her unwillingness to delve into the reasons for her sudden departure from her home planet was all the excuse Gillen needed to nod and smile. "Don't worry, Allaire. I'll come get you. Stay calm."

Samantha flipped the microphone switch and turned to Gillen. "Our first stowaway."

"Let's make it our last."

Pacing quickly over to the Hexagon, Gillen typed in a command on the keys of the control board and then opened the thin glass guard of a toggle switch. His forefinger and thumb pressed against the metal while his eyes watched for an indication that he had witnessed countless times; the red bulb turning green and the opening of the terrestrial Hexagon.

The bulb remained solid red.

Samantha examined the screen. "Try reentering the command line. One of the technicians had an issue with that last week."

Gillen nodded while clearing the code and then entering the lines which would authorize the unlock mechanism. The lines of code reflected from off their pupils as they squinted to confirm what had been entered. In acknowledgement that it was correct, Samantha flipped the glass guard herself and pressed the metal toggle switch.

The color of red was as blinding as it was unmistakable, and Gillen and Samantha stood idle for a moment, him with his hands on his hips, her with arms crossed against her chest, both with an expression of discontent.

"That's curious," Gillen mumbled, leaning over the keyboard while trying to assuage a simmering anxiety within himself. "Okay then. Next step is to attempt an unlock from the Hexagon on Ortelius."

Samantha nodded and paced back over to the workstation along the opposing wall. After performing a series of similar motions to that which Gillen had done, she pressed a toggle switch on the panel and waited for the command line on the screen to change. Gillen was watching her from across the room, his eyes fixated on the confidence of her movements, the familiarity she had with the machinery, and the almost imperceptible change to her body language the moment after her fingers left the toggle switch.

"No error response?" Gillen asked flatly.

"No response of any kind," replied Samantha, still facing the board. "It's as if we're entering commands the system doesn't even recognize."

Gillen realized he was biting his lower lip and moved instead to squaring his jaw. His head moved from Samantha back over to the monitor and then up again at the red bulb above the Hexagon. For an instant, he felt his shoulders weaken under the burden of worry, and his mind wander to wishing that the light would arbitrarily turn green. That the Hexagon would open of its own accord. That it would respond as it always had before, if the proper sacrifice was offered in a particular way. That the binary world in which it existed would grant them special privileges to bypass reality just this once and allow them access to Allaire through the realm of superstition.

The red bulb remained, and the only change could be seen in Gillen's countenance as he cursed his wandering thoughts and took a deep, conscientious breath. Straightening his posture, he marched over to the workstation and flipped the microphone switch. "Allaire?"

The teenager looked up. "Hi, Dad."

"We'll have this worked out shortly. Just stay put, and I'll have you down soon."

"All right," she said softly.

Gillen shut off the microphone and turned to Samantha. "What time did Walter leave today?"

"A little before me."

"Try calling him at home. I'm sure he can talk us through whatever it is we're missing here."

◂ ◆ ● ● ● ● ◆ ▸

"I'm glad you called," Walter Iselin said, entering the laboratory with an energy and confidence not known to priests and potentates, but instead to architects and engineers. For a man who had just turned sixty, he retained all of the vitality of his younger colleagues, and in many instances, his drive to achieve left them scrambling to catch up. Even the room seemed to acknowledge him, casting halos against his silver hair as he walked past the intervals of lighting and up to where Gillen and Samantha stood at the workstation.

"Thanks for coming in, Walter," Gillen said, his voice feigning courage.

"How's Allaire?" Walter asked.

They pointed toward the monitor with her visage layered behind the screen. Walter examined the scene as one who was a first responder: objectively, empathetically, and rapidly. Within seconds he had ascertained the main obstacles and was off on a new course of action. Withdrawing his glasses from his breast pocket, he slid them just far enough on his nose as to zero in on the sweet spot of his vision, and began digging into the command lines Gillen and Samantha had been executing.

"You think perhaps this is a programming issue rather than a mechanical one?" Gillen asked.

"There's a faulty premise in almost every contradiction. We've all made an assumption about this problem that is incorrect. That's what I'm searching for."

The characters on the screen appeared as if they were being projected from within Walter's glasses, each line of code being generated from inside his mind's eye. His fingers struck each key with authority, as if pressing the tiny squares harder would increase their precision. Without so much as a warning, he shot up from his chair at the workstation and marched across the room toward the Hexagon. He then proceeded to flip multiple switches on the control panel, working the board with the intuitive nature of an operator who knew what to push and what to avoid.

His forefinger and eyes in tandem followed a command line on the screen before flipping open the glass guard and hitting the toggle switch. Walter had been looking up at the red light before his action and had the expression of one who already knew what to expect. The fact that the light remained solid red was merely a confirmation that he could check another variable off his mental list.

"Let's try it again," Walter ordered.

The refrain was repeated as they worked out each permutation. Like a multiple choice quiz, Walter was looking for and then systematically removing only the wrong answers. Gillen and Samantha contributed, but it was Walter who charted out the course.

"We'll get her down," Samantha whispered to Gillen after yet another wrong answer was discovered.

"I know," he replied.

Suddenly, Walter stopped moving. Like the motor of an engine cutting out without warning, the momentum of the room stalled. He stood stoic in the center of the laboratory, not so much lost in thought as trying to push away every ancillary one. Gillen latched onto his intense gaze and followed its train to the closed circuit monitor in the workstation. The scene itself had not changed. Allaire sat at the desk, leaning against her elbows, her head tilted forward, her shoulders slouched, surrounded by indicator lights blinking at random intervals.

Walter approached the workstation with a look of suspicion. He reached for the microphone knob and hesitated. His eyes focused on the upper right-hand corner of the screen. A haze of pale light from the lunar Hexagon cast a blurred sphere within the boundaries of the black-and-white frame. Flipping the switch, he said, "Allaire?"

She looked up at the board. "Grandpa Walt?"

"Hey, kiddo. How are you holding up?"

The girl seemed to blossom ever so slightly, moving herself closer to the microphone. "I'm all right. I'm really sorry about this..."

"Don't worry yourself," Walter reassured her, his voice low and warm. "Say, can you do me a favor? Can you look behind you and tell me if you see the light on top of the Hexagon?"

"I can see it."

"What color is it?"

"Green."

Gillen smacked the desk. "I'll be damned."

"Thanks, Allaire. I'll get back to you."

Samantha shook her head. "How is that possible?"

Walter nodded. "There's your faulty premise."

Gillen marched back over to the Hexagon and glared at the red bulb, his hands on his hips, his eyebrows furled. "That was the very first failsafe we designed into this system. If one Hexagon is locked, the other one by default cannot be open."

"Thus preventing a traveler from getting stuck in the Alignment," Samantha added, as if reciting a catechism.

"Obviously, Allaire made it through the Alignment," Walter said, "but after she arrived on Ortelius and the engineers closed the Hexagon here, the lunar Hexagon malfunctioned and didn't obey the trigger."

"That explains why none of the command lines are working," said Gillen.

"And why there were no error messages," added Samantha. "We were entering commands outside the parameters of the very failsafes we built to prevent this."

"But how the hell could this happen?" asked Gillen, moving back to the workstation. "The lunar Hexagon is tethered to the one here. Open/close. Lock/unlock."

"It malfunctioned," reiterated Walter.

"No, that's not how it would have malfunctioned. If for some reason one of the Hexagons didn't obey a trigger command, and the other Hexagon locked, by default, the mechanics of the system, outside of programming, would automatically resort to locking that Hexagon too, restricting access to the Alignment from both ends. That action is hardware, Walter, not programming. The same thing would have occurred if the Alignment itself had collapsed. No tunnel; no portal."

Walter and Samantha exchanged glances. "But Gillen," said Samantha, "the Hexagons don't actually close the Alignment, only human access to the Alignment. That way we never lose communications with Ortelius."

"Correct," Gillen said, snapping his fingers. "So if we still have communications, that means the Alignment is stable. And if one Hexagon is locked while the other is open, that means this is a mechanical glitch on the lunar Hexagon only."

"Or a mechanical *alteration*," stated Walter.

Their perplexed reactions to his statement belied their remaining composure. The words permeated the air, unable to penetrate antagonistic ears. Gillen was surprised by his own lack of objectivity toward the suggestion, but what bothered him more was the emotion to which it was tied.

"You... think someone betrayed us?" Gillen asked incredulously.

Walter tilted his head ever so slightly. "Careful, Gillen. 'Betrayed' is a lover's term."

Samantha interjected with fervor. "Why would someone do that? For what purpose? Especially this close to the announcement."

Walter meandered back over toward the Hexagon. "You may have answered your own question. In three days we're gonna unveil this marvelous achievement to the entire world. Led by the first ever lunar ambassador. Airtime has already been secured. Minor details of the project have already been leaked to the press. Anticipation is building. An incident like this could undermine the stability of the entire thing."

"But this isn't representative of how the operation is going to work," replied Samantha. "Ortelius will always be occupied by a technician during visiting hours in the event a traveler gets marooned by mechanical or programming failure. A guest would not be permitted access to Ortelius without a technician on premises."

"What about a stowaway?" challenged Walter.

Samantha sighed. "A stowaway, no stationed technician, and an inexplicable mechanical failure?" Walter nodded. Samantha turned to Gillen who could offer little in defense. Shrugging, she said, "This just isn't a contingency we factored in."

"It's possible someone did."

"Who?"

Walter pointed toward the Hexagon screen. "Check the timestamps and see who the last person was to close the Hexagon."

"I can tell you that right now," said Samantha. "It was two of our engineers, Barry Sjöstrom and Richard Kaine."

"Where are they now?"

"Sjöstrom went home for the evening. I said goodbye to him when he left. I assume Kaine did the same."

"Get them back here. If this is a mechanical failure, and it's due to an inadvertent puncture or dislodging of some vital component of the Hexagon while transporting the last of the microwave relay through the Alignment, then they'll be the ones to know about it."

Samantha nodded and walked over toward the phone. Gillen then turned to Walter. "And if it wasn't inadvertent?"

"I believe the word you meant to say earlier was sabotage, and it could be for any number of reasons. Perhaps they were against the addition of the embassy. Perhaps they have Soviet sympathies. Or maybe this is a personal vendetta."

"Against you?"

Walter remained mute, his tongue shifting against his upper and lower mandible. Gillen hesitated. "Against me?"

"It's possible."

"But why? They didn't know Allaire was on Ortelius."

"What if they did?"

CHAPTER 5

LIVING REQUIEM

The city of San Francisco was a series of fragmented images, blurred and colorless, as Gillen viewed them from the passenger seat of Samantha's vehicle. Speeding along the interstate, Gillen watched the Bay Bridge in the rearview mirror begin to recede into the landscape, and something about that visual left him with a sense of lethargy. He quickly looked over at Samantha instead, desperate to remain in the moment, to not be dragged back into the despair of one year ago and to avoid the momentous toll escaping from that despair had taken.

"Barry Sjöstrom is on his way," she had told Gillen and Walter after the phone call. "He said he overheard Kaine on the break room phone just before he left. Apparently, Kaine was calling to find out when the last train was leaving for New York."

Gillen blinked and stood rigidly next to Walter, fighting off the onset of nausea that comes with a surge of adrenaline. "He wasn't scheduled for vacation this week, was he?"

"I don't believe so," Samantha had said.

Walter was squinting at his wristwatch. "I've taken that transcontinental route myself. If memory serves correctly, the last train leaves the station just after eight o'clock."

Gillen had glanced over at the abundance of wall clocks near the workstation and sighed heavily. It was almost seven thirty. "So what are you suggesting? That we go after him?"

"Try to intercept him at the station, yes. Or on the train itself. Worst case scenario, you get off at the first stop in San Jose and take the next train home. But at least you'll have the chance to talk to him. Size up what he's doing... what he's done. In the meantime I'll rally the troops here and we'll start examining some other contingencies."

Before leaving, Gillen had stolen a glance at Allaire in the monitor. He wanted to talk with her just once more. Reassure her that they were working on things. That she would soon be down. Inquire as to what had compelled her to sneak back onto Ortelius. But for the moment, she appeared calm and content, the soft shadows of the camera cocooning her within the safety of its lens.

"I love you, champ," he had whispered, before kissing his forefinger and pressing it against the screen.

The train station was bustling and had the distinct odor of acidic steam. Gillen and Samantha marched along the platform next to the passenger cars, her trench coat open and flapping as she walked, his tied tightly against his body. The ticket lines had been strangely vacant, leaving Gillen to suspect that most of the riders had already boarded, including Richard Kaine. He glanced down at his wristwatch to confirm the time, a time progressively advancing past the roman numerals on the face of the giant clock in the terminal.

It was three minutes to eight.

"That woman is watching us," Gillen whispered to Samantha as they walked, the clicking of her heels and of his shoes not quite in synchronicity.

A woman in an evergreen colored dress suit leaned against a stanchion in the terminal several yards ahead. The piercing hazel of her eyes had captured Gillen's wandering gaze, and the hazel was following their movements in lockstep.

Samantha shook her head. "Don't worry about her," she said as they approached a vestibule. "You have the tickets?"

Gillen blinked and reached into his vest pocket, fishing out the tickets and handing them to the conductor. In a series of motions Gillen found himself inside the lounge of the passenger car, seated in a leather chair next to a large window, with Samantha seated opposite of him, riding with her back against the future.

Running the length of the cabin, recessed lighting brought the beauty of the mahogany wood to life, along with the decorative fixtures consisting of the sharp, elongated lines of art deco. Their chairs' upholstery had a series of gold rivets lined along the length of the arms, and Gillen found running his fingers along those bumps to be a soothing act. Between him and Samantha, a small circular table upheld two tumblers and an ivory ashtray.

"Whiskey sour," she smiled, "settles the nerves."

"I prefer scotch."

"Want me to flag the waiter?"

Gillen had already downed the glass. "This'll do."

The landscape outside the window was rapidly changing from urban to rural. Dusk had overtaken the line leaving the passengers in phosphorescent tubes snaking along the ground, slithering along wooded wilderness and cutting through mountains. The locomotive led the charge, a single headlamp slicing through the blackness like a saber vanquishing a specter.

Samantha withdrew a cigarette from a fresh pack and flicked the lighter, a compact metal square emblazoned with a sunburst. The amber tip of the cigarette pulsed to life, as if activated not by the oxygen from her lungs, but by contact with her mind. "In a few minutes, I'll start searching the forward cars, you head toward the rear."

"What if we don't find him?"

"Then we start knocking on doors in the sleepers."

Gillen gazed out the window, his fingers pressed up against his lower lip. "It's possible Kaine had nothing to do with this," he said solemnly.

Samantha was seated confidently, her jacket still open, her legs crossed, her black capri pants seeming to point toward her black heels. A thin waft of smoke drifted up from the cigarette toward the arched ceiling of the cabin, like a string of incense in which Allaire was the meditation. Samantha hesitated before drawing in another puff and then reaching for her glass. "That is also true."

The waiter walked by with a tray and bent himself slightly at the waist. "Another drink for you or the lady?"

Gillen shook his head. "None for me, thank you."

Samantha also shook her head and the waiter walked on. Her eyes then redirected to Gillen, who appeared to be sinking into himself. Parting her lips, she spoke directly, her voice having all of the tonal qualities of a motion picture leading lady. "I'm trying to recall how old Allaire was when she began ice skating. Was she five or six?"

Knowing full well what Samantha was doing because it was the same distractions he would often use on Allaire, Gillen reached down for what was left of his drink and nodded understandingly. "She was four," he said, gazing thoughtfully at the glass, and specifically, the ice melting within it. He seemed to resign his posture to that of a man affording a moment of reminiscence as he continued, "She wanted to start when she was three, but Cate and I decided to wait an extra year."

"Why was that?"

Gillen chuckled. "Allaire wasn't exactly the most... coordinated child we had ever seen. In fact she was quite accident-prone. Walking into walls. Tripping over nonexistent hazards. Falling off the divan from a seated position. Cate was terrified that Allaire would break her neck in the first week of practice. Of course she didn't, but Cate never could shake that overprotective instinct."

"And yet she was Allaire's biggest supporter."

"You noticed?" Gillen said, genuinely surprised. "Well, yes, I suppose it was obvious. Cate never missed a tournament, and attended more practice sessions than I could. We were both so proud of Allaire, but for Cate it was something more. Of what, I'm not precisely certain. Maybe a confirmation of sorts that Allaire wouldn't face the same ailments that Cate had, or that if she did, Allaire would be strong enough to handle them."

"Did Cate not think she was strong enough to handle her own ailments?" Samantha asked.

Gillen shifted in his seat. "Cate had a lot of rough years; first spaced out, then all in a row. I watched the toll it took on her—"

"The toll it took on both of you."

"—and knew Allaire's fate seemed to be on her mind."

Samantha said nothing, but then nodded. "Cate had to endure a lot."

Gillen exchanged glances between the tumbler and Samantha while continuing to run his fingers along the rivets in the leather. "Yeah."

The ambient chatter of the passenger lounge served as a deflection to Gillen. Men, women, a few children, were seated together, separately;

some couples, some meeting for the first time, a few settling in for what would inevitably become a clandestine tryst.

In contrast to the streets and establishments of San Francisco, the shock of Sputnik had worn off for the evening. A pensive sort of peace etched most faces, the kind experienced when delaying the problem of the current moment by transferring it to the next. The mental reprieve was collectively welcomed by the passengers of the transcontinental route as they barreled across the landscape, the wilderness, and into the general direction of Richard Kaine's destination.

"Shall we get started?" he asked Samantha, who was setting her drink back down on the small table.

"That's excellent whiskey."

"I prefer scotch."

Rising from their seats, Gillen sauntered off down the aisle, his hands in his pockets, heading toward the vestibule and connected cars, while Samantha turned to face the rest of the dining area and forward cars. Before leaving, she spun her heels back toward Gillen as he vanished through the connector door, her eyes holding their gaze as if she could still see him. As if the fact that his body had momentarily occupied the space was enough for her to maintain a visual. She refused to even blink, waiting for the evaporation of his apparition like a wet footprint on hot pavement.

While standing, she noticed the gentle rocking of the floor beneath her, and what little liquid remained in her glass appeared to be trying to stir itself. She gracefully spun around to observe the rest of the car before proceeding down the long aisle with calculated intention, eyes shifting back and forth at the faces of passengers marking each one off systematically. When she reached the end of the cabin, she turned back around and began examining the windows, doors, and exits surrounding her. Through the vestibule and into the next car, she did the same, leaving behind little notice other than the click of her heels and the lingering glare of the occasional rider.

Upon returning to the lounge car, Samantha and Gillen spotted each other after entering from their opposing vestibules. Their eyes smarted from both the intensity of the lights as well as from the uncanny timing of their reunion after combing the train. The center of the aisle was bottlenecked by a dessert cart as a waiter skillfully set each plate in front of a patron. Samantha flashed a weary smile toward Gillen who was starting to appear as though standing would be too great an expectation. She took a step forward in preparation of the clearing of the aisle, before quickly glancing at Gillen and then over at the shadowy landscape speeding past the windows like film at a high frame rate.

Her eyes veered back toward Gillen. His gaze was locked onto a single person seated with his back to the wall of the car, just ahead of the dessert cart. Gillen's stare was a strange combination of relief and daggers. Samantha followed the line of sight and narrowed her vision onto a man in a gray suit, his hat sitting atop his lap, his arms folded nonchalantly against his torso, his head slightly askew as he dozed.

Samantha felt her pulse quicken as Gillen took another step forward. The tiny wheels of the cart squeaked as the waiter maneuvered it by the passengers and down the remainder of the aisle, clearing a path for Gillen. With calculated precision, he stepped lightly and rapidly toward the man, giving little notice to Samantha who was following his lead. When the two reached the minimal floor space in front of the sleeping gentleman, Samantha instinctively placed her hand on Gillen's arm, uncertain as to the reason for her action, yet astonished by the instigative power of his single word.

"Richard," Gillen stated.

The man's eyes opened quickly. A solitary blink was all it took for him to confirm that he had indeed been pulled from his hypnotic slumber. His countenance was that of a man in his forties who had gained a decade of appearance through some lengthy ordeals. Gillen knew the face well, but in that moment, Richard Kaine looked paradoxically different. It was the visage of a man who had once been a corpse and had just now been reanimated. The eye sockets were sunken, the eyes were sterling blue. The cheeks were gaunt, the skin was without blemish. The lips were chapped, the jawline was poised with something to say.

Gillen stared at Kaine for a moment longer than necessary, half in hope that this man was a mirage, half in dread that he was a mirror. "We need to talk."

Kaine slowly shifted glances between Gillen and Samantha. At first, he seemed to be sizing up the situation to which he had awoken, yet his settled expression was that of one trying to understand how what he was witnessing was even possible. Swallowing the stale air in his mouth, Kaine said, "What about?"

"You don't know?" Gillen responded, motionless as the rails upon which they were all riding.

The look on Kaine's face transcended concern. He was downright curious. "Can't say that I do, Gillen."

The loud crack of a teacup taking a hard landing on a saucer caused Samantha's focus to momentarily dart. Gillen's did not. "What happened to the lunar Hexagon today? For the first time ever, they're out of sync."

Kaine straightened his neck as he addressed them. "Why would you think I would have anything to do with that?"

Samantha said, "You and Barry were the last people through the Alignment. After you moved the pallets onto Ortelius, you locked the Hexagon and left. We're wondering if you recall any damage being done to the lunar Hexagon during that transition."

"Why don't you ask Barry, then?" said Kaine, calmly.

"We did," responded Samantha. "Which is why we're on this train bound for New York speaking with you." Kaine's expression didn't change, but the rigidity of his jawline seemed to soften. Samantha asked, "Why are you on this train, Richard? Tomorrow's a school day."

"I'm heading out of town for a few days. I meant to tell you."

"This is a first. You've always informed us of unexpected travel plans before."

Kaine nodded slowly, as if waiting for them to ascertain a truth and yet knowing they never would. "Must have slipped my mind."

The train started a curve along the formation of a hilly terrain, the light from the cars casting long beams against the landscape it hugged. Gillen dug in his heels against the gentle pull of the train as it completed the curve. He then said slowly, almost without effort, "When we stop at the station in San Jose, we're all getting off this train, hopping on the next train back to San Francisco, so that you and Barry Sjöstrom can help us fix the Hexagon... *tonight.*"

The train began a slight grade down a hillside, causing the cars a moment of subtle rocking, and in doing so, gave Richard Kaine the appearance of methodically shaking his head at Gillen. When the terrain leveled out, all that was left were the monolithic stares between Gillen, Kaine, and Samantha, three individuals siloed within the cabin of passengers.

"In that case," began Kaine, his voice dry and tight, "I'll need to go collect my things."

Gillen outstretched his arm but did little in the way of moving as Kaine arose from his seat and side-stepped into the aisle. Samantha followed Gillen from behind as he walked behind Kaine, who towered over each rider he passed. Through the vestibule and into subsequent cars, the trio all headed in the same direction, walking against the pull of the train, proceeding into a past that was a mere millisecond behind the rest of the passengers, and yet was in the past just the same.

As they entered the sleeper car, Gillen looked back at Samantha who was obviously running a few scenarios through her mind. When he turned back toward Kaine, the man had stopped, was facing them, and was opening the door to his room. The compartment was small without being cramped and contained all of the necessities of a lengthy transcontinental journey. The bed had been folded back against the wall, the luggage stowed away neatly underneath a dresser drawer, and next to the single window in the space, a rack giving a brown overcoat the appearance of levitation.

Kaine approached the overcoat first as Gillen and Samantha stepped inside the compartment. As if with muscle memory, Kaine lifted the overcoat from the rack with one hand and flung it over his shoulder. Then with his free hand, he reached into the breast pocket of the overcoat and fished out a compact revolver. Gillen's eyes narrowed in on the gun with interest but not concern. Logic dictated that Richard Kaine would not shoot them in his own compartment with the door wide open.

"Funny thing about a dream," Kaine said, placing the overcoat back onto the rack. "When it starts in someone else's mind, and you become a part of it, in that moment, it all seems to make sense."

No one in the group moved. Gillen and Samantha remained in front of the open door, Kaine standing resolutely against the window. He continued, "Walter painted a mental picture for us all. One of such vivid color and clarity. Skipping innumerable steps which would have otherwise pushed the outcome well beyond the span of our lifetimes. Walter dreamt of a shortcut, a possibility that a naturally occurring phenomenon just waiting to be discovered could make the dream come true in the present. So he built a team, and we found that shortcut. Now, there's a city on the moon."

Gillen found himself nodding, fighting off the onslaught of emotions tied to those memories. "That's right."

Kaine hesitated before taking a step toward Gillen and Samantha, the revolver in his hand resting against his crossed arms. "Jack once told me that this project was going to forever change the world. That even beyond those who ventured out to visit Ortelius, those who simply knew it was there, that it existed, would live their lives in a new way, with a newfound realization that if the nearly impossible itself was achievable," Kaine paused, a weary smirk punctuating his sentence. "Well... you'll forgive the expression, then the sky was the limit."

The train again rocked the floor on which they stood, causing Gillen and Samantha an instant of counterbalance; however, the motion seemed to bypass Kaine entirely, whose stance appeared fixed not to the laws of gravity, but to a predetermined course of actions in which a shimmy played no role. "Do you remember him saying that?"

Gillen knew they would soon be arriving at the station and that decisions would start being made with or without them. He blinked and shot a glance at Samantha before answering, "Of course I remember."

Kaine took another gradual step forward and whispered, as if just to Gillen, "Do you still believe it?"

"Richard, listen to me—"

"Because I do. I'm still dreaming, Gillen. I still see the vision, even if reality has changed, albeit not for everyone."

"Richard..."

Kaine's final step closed the distance in the room, and as he stood in front of Gillen, he looked down at him not as one who was playing intimidation tactics, but as one pleading for his life. "Tell me to still believe," Kaine said, begging. "Please tell me that this is real."

"Richard—" but Gillen was interrupted by the sight of his own hand enveloped by Kaine's as the man slowly lifted it toward their faces. Kaine's hand was muscular and contained an inescapable strength as the color drained from Gillen's fingers.

"You would never lie to me, would you?" Kaine asked, while sliding the cool handle of the revolver into Gillen's captive hand. "I know Jack would. But you wouldn't, right?"

"Richard, calm down," Gillen said with a parental levelheadedness. With his free hand, he reached for the barrel of the weapon, trying to pry it out of his own fingers which Kaine had secured tightly around the handle and trigger.

"Promise me that you wouldn't lie to me, Gillen," Kaine reiterated, his eyes unblinking.

"I have no intention of lying to you, Richard, but we need to discuss this without—"

"Because if you did," Kaine said, changing both his tone and the positioning of the gun, the barrel now pressed tightly against his own temple, "then none of this matters, and I'd have destroyed myself for nothing."

"Richard, stop this!" Samantha ordered, joining Gillen in trying to pry Gillen's fingers from off the revolver and out of Kaine's hand.

"Do you keep your word? Do you?"

"Richard..."

"Because if you don't, you might as well just put me out of my misery."

Samantha wedged her body in between the two men and began shouldering Kaine back. "That's enough, Richard," she said, her entire body weight pressing into his sternum.

Gillen gazed at Kaine in bewildered horror, at the sight of the weapon in his own hand, and at the deeply suppressed feeling only ever so slightly rising to the surface. A feeling of oncoming sickness.

Like a virus one suspected was inevitable but the symptoms have yet to manifest. It was the nascent yet obscene sensation of Gillen looking into the face of Richard Kaine, and wishing he had the courage to pull the trigger.

So abhorrently shocking was the instant, that at the moment Samantha freed Gillen's fingers from Kaine's hand, Gillen found himself stumbling backward against the interior of the compartment, hitting the wall with a thud.

The revolver clattered to the floor and no one looked at it. No one looked at each other. They simply inched themselves away from each other and tried to find their internal mechanism for decompression. Kaine leaned against the window, lost in the torrent of his own consciousness. Samantha stood with a hand pressed against the foldaway bed, trying to compartmentalize what had just occurred. Gillen had his back up against the wall with his legs outstretched just enough that his heels could keep him standing, his bruised hand being massaged by the other.

"I can't help you," Kaine whispered. "I'm so very sorry."

"Here, Gillen," Samantha said quietly while helping him stand upright. She could feel him quiver from the sudden weight placed on unprepared legs. His first two steps were cautious, as one arising from bed, and as his stature straightened, the image of Richard Kaine continued to be a carcinogen in his body.

"Ladies and gentlemen," the overhead speakers said, "we'll be arriving at San Jose Station momentarily. Again, next stop, San Jose."

Gillen stepped out of the compartment and began pacing the aisle. Samantha appeared torn as to whether to follow him or stay with Kaine, but her loyalty to Gillen won out and she quickly joined his frantic walk.

"Just breathe, Gillen."

"I'm all right," he pressed, flexing his hand.

The vestibule door opened easily and Gillen and Samantha made their way back into the dining car. Making his way past patrons and porters, Gillen found an open stool at the bar and leaned in on the beveled wood, its veneer a degree of sheen to be admired without being reflective as that would be the last thing a drinker would want to see.

"What can I get for you, sir?"

"Scotch, water," Gillen said, gesturing with his forefinger and thumb the amounts of each.

Samantha stood behind him, exchanging worried glances between the window of the vestibule and the bar. "What should we do about Richard?"

The sensation of drag hit them both simultaneously as the train began to decelerate. A sip from his glass acted as an elixir, granting instant, albeit temporary, relief from the worst of the residual tension. Gillen knew it was impossible for the alcohol to have an effect that quickly, and thanked his acquired muscle memory for doing some of the psychological work. After another sip, he set the glass down on the coaster and turned back toward Samantha who was continuing her lookout for Kaine.

"There's nothing we can do," he said, in the tone one employed when trying not to sound defeated. "Whatever he did or didn't do, he's of no use to us in that condition. Hopefully Barry can..."

Samantha squinted toward the window again before turning back to Gillen. "Hopefully Barry can what?"

Gillen's focus had narrowed on someone at the end of the dining car. His body rose cautiously from the stool as his hand tossed an undetermined amount of dollars onto the counter. With an unblinking glare, he moved past Samantha and squared his jaw. "There she is," he said.

"Who?"

"The woman from the train station terminal. The one in the green dress suit who was watching us."

Samantha, hesitant to retrain her attention away from the vestibule window, turned around and spotted the woman who had just finished a cup of coffee at an end table and was preparing to leave. "Why is that a problem? She was probably just waiting to board, same as us."

The woman tied her gray overcoat and reached for her clutch purse next to the ashtray. The instant she was erect, her eyes locked onto Gillen's and her body involuntarily jerked. Gillen took a step forward. "I know her..."

"Who is she?" Samantha pried, resting her hand on Gillen's shoulder in hopes of reeling in a needless distraction.

The woman met his gaze for only an instant, but in that gaze was an expression that Gillen had once known and only now realized that he had forgotten. It was the look of remorse directed at him for something outside of his control. For the indefinable aura he unwittingly projected into the world which justified their constant stares of sorrow. Whether they saw him assisting Cate through a rough public moment, or whether they simply knew of his life as a caretaker, the acknowledgments were always the same. The woman's momentary glance had triggered the emotion deep within Gillen which he had despised more than any other. She had looked on him with pity.

Gillen stood motionless, his chest having felt filleted. The shock of the emotion was only eclipsed by the curiosity as to why she had expressed it in the first place. Cate wasn't there. Cate was dead.

The woman glanced down while plotting a course of action. Gillen narrowed his eyes as the rocking from the train ceased and the scenery outside the cabin came to a standstill. "I know her," he repeated to Samantha, and slightly tilted his head as he registered the woman's athletic figure, short brunette hair, and haunting hazel eyes. An eerie sense of nostalgia tingled his spine as two realizations dawned upon him. The first was who this woman was. The second was why it was impossible.

He stepped past a cluster of riders loitering in the aisle as the woman turned to leave. Reaching out his hand in protest, he yelled, "Danielle!" But she had vanished through the vestibule door.

"Gillen," Samantha said, struggling to reach him amongst the passengers standing to disembark. "Where are you going?"

He turned to address her. "I'll meet you on the platform, stay there!" With a seamless motion he bolted across the diner car and unceremoniously shimmied his way through the teeming throng of passengers at the door. Wresting the handle away from another patron, he exited the car and found himself in a second lounge area. His eyes danced wildly from one rider to the next, scanning the room for that overcoat, that hair, that walk.

That was Danielle. I know it was.

The second car was packed, yet these passengers seemed to be on this trip for the duration, for they remained seated, drinking, playing cards, smoking, and chatting with fellow riders. Gillen's vision shifted frantically from one section of the car to the next. The woman's swift departure was incongruent with the laissez-faire attitude of the room. He moved forward gradually, each step an exchange of energy for vantage point. The train station's platform was well lit and could be clearly seen through the long, lounge car windows. As he sidestepped his way down the aisle, his head rose and ducked in accordance to the various visuals obstructing his view.

Dozens of riders began to disembark, flooding the platform with shuffling bodies and porters carrying luggage. Beyond them, dozens more passengers stood along the terminal stanchions awaiting their turn to board. Gillen's clear view of the platform had diminished and he was quickly running out of car. Reaching for the vestibule door, he left the lounge behind and breathed in the cool evening air of San Jose that strangely smelled of fruit.

"Gillen!" Samantha called out from the vestibule steps. "Where are you going? What about Richard?"

Gillen had lost interest in Richard Kaine. Giving a firm tug on the forward rim of his hat, he penetrated the bustling crowd and felt his shoulders motioning side to side as he weaved around passengers and carts. A woman caught his attention as she walked along the platform, her brunette hair bobbing in the breeze.

Not her...

Shifting his focus the other direction, he steadily approached the vast open space of the station terminal and the clusters of passengers waiting for an available porter. The number of gray overcoats was staggering, so Gillen maintained his visual on faces and hair only. She had short, neck length brown hair that had come to a frilly curve toward her chin. He also vaguely recalled a thin white headband. There had been a clutch purse of some kind, a green dress suit, and white heels. But none of that was as helpful as her walk. Her stride. The way she moved stood in contrast to her contemporaries, for her feet did not seem to struggle against the pull of gravity, but instead propelled her forward with power and ease. It was the walk of one who was not fighting to stay on top of the earth, but of one who had discovered an equilibrium with it.

Danielle.

The terminal got darker the deeper he went, yet it was not for lack of light. Strategically placed fixtures did their best to illuminate, installed along support columns at various intervals. Gillen found them to be problematic, as they pushed back the shadows and cast long horizontal images against the cement floor, making it appear as if someone was standing just beyond the corner of each stanchion. Spinning back for a moment, he did a panoramic of the station and noticed that most of the passengers were now behind him. Fearing that he had missed her, he contemplated heading back into the crowd, and perhaps back onto the train.

His leather soled shoes scraped the cement while performing a pivot before his entire body froze in place. It was not his eyes that had detected her: It was his ears. The faint clicking of heels echoing from an adjacent corridor had him turning back toward the end of the terminal. Unlike many of the shadows tracing the floor, this one had actually moved.

"Danielle!" he called out, his voice bouncing back at him from against the walls.

The corner of the terminal led to a partitioned port with a single glass-block wall with open air exits on either side. When Gillen reached it, he saw an image moving rapidly away, shapeshifting through the distortion of the glass block. The nighttime air pressed against his cheeks as his shoes pounded the pavement, and again, the scent of fruit permeated his nostrils. Once outside, he spotted the woman across the street, walking briskly toward an alleyway conjoining two large warehouses. The structures were only a few stories tall, but seemed to stretch along the rural terrain for miles. Rows of vents and transom windows lined the weathered exterior of the buildings, and in faded lettering, a giant sign advertised the name and logo of a distribution company.

As Gillen crossed the boulevard, another woman appeared behind him, trailing his lead by several hundred feet. Samantha had exited the terminal on the opposite end and had spotted Gillen just beyond the glass-block wall. She too noticed his target seconds before the woman vanished into the alleyway, as well as Gillen's subsequent pursuit. Still perplexed as to his motive, Samantha reluctantly continued to follow him as the last of his coattails disappeared into the darkness.

The woman had increased her pace from brisk to frantic in an effort to lose the indomitable presence of Gillen in pursuit. With agility she maneuvered along the cement alleyway, avoiding cracks in the pavement and even dodging a sewer grid, showing tremendous confidence in the stability of her white heels. Her arms motioned back and forth in stride with her legs, gaining traction and speed against the resistance of the wind.

Gillen charged into the alleyway with the smack of each step reverberating off the thin walls of the warehouses. His vision jostled as he attempted to keep her in focus while running, painfully aware that she was still well ahead of him. The burning in his leg muscles spoke of his sedentary, urbane lifestyle, made all the more pronounced as the pavement beneath his feet turned to cobblestone. With each step sending a bolt of discomfort through his frame, he wondered how long Danielle could maintain her current pace without diverting.

His thought proved true as the woman disappeared around a corner where two sections of the warehouse separated. Gillen struggled to keep pace against the unforgiving bricks beneath him, his knees now taking the brunt of the punishment. With mere seconds before he would turn the corner, he wondered if his lungs could propel him much farther or if his raspy panting was merely another indicator of his substandard physical condition.

Angling himself accordingly, Gillen ditched the alleyway in favor of the corner the woman had taken. The relief was instantaneous. The ground beneath him was now a soft asphalt, used for easy transport of pallets and crates. Through the vents above, Gillen could now clearly make out the contents of the warehouse and even which areas were dedicated to which fruits. These were storage warehouses for the farmers who populated the San Jose acreage surrounding the train station, the scent of tangerines and mangos a welcome distraction as Gillen continued his dash toward the woman.

"Danielle!" he called out again.

Her momentum was indefatigable. The breeze rustled the edges of her overcoat as she ran, all the while being stalked by her enlarged shadow against the warehouse wall. Gillen also was being pursued by his own silhouette, and behind it, the reflection of Samantha who had just turned the corner. The three individuals raced in alignment along the side street, guided from above by the moonlight of a starless sky.

"Gillen!" Samantha called out.

"Danielle!" Gillen replied.

The long stretch of warehouse was ending, giving way to another alley which led back to the main road. Gillen watched as the woman vanished around the alleyway corner, her being momentarily ablaze by the amber floodlight anchored above a fire door. Once she was out of sight, Gillen felt his adrenaline surge just as it had the last time he had lost visual on her. Despite his body's protests, he continued running.

A shower of iridescence passed over him as he turned the corner and saw a cracked, full-length mirror leaning against a dumpster beneath the flood lamp. The amber hue ricocheted off the glass in prismatic detail, casting light and color out into the deserted alley. As Gillen passed it, his eyes were drawn not to the spectacle, but to the woman running in the mirror. She had reached the sidewalk and had begun darting across the four-lane street. He focused in on her and wondered if she was heading back toward the train station. His periphery alerted him to something else.

A single glint of chrome flashed off in the distance. The moment had been hardly noticeable. Yet Gillen blinked and turned his vision toward the road in curiosity of the surreptitious strobe. The woman had cleared the boulevard diagonally and was now running away from the train station toward a series of small stores. With a slight hop, Gillen felt the boulevard partition underneath his feet as he cleared the first two lanes and started for the next.

His eyes remained peeled on the woman until he heard the unmistakable screeching of tires skidding on pavement. At that instant, he realized what the glint had been. Whirling back around toward the road behind him, he gasped aloud at the sight of a pitch-black vehicle careening around Samantha who had also not seen the oncoming disaster. With headlamps as dark as the tint of the car, it wheeled violently to the right as Samantha screamed. She leapt from her spot on the street, narrowly missing the chrome bumper, and landed a few yards away from the impact as the vehicle swerved to a gyrating stop along the sidewalk.

Gillen gazed at the scene in horror, too stunned to blink or move. His mind ordered his muscles to submit and with strained dexterity he began to walk toward Samantha on trembling limbs. Stumbling forward, he knelt down next to her as she slowly pushed herself into a sitting position. His hands cupped her face as he looked into her eyes to reaffirm that she was alive. Samantha nodded in reply. When he removed his hand, he saw an imprint of blood on his palm. He gazed up to see a trickle of crimson on her cheek from the impact of her face to the gravel. She had a bruise on her forehead and some soot on her neck, but other than that, she appeared more stunned than scathed.

The driver of the vehicle was already gazing at Gillen when the two locked eyes. The man made no attempts to roll down his window, to exit the car, to check on Samantha, to lambast them for their recklessness, or to acknowledge his own. He merely stared with an expression devoid of interest. It was not the face of a sociopath. It was the face of a drunkard.

As Gillen helped Samantha to her feet, the vehicle carefully drove back onto the road and slowly barreled its way into the twilight, the glint of bumper chrome turning to silhouette against the backdrop of headlamps beaming into the night.

"Are you all right?" Gillen asked, his voice cracking just a little.

Samantha's head motioned in the affirmative, yet her eyes held the reflective moisture of one still processing the cheating of death. "I'm okay," she whispered. Then, without a moment's pause she added, "Gillen, who was that woman?"

He did not answer her until they had cleared the road, all the while hobbling on shaky legs and vengeful joints. When they reached the sidewalk, he drew in a long breath and said, "That was Jack's ex-wife."

"Danielle DaLette?"

"She went back to her maiden name after their divorce. Hoyne."

Samantha shrugged. "Okay. Danielle Hoyne then. Why in the world were we chasing her down?"

Gillen's reply was abrupt. "Because Danielle Hoyne is supposed to be dead."

CHAPTER 6

THE EVENTS OF THIS DAY

Samantha held a cigarette to her lips as her other hand fumbled with the lighter. With trembling fingers she tried to strike the flame. Gillen reached across the booth within the mostly vacant train station diner and gently took both the cigarette and lighter. After a couple of puffs from his own lips, the tip of the paper crackled to life and he handed the cigarette back to Samantha.

"I'm sorry," Gillen said softly, "about what happened out there. I can't... imagine living with myself... if something awful..."

"I should have checked the road before crossing," Samantha replied, dismissively. "Now, tell me more about Danielle Hoyne."

Gillen blinked and gazed down at his coffee cup on the table. "Mr. Rainer?" the nurse had said in the hospital waiting room. "The doctor will see you over in this hallway."

Brace yourself. Cate is already dead.

Gillen remembered rising slowly from the seat and marshaling one foot in front of the other. The memory had all of the chaos and sterility of the hospital environment still woven into the fabric of the images. As he turned the corner, he witnessed the doctor heading toward him from down the corridor, the lights from above causing interval flashes against the man's head mirror as he walked. The doctor was about Gillen's height, slim, with narrow, dark rimmed glasses and wearing what Gillen suspected was a perpetual five-o'clock shadow. His countenance was both rugged and poised, not because of genetics, but because of necessity.

"Mr. Rainer, I'm Dr. Thomas," the man said disarmingly. "I was the physician on call when your wife was brought in."

Gillen nodded blankly. *It's all right, Doctor. Just say the words.*

"She... came into the hospital unresponsive. By that time, there was little we could do to revive her. She died this afternoon."

Gillen had stood there, nonplussed. The words had reached his ears with little purpose beyond the confirmation that his intuition had been right. Cate was already gone.

"I'm terribly sorry for your loss, Mr. Rainer."

I love you, Cate.

"Tell me, Dr. Thomas," Gillen had said, his throat closing up, "because... I just need to know."

"Yes?"

"Did she suffer?"

"Probably not. The impact of hitting the water from such a high point most likely rendered her unconscious before she drowned."

"No," Gillen corrected. "I don't mean from the water. I mean from the glass shards... of the windshield... when she went through it."

Dr. Thomas had hesitated before answering, seeming to measure his words with the same amount of concern that he gave to his patients. "Your wife didn't have any lacerations that I saw, Mr. Rainer."

Cate jumped, you fool.

"Gillen?"

His eyes darted up from the coffee mug to see Samantha glaring at him quizzically. She said, "I'm all right. Really. Now please, tell me about Danielle Hoyne."

The diner was quiet as most of the passengers from the station had either boarded or left. Gillen and Samantha sat across from each other in a booth that was positioned against a giant window accented with jade-green tile. The table between them had a speckled white coating that smelled of condiments and cardamom, and on the table was a cup of coffee and a cup of tea, each with an individual hand around their mug absorbing the ambient heat.

"There's not much to tell," Gillen finally blurted. "Of course, I knew Jack for years before he met Danielle. I even suggested to Walter that he should hire Jack for the engineering role at Iselin Amalgamate. Cate and I had watched him cycle through one short-term relationship after another. When it came to women, Jack certainly had a type. Nothing in his life really changed until he met Danielle. She was different from the others. Then one day, I hear they went to the courthouse and got hitched. Some time after that, Jack tells me they're splitting up. He says Danielle moved out and moved on... to Los Angeles, I believe."

Samantha nodded as she followed the timeline of the story, interspersing sips from her tea and puffs from her cigarette. "Go on."

"Well," he said, seeming more fatigued. "A few months later, Jack tells me and Walter that they finalized the divorce. So we take him out for a drink but he doesn't stick around. After that night, I saw Jack even less outside of work hours, and even then he was pretty despondent. Six months goes by. A year goes by. Then one day Jack randomly mentions that Danielle had passed away from some illness. Diphtheria, I think. He was quite shaken by the news, which led to his further emotional and mental decline."

"Fascinating," Samantha whispered, as the steam from her tea drifted between them. "So that would mean Danielle died around the same time as Cate? About a year ago?"

Gillen pursed his lips and nodded. "Unless Jack lied about her death."

"What makes you so certain that the poor woman we just chased all around tarnation was Danielle Hoyne?"

Around the soda fountain, the proprietor of the establishment had taken charge of a broom and began sweeping the far end of the diner. He maneuvered the handle with proficiency and seemed to have a motion in place so as not to miss a single crumb. Gillen stared at the man for a moment and then thought to himself that being a witness to excellence was something he never wished to take for granted.

The instant gave Gillen strength to lift the cup from the saucer and bring it to his lips. The emotion it triggered was not so much from the coffee but from the aroma. *That bakery near my house. Buying doughnuts and coffee beans for the family on Saturday mornings. How old was I?*

He remembered her hair. It was dark umber and had cascaded down her adolescent cheeks in gentle waves. She owned a subtle beauty, neither striking nor forgetful. It had been nearly twenty-three years and Gillen had never forgotten that version of her. She existed in his life as a phantom, relegated to the deepest recesses of his memories and resurrected only in his dreams. Their courtship had been so short, their interactions so brief, and yet somehow, in the auspices of providence, his love for her had remained unbroken. A thread, woven through a fragment of a lifetime, had tethered his heart to hers, and that inseparable connection had withstood the test of time.

Gillen Rainer had been seventeen when he first laid eyes on Danielle Hoyne who had been all of sixteen. They had met at the bakery, both running the same task for the same items for their individual families. It began as a ritual every Saturday morning, and soon he was no longer complaining about the errand, but demanding it. On the third encounter, he finally mustered up the courage to introduce himself. While standing in line, he sensed her presence behind him. With sweaty palms and a palpitating heart, he had pivoted on his heels and thrust out his hand. "What was your name again?" he had opened with, surprised at how suave it had sounded.

If he had been expecting a coy response, she set a new expectation by staring him straight in the face and cocking her slanted grin. "Danielle," she said reaching for his hand. "What was yours again?"

Her hand slid into his with the ease of one neither overly confident nor reserved. It was the handshake of a girl comfortable in her own skin. He smiled as he suddenly felt unsteady on his feet. "I'm Gillen. It's nice to finally meet you."

Danielle nodded, her curious smirk seemingly an indelible part of her facial features. "Gillen. That's an interesting name. Does your family call you Gil?"

"Thankfully not."

"Agreed," she replied, and they both laughed nervously. "It's nice to finally meet you too, Gillen-not-Gil. So tell me, how is it that we always seem to be at this bakery every Saturday morning?"

"Especially since the doughnuts here aren't that good," he whispered, momentarily leaning forward.

"Frankly," Danielle said, "I was out voted. My father and mother both insisted on it and so did my two younger sisters. I much prefer the little stand over by the promenade."

The next Saturday morning, the two met again at the bakery and ordered the same items for their families. "Coffee beans and doughnuts?" Gillen had asked.

"Coffee beans and doughnuts," Danielle had replied.

"And something extra for you," he added, placing a small bag into her hands.

The paper crinkled as she unwrapped a perfectly round cruller from the promenade stand. She gazed at it for a moment longer than Gillen thought necessary, and for an instant, made him wonder if he had somehow missed the mark. When her eyes rose back to meet his, her expression still had the indelible smirk, but with more warmth around the edges.

"I had a feeling all week that you were going to do this," she said, her voice relaxed and mellow. "As soon as I was back home last Saturday, I had this thought, and I knew."

Gillen laughed in relief. "Really? Am I that obvious?"

"Yes," she said. "Well, your character is."

"My character, huh? You could tell I'm a romantic?"

"I could tell you're kind."

Saturday mornings at the bakery quickly became a much longer errand. Each had initially claimed to their families that it was due to longer lines, so they were encouraged to head out earlier in the morning, which only gave them even more time to stand and chat about the challenges of school and cities they wished to one day visit. Their conversations flowed like a torrent, interrupted by brief moments of repose where they simply gazed into each other's eyes and wondered why every day wasn't like this.

That was the morning Gillen had suggested, "May I... walk you home?"

Danielle had shifted her hips as she laughed. "Of course, silly."

Hand in hand, the two sauntered down residential sidewalks, each carrying their grocery bag. They both felt keenly aware of the occasional stares of either amusement or disapproval they received as they passed by single family homes with children playing in the front yards, mothers sitting on porch steps, and fathers stretched out on their lawns while reading the newspaper. Gillen had asked Danielle if she was still comfortable holding his hand. She had replied, "Why wouldn't I be?"

Gillen had difficulty withholding his smile, and decided to never think about those stares again.

The following Saturday, Gillen had made sure their orders were first in the queue, guaranteeing them more time together outside of the bakery. The bell above the door had barely finished its peal before he had the two bags and Danielle back on the sidewalk and detouring for a nearby park.

"You know what I think?" Danielle had said, offering Gillen a bite from the cruller he had secured for her from the promenade stand.

"Thank you. What's that?" he responded.

"I think you and I are going to have to find another way to see each other soon."

"You mean in addition to Saturday mornings?"

"I mean instead of."

The two sat on a park bench overlooking a grassy hill that gave way to a breathtaking view of the bay. The sunlight gleamed off the waves on the water, glistening like sparks of electricity across a circuit board. Shifting his vision back toward Danielle, he leaned in a bit and flashed an exaggerated frown. "Why is that?"

"My father said we have to cut back on frivolities for a little while. My younger sister is sick."

"I hope with nothing too serious."

"Hard to tell," she said. "Emily has been losing weight for the last few months and just this week started having trouble getting up the stairs to her bedroom. Last night they called for the doctor to come after she fell from a standing position next to the kitchen sink. It was as if her legs just completely went out on her."

"Is she all right?"

"Just a bruise, but she doesn't seem the same." Danielle spoke softly and directly, as if retelling a sequence of events. "Last Sunday, the pastor at our church added her to the congregation's weekly prayers. He said that he would stop by tomorrow after the service and lay hands on her. Ask God to heal her, I guess."

Gillen nodded thoughtfully, his mind factoring numerous things at once. "Do you think that will help?"

Danielle shrugged. "Father says it will. But until then, no more trips to the bakery. Today was it for a while."

Gillen's arm had already been stretched out against the back of the bench when they began eating. He had enjoyed the sensation of her dress up against his skin along with the tangles of her hair that curled at the ends against his arm. It was the thrill of a brush with femininity. Yet as she spoke, Danielle had leaned in more toward him, turning to witness the reassurance of his face.

As he gazed at her, Gillen said, "How can I help?"

Danielle did not immediately respond, for it was a question without an answer. Both the physical and the metaphysical needs for her sister were being treated by their respective experts. The rest was out of her hands. Danielle stared at Gillen a moment longer, her eyes shifting hopefully for some new revelation to dawn upon them. And then, rather without warning, she let out a brief sigh and slowly began leaning in toward him.

The intention of her movement would have been obvious to any onlooker, and they would have been wrong. For only Gillen knew her true intention, and lowered his shoulder for her as the soft flesh of her cheek pressed against his shirt and she sank her slender frame into his embrace. With kismet energy he had held her, his arm tucked underneath her head, his free hand caressing her cheek, and his mind formulating what would be his first ever prayer. *God... if you're listening... please heal Danielle's sister. Amen.*

The summer had progressed, and with it, the blossoming love between two youthful teenagers. With the bakery now out of the question, Gillen had made a point to swing by after school on occasion to lend a textbook... or a cruller, the ironic chicanery in the fact that the two lovers didn't even attend the same school. Nevertheless, Gillen had boldly made his presence known to the Hoyne family on multiple visits during which he would stand in their yard chatting with Danielle, or sit on their porch and study with the girl he couldn't imagine his life without. He had met the other sisters, introduced himself to the mother, and gone so far as to offer a helpful hand to the father as the man steadied himself on a ladder.

Danielle had watched with pride and curiosity, the former due to Gillen's gallantry in trying to infiltrate the family, and the latter due to their almost total disregard for his existence. Courtesy was not dead within the Hoyne residence, and Gillen was routinely offered a beverage during his increasingly frequent visits. However, as certain as each family unit had their unique internal balance, such was the case that Gillen Rainer suddenly seemed too much of a counterweight.

"So they don't want me around anymore?" he had asked incredulously one afternoon in the park,

Danielle nestled up against him underneath an oak tree.

"They didn't say that," she said in a tone void of exasperation. It was instead the tone of regret. "I don't think it's about you, really. I think it's about Emily. She's getting worse and they just don't want strangers around the house right now."

"That's the whole point," Gillen protested. "I don't wish to be a stranger. I wish to be a part of your family. To help them. To help you."

"And I love that about you," Danielle assured him, her eyes narrowing in on his. "You're the kindest person I've ever met. You make me so happy."

"As you do for me."

"What you and I have will last. My family just feels like they need a little space right now. Some time to process what the next steps for Emily will need to be."

Gillen sighed heavily, shut his eyes, and wondered why any of this was anyone's business but theirs. The emotion was visceral, churning inside of him, demanding a response. Love was more complex than he had envisioned, but the reasons why seemed about as alien as flying saucers from another galaxy. He tried to pinpoint the motives, crisscrossing his actions, their reactions, and none of it seemed to settle the multiple choice question which was: Why should they not be together?

He had opened his eyes and regained control of his emotions. The simmering faded, the confusion tabled, and the awareness of his dwindling time left with Danielle repositioned itself as his foremost thought.

"We'll find a way to make this work," he had said matter-of-factly. *That's the only correct answer to this equation.*

The sunlight from behind the trees was being filtered through the leaves and had cast a series of long rays along Danielle's auburn hair. As the breeze rustled the branches the rays motioned against her like waves, hypnotizing Gillen's vision with the image of his ideal.

"Danielle," he whispered gently.

"Yes?"

"I love you."

The words had appeared on his lips before his conscious mind had formulated them. These words had instead derived from his subconscious, from his deepest values. As soon as he spoke them to her, he couldn't imagine a parallel universe in which he hadn't.

What proceeded was not their first kiss, but what years later Gillen would recall as their first. Danielle took his head in her hands and drew him to her lips, his arms wrapping around her torso and securing her place by his side. In tandem they sensed their love breaking through the confines of caution like a supernova, reaching out into the farthest recesses of their individual minds and tethering them to a unified purpose. This moment, their moment, belonged only to them. Their lips then parted and their foreheads touched; their eyes locked onto each other in confirmation of a decision which required no verbalization. Only action.

Danielle had never been to Gillen's house, which rested along a row of other two-story homes in an only incrementally better part of town. Gillen had previously told her about his father and mother, his younger brother, Alden, and their lazy dog, Fritz. He had even shared a few details about Danielle with them. However, on that day, there would be no introductions for Gillen's father was at work, and his mother and brother would be visiting his aunt. As Gillen reached for the front door, his heart was pounding.

Leading Danielle by the hand through the living room, kitchen, and stairwell, he had motioned that they would need to ascend to the second level of the house. She nodded and smirked in the way only Danielle could, and for a moment, he watched her from behind as she began up the steps, her fingers slowly circling the newel post before sliding up the wooden railing.

When they arrived at the landing, Gillen opened his bedroom door and grimaced upon seeing his unkempt bed. *Of all the days to forget...* Much to his relief, the rest of his room was in decent shape and even had the pleasant scent of midafternoon air due to an open window. Gillen stepped to the side as Danielle gradually walked in, seeming to adjust to the environment of his room and the memory she was about to create there.

Gillen turned to face the window and asked, "Shall I draw the curtains?" By the time he had finished the task, Danielle had already begun unbuttoning her dress.

The afternoon had approached evening, and they both knew it was time to go. They stood at the landing holding each other, fingers running the length of arms, lips placing finishing touches on necks. Each had been aware of how little they knew going into that room, and yet, through the instances of curiosity and tenderness, they had left the bedroom older and with a new found trust in their ability to interpret one another.

"I'll see you soon," Gillen had stated, not as an inquiry but as an imperative.

"Yes," she responded, "you'll see me soon."

That day changed Gillen's life, for he knew that love was not just an abstract sentenced to live two dimensionally between the pages of novels, but a powerful, life-affirming action between two individuals who shared the same values. Danielle Hoyne was now a permanent value.

The week that passed infused Gillen with confidence in his thoughts, in his decision making, and in his relationships. He found discourse with his neighbors more interesting. The nuance of literature became more pronounced. And even his chores seemed to serve a grander purpose in building his self-esteem. His mother was the first to notice, followed by his father. Gillen replicated a familiar smirk and said, "I'm happy to be alive and I'm happy to be me."

The effervescence carried him through until that Sunday afternoon. The day was warm and breezy, yet the atmosphere held the static of oncoming rain. Gillen sensed it as he bounced down the stairwell and out onto the patio. The summer air struck him with complexity, as if it were overcompensating for the approaching storm. He shut his eyes and breathed in the memories of Danielle, her mere existence inflating his lungs to capacity.

As he opened his eyes, he saw her, walking up the street from afar. Her sudden manifestation caused no surprise to him, but rather a calm affirmation that they were indeed inseparably linked. Walking next to her was a man. Narrowing his focus, Gillen recognized the individual as Danielle's father. The image gave him no hesitation, no trepidation, only the intuitive knowledge that if he was to do anything in this world, it was to plant his footing solidly on the porch.

Danielle's father pushed the old wooden gate open slowly, his other hand firmly on his daughter's shoulder. His face was friendly, the kind that no matter the degree of tumult he had experienced, would always err on the side of negotiation. Danielle's face however, was easier to read, showing all of the hallmarks of a sleepless night of weeping.

"Hey, Gillen," the father tried to say nonchalantly while stopping himself and Danielle short of the porch step. "How are you today?"

For a moment, Gillen withheld his reply, not because he didn't have one, but to watch the man wait. "I'm doing fine," he said evenly, then shifted his eyes to his love. "Danielle, are you all right?"

Both of the Hoynes stood just below Gillen on the walkway, each crestfallen, but not for the same reasons. Danielle stood broken before him because she was still a teenage daughter. The hovering force dictating Mr. Hoyne's actions was yet to be determined.

"Gillen," the man said gravely, "we came here... to tell you something. Something difficult."

"Is Emily all right?" Gillen interjected, throwing Mr. Hoyne off track.

"Umm... she's about the same. No, this... this is about you and Danielle."

Danielle's eyes were staring, burning into Gillen's periphery, yet every time he shifted glances toward her, she couldn't bear it and looked away. "What seems to be the problem?"

The father clicked his tongue before saying, "Gillen, it's been really nice having you stop by the house, meet the family, and be there for Danielle during this rough time. I've noticed it, and it was appreciated. It really was."

Gillen blinked and again looked over at Danielle who appeared as if she was going to be sick. Mr. Hoyne continued, "But you must understand, that right now, what we're facing, with the world the way it is, with Emily taking up so much of our concern, it's crucial that the family be what it's supposed to be right now. A family."

Gillen found himself nodding ever so slightly. "I see."

"Understand, Gillen, that your friendship to Danielle has meant a lot to us. She needed a friend.

But now things have changed. And we just want what's best for everyone, including for you. So we feel that... until things get better at home, until things settle down a bit in the world, that it would be best if you and Danielle don't spend any more time together."

The silence of the neighborhood was unusual, and for a moment, Gillen wasn't sure if no one happened to be around or if he had been rendered mute by the noise of his pulse pounding into his ears. Taking a long, deep breath, he squared his jaw and addressed only Mr. Hoyne. "You misspoke when you called Danielle my friend. She is my *lover*."

The man didn't move, hardly blinked, and Danielle simply stood there with the presence of one unable to awaken from a nightmare. The flow of time seemed to be altered with each second containing a full and complete realm of reality fully disconnected from the next. For Gillen, it was where the primitive merged with the rational. He sensed his muscles tighten, his eyesight sharpen, and his mind zero in on who the real culprit was in the situation. A culprit who was speaking vicariously.

"Why are you choosing to do this?" Gillen finally asked.

Mr. Hoyne sank just a little under the bearing of the question. "I've already told you."

"No. I don't mean why are you choosing to break Danielle and I up. I'm asking why you're letting someone else decide what's best for us."

Gillen's eyes remained locked onto her father's, but in that instant his peripheral caught sight of the first signs of life coming from Danielle. Mr. Hoyne cocked his head at Gillen, his face contorted in confusion, unable to reconcile the script he had been given with reality. Incapable of mustering a reply, the man rubbed the back of his neck and avoided eye contact.

Then, much to both of their surprises, Danielle found her voice. "Pastor said that God is punishing the family for what you and I did, Gillen. That God is punishing Emily..." Her voice trailed as tears filled her eyes.

The space between the Hoynes and Gillen was only a few feet, but seemed eternally distant in context of the words that hung in the air. The statement had found its way into Gillen's brain, but seemed unable to penetrate his cognition, like hieroglyphs without a primer. So foreign an utterance was the vocabulary originating from the pastor, that without a point of reference or a metaphysical glossary by which to orient himself, Gillen was left with no other recourse than to allow his body to detoxify the statement from his mind by any means necessary. With a giant, purging reflex, he doubled over laughing.

The striking scene caused Mr. Hoyne to bristle and Danielle to regain a shred of her composure. The laugh echoed off the edges of the homes on either side of the Rainer house, and seemed to permeate the neighborhood for blocks. It lasted for only a few seconds, and much like the wheeze at the conclusion of a violent cough, he caught his breath and wiped a solitary tear from his eye.

Gillen said to Mr. Hoyne, "There is nothing in reality, in the real, physical, tangible world, that could explain any connection between Emily's mysterious illness and the love shared by me and Danielle. And nothing your pastor says could ever make it so."

He then addressed his love. "Danielle, you know who you are to me. That will never change. I recognize that you're in an impossible spot right now and I have no intention of making it worse for you. I love you, and hurting you is hurting myself. So promise me something, just one thing, would you do that?"

Danielle smiled through her tears as she gazed into the face of her happiness. "Anything."

"Promise that until this is over, that until those who feel the need to interfere in our story have come to their senses, that when you think back to what we have shared and who we have become as a result, that you will not remember this day. That you will make a choice not to bring the events of this day to the forefront of your memory. Ever. Would you do that for me?"

Had her father's hand not been firmly planted on her shoulder, and had the steps leading up to Gillen not suddenly seemed like a mountainous climb, Danielle would have lunged forward into his arms and assured him that never again would this day come to mind. But instead she stayed put, resigned to her predicament, yet beaming with the sort of security one has when knowing that rescue is imminent. "I promise," she whispered back, "this will never be part of our story."

◂ ◆ ● ● ⬤ ● ● ◆ ▸

The memory evaporated. The diner suddenly felt like a foreign environment as Gillen repeatedly blinked and brought his attention back to the booth. A wellspring of emotions bottlenecked at his throat, a wave of exhaustion overtaking his senses. Only then did he realize that the proprietor was standing at their table, having asked if there was anything else he could bring them. Gillen shook his head instinctively and dropped a half dollar on the table. As the man walked off, Gillen again became aware of Samantha sitting across from him, gazing at him through her honey-brown eyes. She had finished her tea and was snuffing out the remainder of her cigarette into the ashtray.

"You loved her so much," Samantha said, witnessing the anguish on his face.

Gillen reached for his hat on the jade-green tile and began sliding himself out of the booth. Wearily he responded, "It doesn't matter."

ARTIST-IN-RESIDENCE

High above the Iselin Amalgamate building, and beyond the reach of the towering Golden Gate Bridge, a full moon watched over the city. A simple lifting of the head would fill one's vision with the dark volcanic plains pockmarking its northern landscape, Shackleton crater coming to a point at its southern, and somewhere in-between, the lunar settlement of Ortelius.

"She's up there," Gillen said as he and Samantha made their way to the foyer entry doors, a statement which brought him in equal parts grief and wonder. Once back inside the laboratory, Gillen hung his hat and overcoat on the rack and gave a reaffirming tug at the hem of his gray vest. Rolling up the crisp white sleeves of his shirt, he assessed the scene before him. Several additional people were now moving about the workspace, men and women who had left their homes and families in the middle of the night to attend to a rescue operation.

"How's she doing?" Gillen asked, directing his question to just one man.

Walter turned away from Barry Sjöstrom and two other technicians and stole a few steps toward Gillen and Samantha only to motion for them to join the group. "You must see this."

As they hovered behind Walter, the desk of the workstation was littered with white sheets of paper covered in pencil drawn diagrams. Above the desk a palpable energy crackled from the monitor, and Gillen moved in slowly to determine what he was witnessing.

"What's she doing?"

From behind the glass of the screen, Allaire Rainer stood adjacent to the lunar Hexagon, her eyes rotating shifts between staring up at an exposed electrical panel and down at a clipboard cradled in her arm. In her hand, a pencil, sketching exactly what she was seeing on each section of the Hexagon, before flipping the paper up toward the camera for those on earth to review.

"I'll be damned," Gillen whispered, mouth agape, eyes unable to watch anything else but the brilliance of his daughter on display.

Walter turned to Samantha. "This was Allaire's idea. She started sketching the Hexagon out of boredom and then asked if a more granular sketch would be of any usefulness. She's been at it for hours now."

Samantha nodded her head at Allaire with a beaming grin too proud to withhold. "Attagirl."

Aesthetically, the strewn lines on the desk flowed from page to page like the spirited attempt of an art student's recreation. Outlines, diagonal arrows, parallelograms, and scribbled additions by the technicians themselves, lay next to metal binders with reams of the original printed schematics. The painstaking work of cross-referencing each section was only slightly anesthetized by the permeating smell of fresh coffee.

"I'll have some," Sjöstrom waved toward Lisa, who was holding a carafe in each hand. Around the workstation and adjacent drafting table, small puffs of coffee steam waltzed with cigarette smoke, emissions of the fuel needed to power each individual.

After catching Walter up on their perilous encounter with Richard Kaine — and emitting the incident with the ghost of Danielle Hoyne — Gillen and Samantha joined those at the drafting table as a large arc lamp blazed down on the lines and words and numbers, interrogating for discrepancies. "So what do we know thus far?" Gillen asked the group.

"Structurally speaking," one of the engineers said, "the lunar Hexagon seems sound."

"So no external damage, inadvertent or otherwise?"

"Correct."

Gillen nodded. "That's in line with Sjöstrom's story. What about hardwiring? Panel boards?"

A technician spoke up, his gruff voice a match for his weathered face. The creases of his mouth were a subtle grin, as if tethered to the perpetual inner workings of an overactive mind. "That's where it gets interesting," he stated. "All of the cabling and circuitry that we've seen so far are in order, except for this." The man's stubby finger jammed against the diagram in question. "Your daughter's sketch of this section needs to be confirmed. Because if she's seeing something there that isn't in our binder here, then we'll have to trace the origin of this phantom cable."

Gillen grabbed the page from off the table and smiled. "Good work." Pacing back over to the workstation, he spotted Walter seated alone at the console, finishing the sketches of yet another page from their lunar artist. Gillen sat down next to him and observed the seriousness, almost reverence, with which Walter copied each line. His head would lift up and his eyes would peer through his glasses to zero in on the diagram Allaire was holding up to the camera, followed by a sudden return to his hunched posture so as to infuse his drawing with acute precision.

"So Ortelius now has its first artist-in-residence," Gillen said.

The two chuckled the weary laughter of circumstantial awareness. Gillen then said, "So ordinarily, aren't Tuesday evenings your poker nights?"

Walter's hesitation was only noticeable in the pencil's inertia. Taking a moment to push his glasses further up his nose, he said, "That's right, Tuesdays were poker nights, weren't they?"

Gillen nodded slowly, taking a cautious sip from the steaming coffee mug before him. "Well, for me they were home early because I have no poker face, but yes."

Walter continued drawing. "Those were fun times. For a while."

Gillen smiled, then frowned, then regretted broaching the topic. "Yeah."

After adding several clarifying notes, Walter swooped up the page from the desk and pressed the microphone switch. "Great job, Allaire. That was a complicated one for sure. Give us some time on this and we'll get back to you."

Allaire nodded and set her sketch down on the drafting table next to her. As she walked back to the lunar workstation, Walter left the workstation at which Gillen was seated and marched back over to the group. Gillen swiveled his chair closer to the microphone and leaned in on the desk. "Allaire?"

Her eyes bolted upward. "Hey, Dad!"

"How are you holding up?"

She shrugged. "My hand is starting to cramp, but other than that I'm okay. I miss you."

"I miss you too, Allaire. You know you're being quite brave about all of this. I'm proud of you."

"Even though I caused the mess?"

"You didn't cause it, you just got stuck in the crosshairs. If not you, then it would have happened when someone else was up there, albeit next time with a technician on site too."

Allaire nodded slowly. Gillen then asked, "What were you doing up there, anyway?"

The video feed on the monitor crackled as Allaire tugged at the ankle-length hem of her capri pants and gazed down at an empty section of floor.

She spoke softly, responding to Gillen as if he were sitting right there in the room with her. "The night you brought me up here, to see everything for the first time, I was using the tuner to listen to the radio stations from earth. It happened right before we were getting ready to leave. You were over by the Hexagon, and I was sitting here. Suddenly, I heard it. That song."

Gillen leaned in on the workstation desk. "The... song from your dream?"

Allaire nodded. "Yes. The one I remember Mom singing to me when I was young. Only I can't really remember it, except for those first few notes." Pressing her lips together, Allaire drew in a breath and hummed the nine notes that had sent chills down Gillen's spine. "Remember?"

This time it was Gillen who was gazing off into a void. "I wish I could."

"The song started playing over the speakers, the whole thing, and I wanted to hear it better so I tried to increase the volume, but I grabbed the tuner dial instead by accident. The station and the song were gone."

The diagram in his hand acted as a touchstone to his fingers, anchoring him to this world and away from the tempestuous line of thinking darkening the perimeter of his mind. A line obsessed with why he didn't know a familiar song chosen by Cate to serenade their daughter. Of shame when he brought her face to memory. And of guilt when he thought of the reality that he was still refusing to face. *Cate jumped, you fool. I guess you didn't know her as well as you thought.*

"That's why I came back," Allaire summarized. "I know it sounds silly," she added, unable to look at her father on the monitor. "But I just had to come back and see if I could find it. If somehow it might still be playing. I just... I have to hear that song again... even once more. Those notes make me feel a connection with Mom that I don't get from anything else. I have to remember. I must make myself remember. Maybe then I can..."

Her voice trailed and her eyes searched. Gillen said with finality, "Find closure."

The mocha in her eyes were reflective as she looked up at the camera and smiled. "Yes."

Gillen felt startled as the large hand of the engineer landed on his shoulder. "Mr. Rainer, did you ask her yet?"

Clearing his throat, Gillen sat upright and nodded. "Right. Thanks for the reminder. Allaire? We need you to double check something from your diagram on page twelve. Can you pull that one back out?"

Walter marched back over to the workstation and set his coffee down on the console. "Is she checking?"

"Yeah."

"Okay, I have it," Allaire said.

"Great," Walter interjected. "We'd like you to confirm this cable here, the one I have circled. Can you see which one I mean?"

After squinting at the monitor for a moment, Allaire said, "Yes, I see it."

"Go back over to the main panel on the lunar Hexagon and tell me if that cable indeed exists."

"Okay, Grandpa Walt. No sweat."

Walter smiled, turned off the microphone, frowned, and said to Gillen and the engineer, "If that thing does exist..."

The engineer grimaced. "Exactly... a cable that large, and in that section of the panel—"

"Makes no sense, unless someone made a modification—"

"One that's leading circuitry away from the Hexagon..."

Walter nodded. "If that's correct, we're going to have to somehow show Allaire how to trace a cable through a series of panel boards."

"Without a technician present? It's gonna be a long night," replied the engineer.

Gillen sighed heavily and pressed his fingers against his furled brows. "Wait a minute, why can't we just have her sever it?"

"What do you mean?" the burly man asked.

"If that cable is causing the disruption between the Hexagons why can't we just have Allaire cut it? Destroy it."

Walter shook his head. "We have no idea what vital wiring was routed through that cable. If we have her sever it blindly we may lose connection to her altogether."

The engineer disagreed and stabbed the diagram on the desk. "You're wrong there, Dr. Iselin. Page eight confirmed that the lunar Hexagon panel doesn't house anything related to closed circuit feeds or audio. That's all over on the wall."

"Then what do you think the cable contains?"

"Something controlling the mechanisms of the Hexagon itself. Power/shutdown. Open/close. Hell, maybe even a direct line to the rat who installed it."

"Can you hear me?" Allaire shouted from the other end of the room.

"We can hear you," Walter said.

A long pause ensued. Allaire repeated, "Can you all hear me?"

"Yes, we hear you, Allaire..."

The engineer shook his head. "You might try turning our mic back on when you have a minute."

Gillen chuckled to himself. Walter mumbled as he flipped the switch. "Let's see what happens when you two forget to—"

"Can you hear me?"

"Sorry, Allaire," Walter smirked. "We can hear you now, yes. Go ahead."

"Okay," she confirmed. "That cable... it's here. It looks just like what I drew in the diagram."

"Swell work, Allaire. Stay put for a moment, will you?" With that, Walter flamboyantly flipped the switch and turned back to his compatriots. "What say ye, gentlemen?"

"Sever it," Gillen reiterated, pointing at the screen. "Have her slice that thing in half. If it's granting someone control of the lunar Hexagon, this action should remove them from the picture and then we can continue troubleshooting. Until then, everything we try is an exercise in futility."

The engineer was vacillating. "It would be nice to have her trace that thing to see where it leads, but I suppose we can still do that post-cut. All that matters now is getting the lunar Hexagon open."

Walter responded slowly, looking down at his shoes before peering over at one of the many wall clocks. "I have an acquaintance who is a professor down at Caltech. He's a good man to pitch ideas to, but I suppose it's too late to call the university office."

Samantha found her way over to the workstation and caught herself up on the situation. "I'm with Gillen. That cable didn't exist before recently and I can't imagine what purpose it could serve other than bypassing the failsafe mechanism. Have Allaire cut it."

Walter raised an eyebrow and hesitated. "And if we lose transmission with Allaire, then what?"

The engineer leaned against the console, exasperated. "I ran the wiring for the closed circuit cameras myself. There is no way that cable—"

"What if the Alignment closes as a result?"

Samantha said, "If the Alignment closes we reopen it from this end."

"And if it won't reopen?"

"Then we create a parallel Alignment and initiate the same process. Walter, we've opened, closed, and even created parallel Alignments a hundred times. This is textbook. The Alignment isn't the problem here. The lunar Hexagon is."

Gillen watched with curiosity as an anxious Walter nodded in troubled agreement with his team. He rarely saw the man worried. That worried Gillen.

"Allaire?" Walter said into the microphone.

"You gotta flip the switch," said the engineer.

"Damn it. Allaire?"

"I'm here," the teenager said.

"Okay, we think we've isolated the problem and that cable is it. If you'd be so kind as to come back to the workstation, I'm going to tell you where to find the toolbox and electrical gloves, and then we're going to walk you through how to sever that cable safely."

"Mr. Rainer?" Lisa whispered from behind his swivel chair. "There's a call for you."

Gillen glanced at Samantha who flashed him a reassuring look. "We'll take good care of Allaire. Don't worry."

With a grateful touch on her shoulder, Gillen walked past Samantha and followed Lisa over to a semicircular desk. The phone's black receiver lay next to the rotary dial as the cord curled its way off the table. "Hello?" Gillen answered.

"Heya, Gillen," came a voice from the receiver. It was the calm, collected voice of a man reacquainted with sanity.

"Jack," Gillen whispered, almost too stunned to speak. He turned himself away from the heartbeat of the laboratory and sat down in a chair, pressing his shoulder up against some file cabinets and cradling the speaker in his hand. "How are you?"

"Briefly insane, but a little better now, thanks. How are you?"

Gillen swallowed the stale air in the back of his throat and smiled. "Umm, well, it's been a busy day to say the least."

"I bet," Jack said. "I'm sure Walter has everyone getting ready for the press conference."

A simple nod was all the reply Gillen could muster, his mind still processing with whom he was speaking. "Jack, are you still at the hospital?"

"Yep, yep. I normally wouldn't be allowed to make phone calls this late, but I think one of the nurses fell in love with me. Either that or it was pity. It may just be pity."

The man sounded as he used to, which gave Gillen pause. He was not the Jack DaLette of a week ago, but the Jack DaLette of a memory ago. Before his depression, before the divorce, before Danielle, there had been this Jack DaLette. Gillen proceeded with caution. "Well, I'm glad you're all right. You had us worried."

The man's voice lost some of its confidence. "Yeah, well, Walter was bound to make one of us crazy, so I took one for the team."

Gillen laughed yet again with caution. "I understand."

Jack fell silent for a moment, breathing into the receiver as if struggling to withhold excess oxygen. "I'm... uh..." he began, choking with rapidly onsetting emotion. "Sorry, Gillen... for...what I did. For the blood... in my office..."

"Jack, you don't need to apologize for that."

"I do, I do, I do," he repeated. "Because it was unlike me, and unprofessional, and lazy, and stupid, and idiotic. It was pointless. It provided no sense of relief and only served to distract from my ultimate goal."

Gillen bit his lower lip and shifted glances from the small cluster that had built around Walter's workstation and the file cabinets providing some semblance of privacy. "If I may ask, what was the motive in what you did?"

The word popped as Jack let out a laugh. "Closure."

A low-grade headache that had been building for close to an hour was now slowly creeping its way down into Gillen's neck. He cocked his head from side to side but found no relief.

Jack breathed heavily into the mouthpiece, his words moist with the emotion in his eyes. "I miss Danielle so much..."

Rising from his chair, Gillen wrapped his free arm around his torso and began pacing the floor. He was not ready to process this yet. "I'm sure you do, Jack."

"I loved her so much."

Gillen shut his eyes and grimaced. In his mind, he saw the place setting, the linen tablecloth, and a large window overlooking the Bay Bridge. Votive candles found their way around the decanter and flower vase, casting fluttery shadows on the dinnerware. Gillen had had his arm around Cate's chair, whispering into her ear, feeling amorous.

"What did he say her name was again?" Cate had asked, her lips seeming more red than normal, vividly accentuating the maroon of her cocktail dress.

"I wanna say, Dorothy," Gillen answered, uninterested in the tardiness of his friend or his friend's new flame. He wanted to get Cate home and out of that dress.

"I thought you told me it was Dolores?"

"No, Dolores was his last girlfriend of three weeks. She lived in Sausalito but Jack didn't wanna make the drive."

As she poked at the olive at the base of her martini glass with a skewer, Cate's face struggled to withhold an amused judgment. "Our bachelor friend, the cosmopolitan man."

"Something like that," Gillen said, and laid a gentle kiss on Cate's collarbone as she smiled, more amused than aroused. He then said, "I'm going to eat the chateaubriand tonight and then I'm going to eat you."

"Where did Jack say he met her?"

"Some rally downtown."

"Like a political rally?"

Gillen brushed his nose lightly up Cate's neck. "These are all really good questions to ask them when they get here."

The two smiled and shared a brief kiss as Jack and his date appeared from around the corner. Gillen had been the first to turn his head as they approached, blinking once to focus in on Jack, blinking multiple times to focus in on the woman holding Jack's hand. She walked toward the table with confidence and energy, until the instant she locked eyes with Gillen. Her pace slowed considerably, and Jack took that as an opportunity to step ahead of her and slap Gillen on the shoulder.

"Good buddy," Jack said as a curlicue of blond hair bounced against his forehead. He then stepped past him to give Cate a peck on the cheek. "Lovely as always, dear."

Gillen couldn't remember pushing his chair back from the table and standing, for his memory of the event seemed less as if he had risen to his feet and more like the floor beneath him had levitated.

"You two," Jack announced, resting his hand on the small of her back, "this is Danielle."

Oh my God, thought Gillen, his senses spiraling from either a rapid surge of panic or euphoria. There she was. The love of his life. Standing before him. Decades older and yet instantaneously recognizable. Those hazel eyes. That mischievous smirk. The way she walked as if oblivious to the notion that life was guilt. Gillen struggled with lightheadedness as he finished his visual inventory. Her hairstyle had changed, it was much shorter than when she was sixteen, parted on the right with one end coming down to a curve against her jawline, the other side coming to a curve just below it. Her face looked the same to him, and he surmised in that moment the reason. Even as teenagers, he had always beheld her as a woman.

"Danielle," Jack continued, "these crazy kids here are my friends, Gillen and Cate."

Danielle had stopped just inches short of where Gillen was standing, and looked up at him in awe. Her cerulean strapless dress left off at her knees, accessorized with white heels and pearl velvet gloves. Finger by finger she began to remove them, hoping to infinitely delay the offer of a handshake, and with it, the memory of his touch.

"A pleasure to meet you," piped in Cate, admiring her dress.

"Likewise," Danielle whispered, unable to decide where or at whom to look.

Gillen's hand had reflexively sank to the arm of his chair as he cautiously sat back down. As the rest followed his lead, his unsteady hand reached for his cocktail glass and drew some of the fluid past his lips. Adding to the absurdity of the moment, Jack had been absentmindedly chivalrous, pulling out the chair across from Gillen for Danielle and seating himself opposite of Cate. The instant she sat down Gillen could feel the tip of her white heel bumping into his wingtip.

"Well, what do you think, Gillen?" Jack asked, a goofy smile etching his mouth.

Gillen took a deep breath and ordered himself to smile. After a moment's contemplation, he said, "What was your name again?"

The woman cocked her slanted grin and glanced down at the linen tablecloth. When her eyes returned to him, she responded, "Danielle. And what was yours?"

"Gillen," he had said. "It's nice to finally meet you."

Danielle nodded, her curious smirk still an indelible part of her facial features. "Gillen. That's an interesting name. Do your friends call you Gil?"

Gillen fought off the kind of expression that often leads to tears. "Thankfully not."

Standing motionless and with the handle of the receiver pressed firmly against his ear, Gillen opened his clenched eyes and realized that he had been smiling.

On the other end of the line, Jack choked out, "I loved her so much."

So did I.

OPEN/CLOSE

Allaire Rainer set the electrical gloves and cable cutter down on the floor of the laboratory on Ortelius. Next to her, the lunar Hexagon stood with its main panel exposed and two large cables that no longer met in the middle. The girl looked up at the apparatus with perplexity, as if witnessing something for the first time. She then tilted her head and peered up at the ceiling camera.

"Dad..." she whispered.

The team surrounding the workstation included Walter, Samantha, the engineer, and Gillen who had just paced back across the giant room after ending his phone call with Jack DaLette. "How did she do?" he asked, while reclaiming his swivel chair.

"Something's wrong," Samantha muttered, her countenance reading nuance from the situation.

Gillen pulled at the microphone. "I'm here. What's going on? What do you see?"

Allaire blinked incredulously and said, "The light on top of the Hexagon went out, blinked, and then turned solid green again."

No one at the workstation responded. Neither did they celebrate. In stunned silence they absorbed the news with apprehension, like those hearing of mankind's achievement of placing the first satellite in orbit... from Russia.

"That's good, right?" Gillen asked the group, his eyebrow fully arched.

The engineer balked. "That's strange."

Walter concurred. "Yes, it is. Why didn't we hear the unlock mechanism from the lunar Hexagon?"

Samantha pushed her forefinger and thumb against her chin and walked over to the terrestrial Hexagon. She examined it for a moment, gazing at the embryonic field acting as a protective sheath from the Alignment. There was no change. Not even so much as a wrinkle in its reflective fabric as was customary when unlocking the Hexagons. Punching a command line into the screen, she scanned for any failsafe warnings or indication that the Alignment had collapsed.

All was as it should be.

"Should I walk through it now?" Allaire asked the ceiling camera.

"Tell her to wait," Samantha ordered, shaking her head as if the data on the screen only answered questions in the affirmative.

"This doesn't seem right," Walter stated while flipping multiple indicator switches on the console.

"Is it still locked?" Gillen asked, looking for a readout on one of the monitors.

"I'm trying to figure that out," the engineer mumbled.

"Our Hexagon shows no change," Samantha said while marching back to the workstation. "And we absolutely would have heard the unlock mechanism through Allaire's microphone."

"Which there wasn't." Walter frowned. "The only discernible change was the lunar Hexagon light, essentially, staying green."

"Have her test it," the engineer stated, interrupting Walter. "Have her toss something through the field and let's see if it lands on our side."

"Like an empty binder?" Walter suggested.

Gillen shook his head. "That's not heavy enough. We need something with more mass to push through."

"A conference room chair should do it," Samantha said, drawing their attention to Gillen's seat. "Plus they're on wheels so she can roll it into the Hexagon, give it a good running start."

"Allaire?" Gillen said, tugging at the mic.

"Hey, Dad."

"Let's test this thing first. Go grab a chair from the embassy and roll it into the lab."

"Okay. Be right back!"

Walter lifted his hand up to the microphone switch and turned it off. To the group he said, "Let's be thinking about what our next step is going to be."

The teenager disappeared out of the room leaving the team below to wait and think. Each face stared at the monitor with its own version of the same emotional expression: suspicion. Nothing about the actions or functionality of the lunar Hexagon was consistent with the mechanisms and protocols they had put in place. It was as if they were now dealing with machinery outside of their original specifications, like a third party vendor's contraption which had been jerry-built into their ecosystem and had just gone haywire.

Allaire returned to the laboratory wheeling a leather executive swivel chair from the embassy's conference room. Once she reached the workstation, she plopped down on the seat and used the console to give herself a moderate spin.

Gillen smiled when he saw it. *There's still a little bit of kid left in her, Cate.*

Walter said, "Okay, Allaire, here's what you should do. Have your starting position be the console, grab the back of the chair with both hands, and run as fast as you can toward the Hexagon before propelling the chair into the reflective field. And please, be sure not to fall into it yourself or let the chair bounce back at you if it fails."

Walter waited for her reply.

"You gotta flip the mic switch," the engineer chortled.

Samantha rolled her eyes and pivoted the microphone neck toward her. After flipping the switch she repeated Walter's instructions to Allaire and the team braced themselves for disappointment. "I hate to say this," Samantha whispered to the group, "but everything in me is hoping this fails, because if it doesn't, whatever alterations were made to the lunar Hexagon have basically made the operations of it unknowable."

Gillen rubbed his hands together and pressed his knuckles up to his cheek. He knew Samantha was correct. If the embassy chair cleared the Alignment and landed on their lab floor, that only increased his concern about the stability of the whole apparatus. That green bulb did not mean what it was indicating, and Gillen despised being lied to.

"Here I go," Allaire said, before pulling the chair back once, then twice, and on the third motion bolting from her place at the console and propelling the chair forward across the laboratory floor. Like a battering ram, the curved metal armrests slammed into the protective field of the lunar Hexagon, and for an instant, the opening lit up with the metallic glow of a full moon. With her artistic ability as a figure skater to perfectly hit a landing, Allaire rammed her heel against the floor and came to a stop as the Hexagon absorbed the conference room chair in its entirety, leaving behind nothing but a series of ripples in the reflective fluid.

"No way..." said Gillen, as he and the team thrust themselves sideways to view the opening of the terrestrial Hexagon. Their eyes were wide, expectant, mesmerized, and utterly baffled. The Hexagon stood with the unshakable nature of an ancient obelisk. It's message frighteningly clear. There was no chair. It was still inside of the Alignment.

"What in God's name?" Walter said, his eyebrows furled, his jawline drawn tight.

"That can't be," Gillen added. "That's not even…"

"…possible," finished the engineer. "Our Hexagon is unlocked. Isn't it?"

Samantha confirmed. "That's correct."

Gillen swiveled back around toward the workstation and stared into the monitor to confirm what he thought his eyes had just witnessed. "Allaire?"

"Yes?"

"Is what we saw accurate? Did the chair vanish into the Hexagon?"

"Sure did!" she said enthusiastically. "Does that mean I can go through now?"

"There's no way our Hexagon is unlocked," protested the engineer, his fingers irritably rubbing his mustache. "Otherwise that chair would have already sailed through the Alignment."

"I'm telling you," Samantha said, "it's unlocked."

"So does that mean I can walk through now?" Allaire asked the team.

"Let's test it," the engineer balked. "I will push my own chair at the Hexagon and show you that it's still locked."

"Be my guest," fired back Samantha. "But the indicators all confirm otherwise."

"Yeah… sure, just like it did on the lunar Hexagon, right?"

"Can we remain calm, people?" Walter interjected, his voice reassuring and authoritative. "We can either have a conniption or we can focus on what we know."

"I'm calm," the engineer said, standing up. "But I'm also right. Allow me to demonstrate."

As the engineer walked over to the side of the console, wheeling his chair along from behind, Gillen leaned in on the desk. "Allaire? Hang on one more minute. We're testing something out. Go ahead and stand back by the workstation."

Allaire obeyed as the engineer rolled his chair around on its tiny wheels. Instead of ramping up for a sprint, he spun it around a few times with his hand and then launched it forward as if sending a bowling ball down a pin lane. The momentum was sufficient to send the chair sailing across the floor and right into the embryonic field of the terrestrial Hexagon. In a sudden blaze of silver glow, the chair evaporated into the fluid, leaving the engineer stupefied and Samantha wishing that she had not been right.

Back at the monitor, Gillen waited for any sight of the engineer's chair appearing through the perimeters of the lunar Hexagon. He saw Allaire watching too, the hope on her face steadily waning. He knew that the action of movement through the Hexagons was supposed to be instantaneous. Waiting even a moment for the chair to arrive was time wasted. It too was now stuck in the Alignment.

The engineer turned to face Samantha. "Okay, I stand corrected. So what does this mean?"

Samantha sighed and walked slowly over to the coffee pot, her gait still recovering from the near miss with the vehicle. "What this means is that the lunar Hexagon has been unlocked this entire time.

The only thing that's changed since we started troubleshooting is severing that cable. That's why we didn't hear the unlock mechanism, that's why the terrestrial Hexagon thought everything was in working order—because it is, *mechanically* speaking."

The engineer still seemed lost, so Walter stepped in. "The lunar Hexagon was tampered with, there's no dispute there. That cable was installed to fool us, alter the function of the indicator light, control panel, whatever else. But as is clearly evident, the real problem is with the Alignment."

"Another faulty premise we had," Samantha said, sipping from her mug.

The engineer nodded. "Plus, I'm out a nice chair."

Walter stood in the center of the lab and addressed the entire staff. "The abnormalities we have just witnessed are demonstrable of the kind of foresight that was considered when we first launched this endeavor. The next steps in this situation are as clear now as they were when we wrote them. Any anomaly proven to be directly tied to the integrity of the Alignment itself, is grounds for us to manually close that Alignment and open a new one."

There was a murmur of discussion amongst the group, but Gillen remained silent. Like his team, he knew what closing an Alignment meant, but he wondered if they all felt as nauseous about it as he did.

"As a reminder," Walter continued, "this is an exercise we have completed numerous times successfully, with people still on Ortelius I might add.

In fact, I believe that I was the first to volunteer to be temporarily marooned." With that the old man chuckled to himself. Gillen and Samantha exchanged glances from across the room.

"Now who has the most experience in this particular procedure?"

Barry Sjöstrom timidly raised his hand. "That would be me, Dr. Iselin. Well, the mechanical side of it anyway. Although Gillen did most of the original mathematics for stabilizing the hole."

Gillen nodded slowly and got up from his seat. "Guilty as charged."

"Capital," Walter said, trying to sound upbeat. "Anyone else run this sequence last time?"

"Yep," Gillen said, pursing his lips. "The Alignment expert you're thinking of is Jack DaLette."

"I see."

"Yeah."

"No need to be concerned," Walter added, swaying his hands over the group. "Jack's convalescence will have no effect on our ability to facilitate this in a real world situation. We have the team. We have the manuals. And thanks to Lisa, we have the coffee."

The group laughed more than the joke warranted, and Gillen leaned against the console amazed at Walter's never-ending penchant for optimism. The man was not only remarkably rational, but deeply empathetic, two traits Gillen had always thought should be inseparably linked. Walter's rallying speech gave the team what they needed in that hour, a confidence in their own competence, even as the wall clock had long since switched from PM to AM.

Gillen slapped his hands together and paced over to the drawing table with the lamp over it. Samantha and Sjöstrom stood gazing down at some schematics as Gillen joined. With a smirk he whispered, "Man, the boss is keeping us late tonight."

Samantha quickly set her coffee cup down so as not to spill it as she chortled. Sjöstrom too joined in on the weary laughter. Gillen shook his head and reached for a slide rule. "Seriously though, folks, it has come down to this."

Samantha nodded. "Closing the Alignment."

"We can do this," Sjöstrom said, trying to instill confidence in the other two. "I've been present for every new Alignment we've ever spun up between here and Ortelius. Jack wrote the binder on this procedure himself. I'm well prepared to execute this operation without him here. I assure you."

Gillen sighed and placed his hand on Sjöstrom's shoulder. "I have no doubt, Barry." With that he again glanced down at the schematic, but then darted his eyes over toward the coffee pot.

"It's fresh," Samantha said.

Gillen placed his hand on his stomach. "Is there any tea?"

"Lisa can probably find you some tea. She's over by Walter."

Gillen excused himself and walked over to the other side of the lab.

Sjöstrom said, "He's worried."

"Of course he is," Samantha replied. "But not about you, or even about our team. We've done this before, many times. Walter is right. This team specifically was predicated on the notion that this event was inevitable."

"Just not with Gillen's daughter as the one marooned."

"True."

Sjöstrom cocked his head and began shuffling through some papers. Samantha reached out her hand and gently placed it on his wrist. "He doesn't blame you for what happened, Barry. There's no reason you should have noticed Allaire hiding in the lab."

Sjöstrom nodded in tepid agreement, his eyes still zeroed in on the sheets within Jack's binder. "Yeah, but I should have noticed Richard."

He continued flipping through the pages, his index finger and eyes scanning the same lines of instruction. Samantha leaned in on the table, the giant lamp above them casting their shadows across the blueprints of the Hexagon. "What about Richard?"

"He's been acting strangely for a couple of months. I didn't know him well enough to feel like I could pry into his personal life, so I didn't. But I'll tell ya. This one time, what was it... maybe three or four weeks back, I'm walking into the break room to get some creamer, when all of a sudden I see Richard just sitting alone at the table. He's right there, back towards me, all by himself, crying. But not just crying though, like trying to hold it together. Almost... weeping. I just stood there. I didn't know what the hell to do. So I decided sugar would be okay instead of creamer and turned to quietly leave the room. Just as I did, I saw what was in his hand. A photograph. A picture of Richard sitting next to his wife, with a little kid on their lap. A two-year-old probably."

Samantha gestured with her hands. "And he was just sitting there, weeping, while holding the picture?"

"Sure was. Almost uncontrollably. So like I said, I'm about to back out of the room and head to my office, when suddenly it dawns on me. Richard and his wife don't have any kids. Never did. That much I know about the man. So who was that little guy on his lap?"

Samantha shrugged. "Maybe a nephew. Or a neighbor's child."

Sjöstrom shook his head. "This was one of those holiday family photos with a caption. It clearly said: 'The Kaines'. I also got a decent look at the kid, and I'm telling you, that boy was the carbon copy image of Richard. Steely-blue eyes and all. And the way they were holding him, that was definitely a family photo."

Samantha tried to think of another question, or simply another response, but drew a mental blank. All she could picture was the sight of that man squeezing Gillen's hand and attempting to commit suicide on a transcontinental train. The expression on his face, with nothing short of a disdain for living, and the look on Gillen's, with nothing short of murderous rage, shook her to her core as Sjöstrom nodded from across the table.

"It's strange," he whispered. "And so is Richard Kaine."

◄ ◆ ● ● ● ● ◆ ►

"Hey, champ," Gillen said to Allaire as he set his cup and saucer down on the workstation desk. A single string dangled from the edge of the mug as the tea packet to which it was connected steeped in the scalding water. The aroma of peppermint wafted throughout the laboratory.

"Hi, Dad," the teenager said, seated at the lunar workstation and using her elbows to keep her torso upright.

"You must be so tired."

"I'll be okay, Dad. Is that peppermint tea?"

"How did you know it was peppermint?"

"Because you look worried."

Gillen scolded himself for letting his facial muscles betray his inner turmoil. Doing his best to project a more confident countenance, he lifted the mug from off the saucer, sipped from it cautiously, and winked at Allaire. "Tastes just like toothpaste."

Allaire burst out into a belly laugh, a scene which Gillen longingly absorbed. It was a stupid joke but had always made her giggle. He knew those days would all too soon come to an end. He said, "Did you have time to get some food while Samantha and I were gone? There's plenty in the galley kitchen in the embassy."

"Sure did. I ordered a pizza... just kidding."

Gillen laughed. "I've actually done that!"

"No!"

"The honest truth. Grandpa Walt and I were up on Ortelius once and decided to call that restaurant you love on the Embarcadero. They delivered it to the front door of the building, and... well, and... your Mom... she was here working with us that night. Anyway... she brought the pizza up to us. It was still piping hot. And the three of us ate it right where you're sitting. The first pizza delivery to the moon."

Allaire's smile was as wide as it was sentimental. She blinked, gazed down at the desk for a moment, and envisioned an absurd scenario in which the restaurant employee was invited along, eating pizza on the moon, with Grandpa Walt, her father, and her mother. "Sounds like it was fun."

After taking another sip from his cup, Gillen said, "It was. Your mother was a wonderful woman. She made every situation she was in brighter and happier."

"Even with her illness?" Allaire asked, bluntly and without much emotional context for Gillen to grasp.

For a moment, the question bothered him, for he did not know why she was asking. Cate had been a dedicated mother to Allaire, her fiercest supporter, her number one fan. Despite her limitations, she had pushed past her own boundaries, often at her own peril, in order to be a part of her daughter's life. Yet Gillen had always wondered if those sacrifices had been made to the wrong idol. Allaire had thrived on the challenge and stimulation of competition, the rigor of academics, and the limitlessness of creativity. Cate had been the lynchpin for all of that. But if Gillen was honest with himself, painfully, brutally honest, he suspected that Allaire had never felt that close with Cate, which could be why Allaire seemed obsessed with finding her own connection with her late mother via the illusive song that only she could recall from early childhood.

"Your mother," Gillen began, measuring each word with grave caution, "faced a lot of obstacles, just like you and I do. Any lack of patience, or empathy, or affection that you may have experienced from her stemmed from her trying to take care of the family and also exist from day to day. Sometimes she succeeded in that. Sometimes she failed. Sometimes the biggest battle she waged on a given day wasn't in her body, but in her mind. Endless, excessive pain can cause people to be depressed. Your mother often fought times of depression, she knew it and so did I. But one of her goals was to keep that knowledge from you so that you weren't burdened with the responsibility of it. I know she never meant to seem aloof. I know she loved you dearly. I know you made her indescribably happy."

Allaire nodded slowly, taking in each statement as would a prosecutor laying out a case. She then arched an eyebrow and said, "I was actually talking about you, Dad. Did she make *you* happy?"

I love you... Danielle. The thought assaulted Gillen's mind with the power of a floodlight on a shadow. Recoiling from the memory, he took another sip of tea and felt his neck attempt a passive nod. The motion it made didn't feel right. "Of course. I loved her so very much, Allaire."

Cate jumped, you fool.

"So, let me tell you what to expect on your end once we close the Alignment."

◄ ◆ ● ● ● ● ◆ ►

"The Minreth-Hughes equation," Gillen said while standing at the drafting table, giving a triple check at the arithmetic he had quickly jotted down using his pencil and slide rule. Around him watched a resolute Walter, a hopeful Samantha, and an anxious Barry Sjöstrom who was holding his notepad to his chest as if preparing for interstellar battle.

"This is good," Gillen finally said, tossing the scrap paper toward Sjöstrom and placing his hands on his hips. "Let's see if they match."

Sjöstrom nodded and lowered his notepad next to Gillen's page, a string of numbers and mathematical formulas littering the sheet. All that mattered was the final calculation at the bottom of each page, Sjöstrom's having been circled, Gillen's having been underlined.

"Bingo," the men said in unison, and the table took a collective sigh of relief.

Walter slapped Gillen on the shoulder and gave him the shove of a proud father to a son. "That equation changed the game for us, Gillen. And you discovered it."

"No, no, Minreth and Hughes discovered it, I just finally thought of applying it after the umpteenth time of failing to keep the Alignment stable."

Samantha smirked and said, "Leave it to a man to figure out how to coax open a hole."

The three men stood motionless for an instant, mouths agape, before bursting out into stunned laughter. Samantha walked around the table and tapped Gillen on the side of his face. "Come now, boys, I'm not as puritanical as all that."

"Dr. Iselin, we're all set over here," the engineer said from the workstation.

The team hustled over to the console bringing with them just the notepad on which the final calculations had been scribbled. Gillen's keystrokes clicked along in binary rhythm while three other pairs of eyes watched the characters populate the screen, each mind independently confirming what the group had decided.

"Looks good, Gillen," Samantha whispered.

"You got it," Sjöstrom said.

Walter turned to him and smiled. "We're ready to do this. Is Allaire all right?"

Gillen nodded and pointed at the other monitor. "I told her we'd be disconnected for just under an hour. I also recommended she get some sleep. She's mentally prepared to fly solo for a bit."

Allaire sat at her workstation looking up at her screen, listening to music from stations on earth. Walter said, "Does she know that those radio signals are also coming through the Alignment? She won't be able to listen to music until we reestablish contact."

Gillen nodded. "She knows. Listening to the radio is her calming ritual before going to bed. Fifty-five minutes from now, we should find her sound asleep."

"Just in time to wake her up for the short walk back to earth," Walter chided.

Gillen glanced down at his wristwatch and gave his hand a tight squeeze. Leaning next to the side of the console, he breathed in slowly and nodded at Sjöstrom to begin the shutdown sequence. "This is going to be the longest fifty-five minutes of my life," he whispered to Samantha.

Pushing up the protective clips covering two siloed switches, Sjöstrom took one final glance at the console before performing what seemed to be too simple an action for such an important task. The first switch caused no visual changes, but the team could hear gears and mechanisms begin to shutter, along with a high-pitched rattling noise. Gillen's unblinking eyes locked onto the monitor to absorb as much of his daughter as he could before Sjöstrom flipped the second switch and the black-and-white screen went to static.

The sound of power draining from a generator was followed by what could only be described as the momentary suction of air through a vacuum. The silence that ensued lasted exactly one second. Then, with the force of a commuter train passing by a junction, the inertia of the lab was riven by a sonic boom as the swivel chair was purged from the collapsing Alignment. Like a missile it was expelled airborne out of the Hexagon, soaring across the length of the laboratory, jettisoning toward Gillen at the console. The speed at which it flew was too great for Gillen to react, as one of the wheels sliced along the side of his head, knocking him backward as the chair crashed into a window and sent shards of glass cascading onto the floor.

Hunched shoulders and hands safeguarding heads gave way to witnessing the aftermath. The window was now hollow with pieces of its wood and metal frame splintered or missing. The swivel chair lay sideways on a bed of shattered window pane. And next to the console, flat on his back but still conscious, was Gillen, the right side of his face covered in blood.

"Oh God," Samantha muttered, scrambling around the others and kneeling next to Gillen as he groaned.

"Is that from the glass?" Walter asked, kneeling down with her.

"I don't think so... just from the chair. Gillen?"

He blinked repeatedly, dazed from the experience, confused as to why he was horizontal. "I'm okay," he said, even as his palm returned from the side of his head in crimson.

"Help me get him up," Samantha ordered, and Sjöstrom and the engineer hoisted Gillen to a somewhat vertical position. "Let's sit him down over here."

The room gyrated as Gillen felt his legs acquiescing to the direction he was being led. "I'm all right," he assured them, uncertain if he was in the best condition to determine that.

Lisa brought a bowl of warm water and some towels to his side as Samantha wiped away the blood and started dabbing at the actual wound. His vision swam for a moment as he watched the towel return from his skull, each time appearing less red.

"How bad is it?" Walter asked.

"Not the worst I've ever seen. Heads just tend to bleed a lot."

The engineer put his finger and thumb together. "That much. The rest of the chair missed you by that much."

"Isn't it obvious?" Gillen grinned. "Today's been my lucky day."

The group maintained a murmured laugh until a sudden realization seemed to dawn on them all at once.

"What about the other chair?" the engineer asked.

"You don't think..."

Walter's eyes widened. "Where was Allaire sitting when we closed the Alignment?"

Gillen stood up, albeit slowly and with a bit of a wobble. "The opening to the lunar Hexagon faces diagonally away from the workstation on Ortelius. If it shot out of there like it did here, in a straight line, then it would have smashed into...?"

Sjöstrom shut his eyes, rebuilding the laboratory in his mind. "Nothing vital. Some utility panels against the wall or maybe just the wall itself. And that's not even a load-bearing wall, or a water wall, so everything should be okay."

"I'm sure it frightened her, though," Walter said, clenching his jaw. "Damn it to hell. How did I miss that?"

"None of us thought of it," Samantha corrected, dismissively. "There," she said, placing her hand up against Gillen's sand-papery skin. "Bleeding has mostly stopped. You seem fairly normal."

The engineer quipped, "Is he still a wise guy?"

Gillen chuckled wearily. "I'm injured, not reformed."

Walter continued to fume as he marched over to the console and examined the board. "I suppose we learned something new about the nature of the Alignment thanks to all this."

"We learned two new things," Sjöstrom said.

"How do you figure?"

Sjöstrom pointed at the broken swivel chair next to the window and cracked a grin. "That's not our chair. That's the leather executive chair from the embassy on the moon. Which means our chair was expelled onto Ortelius. The Alignment must act like a one-way street. No U-turns."

"So something made it through," Gillen said, his voice laced with some hope. "Imperfectly, I admit. But something finally made it through."

"Correct," Sjöstrom said, his hand hovering over the siloed switches. "Additionally, these are what close the Alignment. However, after I flipped just the first one—the failsafe switch, I could hear the purge starting to occur. That rattling sound. That means in the future, if we ever need to extract something from within the Alignment, all we need to do is initiate the shutdown sequence without completing it. The object will be expelled without us having to close and reopen a new Alignment."

Walter nodded, thinking carefully about what Sjöstrom had just told him. "Well, in the future, let's just not leave any projectiles in the Alignment. After all, brilliant minds and windows are both expensive to replace."

Samantha patted the side of Gillen's head and collected the towels. "I'm going to go wash up. Be right back."

"Samantha? Thank you."

She stood there for a moment, smiled, and then leaned forward ever so slightly. "You're quite welcome, and forty-nine minutes to go."

Gillen sighed heavily as Samantha walked away. *Hold on Allaire... I'll be with you soon.*

◄ ◆ ● ● ● ● ● ◆ ►

The laboratory on Ortelius was humming. All was operating normally save for a few indicator lights pulsing randomly along the utility wall, right next to panels which had been smashed in by the speeding bullet which was the engineer's swivel chair. It lay on its back, with one armrest torn off, covered by a warped panel which had been knocked off its hinges. Comparatively, the damage to the lab was minimal. Yet Allaire Rainer had gazed at the wreckage for several minutes already, not sure what to make of the situation, and desperately hoping the incident had not been her fault.

Exhausted from sitting, she walked into the embassy and made her way around the giant conference table, the lighting in the room giving her reflection on the waxed mahogany a warm, rich texture. She stopped for a moment to view the earth, still a single blue sphere in the center of utter blackness, marvelous in its beauty, loyal in its companionship.

Allaire ran her fingers along the sill until she returned to the entrance of the semicircular space and reentered the lab. As she walked back to the workstation, her lips drew in a quick breath and she hummed the nine notes which were so precious to her. Her mind knew what to expect even as her skin felt chills.

She collapsed back onto her swivel chair at the console and took a glance at the static dancing across the screen. In the background, the ambient sound of gurgling emitted from behind the water walls as they performed their rotational stirring of the tanks. Her eyes drifted to the series of clocks affixed to the panel. Forty-one minutes remained. Sighing heavily, she flipped the switch on the radio tuner and began rotating the dial.

White noise crackled, confirming that, for the moment anyway, she was indeed a castaway on a lunar outpost. She lowered the volume just enough so as to still be able to listen to the sounds of wandering static and rested her head and arms on the workstation desk. Shutting her eyes, the room began to fade.

The needle on the VU meter suddenly spiked, and a low, recognizable voice emitted from behind the fabric of the speakers. "Allaire... can you hear me...?"

PARALLELOGRAM

"I'm sorry to have to tell you this, sir," the operator said, her voice having the kind of insouciance one gets after being perpetually exposed to the more impatient side of humanity. "Ardmore 2-5579 has been disconnected for some time now due to the occupant being deceased."

Gillen held the phone up to his ear, against the side of his face yet unravaged by the unintended consequences of spacetime. "I see. Can you confirm the name associated with that extension?"

"A Miss Danielle Hoyne."

That can't be right. None of this is right.

"Thank you for checking, ma'am." And with that, Gillen hung up the phone and turned to see Samantha leaning against the file cabinets. Her dark, ombré hair was still pulled back behind her head and twirled into a clip, but the stylish wave on each side had long since drooped under the weight of existence. The rest of her apparel was doing a decent job feigning the alertness of someone barely able to stay awake.

"Past loves are interesting," she whispered. "Whether they're ghosts or living, they still haunt us."

The stare between the two was fleeting, their eyes smarting underneath the harsh fluorescent bulbs. "It's been a weird day," Gillen answered, still sensing the wound on the side of his head when he pronounced certain syllables. "How far along is the new Alignment?"

"Almost there," she said. "It seems to be opening faster than usual."

Gillen cracked his knuckles and flashed a passive-aggressive grin. "How peachy of it to finally decide to function."

"We're starting to get video!" the engineer called out from the workstation. The duo paced back over to their second home and found Walter, the engineer, and Barry Sjöstrom hunched over the console gazing at the monitor.

"It's intermittent but it's there," he said. "Another minute or two and we should be fully—"

"What's that?" Gillen asked, squinting at the feed from Ortelius, the picture grainy and distorted. The team leaned in.

Below the vantage point of the ceiling camera, beyond the corner edge of the lunar Hexagon, and past the workstation's console, was Allaire... standing and talking with someone in a spacesuit. The individual seemed to tower over Allaire, glowing in metallic radiance except for a single faceplate shrouded in shadow.

The group fell mute as the unconscionable sight strained credibility. Their minds rebelled, too stunned by the absurdity of the image to examine it objectively. It was a prank, or an optical illusion caused by distorted transmissions from a not fully formed Alignment. What they were witnessing was science fiction, straight out of a serial comic or the latest pulp magazines, but not reality. There was no possible way for another human being to be standing on Ortelius interacting with Allaire Rainer, and that was the momentary judgment of each person at the workstation except for one. Gillen shook his head slowly and reached his trembling hand for the audio tuner.

"Who is that?" he whispered.

Too shocked to move, the rest merely observed and tried to stave off their wildest fears. Allaire motioned toward the spacesuit and the individual within gestured back. She seemed calm, alert, and cooperative. Whatever kind of communication they were involved in, Gillen was certain that Allaire was receiving instructions... and she seemed to be capitulating.

"How... is this possible?" Sjöstrom muttered, slurring his vowels.

"Those aren't our EVA suits," Gillen stammered. "I've never seen... I mean... those were not manufactured by us."

"Do we have a connection yet?" Samantha interjected.

The engineer grimaced. "Patchy."

Gillen flipped the switch and gave the gooseneck of the microphone a stranglehold. "Allaire... do you read me? Can you hear my voice?"

There were no visible indicators that she could hear anything coming from the speakers. She simply stood, back facing the camera, conversing with a manifestation. After another moment, she nodded, seemingly all too comfortable with the situation. The spacesuit took a step back and stretched an arm outward toward the corridor. Allaire nodded in agreement and started to leave the lab.

"What the hell is she doing?" Gillen said frantically, giving the switch another few tries. "Allaire? Allaire, can you hear me? Hey... are you still there?"

The picture on the screen blacked out before returning seconds later, this time with more definition. "Try it again," Samantha said.

"Allaire? Allaire, can you hear me?"

The engineer reached for the controls on the panel and changed the input to the camera view in the embassy. A cursory search revealed nothing, so he switched to the next feed and caught Allaire exiting the long end of the corridor that led to the airlock.

"Umm... why is she heading to the airlock?" Sjöstrom asked.

"Is there a view from that section?"

The engineer shook his head, his eyes darting from the screen to the panel. "Camera three is down. It's been on the repair list for weeks. But we do have a crow's nest view on top of the embassy. It pivots so we can get a full panoramic of Ortelius if she does leave the habitat."

"Why would she leave?" Gillen asked incredulously, flipping the feed switch away from the corridor and back to the lab. As the view stabilized, the image that filled the screen sent a shutter throughout the room.

The man in the spacesuit stood directly in front of the camera, the silvery fabric of his suit acting as his otherworldly halo. His helmet was halfway to being unlatched as his gloves rotated the sphere from off his head, and for an instant, Gillen wasn't certain he had the fortitude to handle whatever he was about to witness.

When the helmet detached, the man seemed to breath in the recycled oxygen of the lunar laboratory before lifting the helmet past his face and gazing up into the camera. Gillen, Samantha, Walter, Barry Sjöstrom, and the engineer, all leaned in toward the monitor to get a better look at the unidentified visitor.

The man's expression was stoic. The eyes, intelligent. His facial features, disturbingly familiar.

"Hello, Gillen," the man said into the camera.

Gillen became acutely aware of two emotions surging through his veins like liquid acid. The first was horror. Of seeing something in front of him so foreign to his concepts of reality that his mind was unprepared to process it. The second was surrender. Of being unwilling to do the work of breaking down the subjective enigma until it became objective, and therefore, submitting his mental faculties to the realm of mysticism. Like an impulse of holistic expulsion, Gillen teetered on the verge of retreat from this image, from this living, breathing man who was by his very nature, incongruous with reality. The temptation was intense, Gillen's every sensation begged for relief from the visual knowledge of what he was seeing.

Yet he knew no good could come from ignoring what was standing before him, and that the only way to compartmentalize the phantasm was to utilize the very tool of survival he possessed... his mind.

With an inward tremor that reached out into his limbs, Gillen centered the microphone and turned up the volume on the console speakers. He parted his lips to speak, uncertain if any sound would emit but knowing he had to try nonetheless. He said, "Who... in God's name... are you?"

The man remained planted where he was, but tilted his head ever so slightly, as if to scold Gillen for his disbelief. "You can do better than that."

The voice was unmistakable. The face was indistinguishable. And with the passing of each second, the motive of the man was becoming self-evident simply in lieu of who he was. There could be no mistake.

Standing there, just below the ceiling camera on Ortelius, was the exact replica of Gillen Rainer. He said, "You knew this was inevitable, Gillen. Why do you sound so surprised?"

Gillen exchanged glances with Samantha so quickly that he didn't have time to register if what he saw on her face was more confusion or terror. The engineer and Sjöstrom each held back their bewilderment, one with clenched teeth and the other with a fist covering his mouth. Walter's countenance was the only one to have evolved, having started with shock and having settled into a scowl.

Gillen drew in a deep breath and exhaled as if the air around him was subarctic. "What are you doing with Allaire?" he asked.

The other man responded, "She's safe. I mean her no harm."

The comment landed with little acknowledgment. "You need to stay there," Gillen ordered, "and we can talk about this together. The Alignment is almost intact."

"Oh, I didn't come here using the Alignment," the other said, seeming to want to show some amusement in his tone yet also having the emotional wherewithal to not.

"Well... either way, stay there. Let's discuss this. Just you and I."

The spaceman looked down at the lab floor and sighed, giving the impression that chatter would be too little too late. He gave the helmet in his hands a spin and looked back up at the camera. For a fleeting instant, Gillen witnessed in himself that expression which he despised above all others. The man in the spacesuit had looked at him with pity.

"Do you remember," the man said, "what Allaire's name means?"

Gillen flipped off the mic switch and turned to Sjöstrom. "How much longer before the Alignment is stable?"

"Thirty seconds."

Gillen hit the switch and said, "Yes, of course I remember."

The man nodded. "Cheerful. In French, Allaire means cheerful. The Parisians create such lovely names, don't they?" As he spoke, the connection occasionally crackled, sending lines of static across his face and giving him the appearance of an apparition. "I'm sorry about this, Gillen, I really am. I know losing her will be unbearable for you—"

Gillen gazed at the timer and then back at the screen. The Alignment was reconnected.

"But you have to try and make yourself understand... that her well-being is what's most important here—"

Gillen bolted from the workstation and tore open the Hexagon's control panel. With unblinking eyes he scanned the necessary confirmations on the monitor before checking to be certain that the hovering bulb was green.

"I am not a bad man, although I could understand why you would think so—"

Samantha joined Gillen at the Hexagon and took over operations of the panel as he readied himself to jump.

"Something you cannot comprehend right now, but one day you will..."

"You're good to go," Samantha said, narrowing her eyes in solidarity with Gillen's mission. "Walter and I will be right behind you once you're clear."

Gillen slapped his hands together and nodded. "Here I go."

"Goodbye, Gillen," the man said, sliding his helmet back onto his head and then reaching toward the lunar Hexagon's panel to press a button.

Gillen took a step backward before tensing his muscles for the leap through the Alignment and into what he suspected would be a violent confrontation with this imposter. But as his foot pushed forward, he heard the familiar sound which had eluded them from the beginning of the imbroglio. A sound which could not have been more improperly timed.

It was the sound of the Hexagons locking.

With a giant mechanical thud, the embryonic field vanished along with Gillen's reflection as he leapt into the Hexagon, sailed through the opening, and landed with a grunt against the unforgiving metal floor at the rear of the apparatus. The impact was immediate and harsh, sending streaks of pain across the inside of his eyelids. The disorientation of seeing the lab sideways lasted only until Samantha reached down for his hand and hoisted him back to a standing position.

"What happened?" Gillen exclaimed while rubbing his right arm and shoulder.

"That bastard locked the lunar Hexagon!" Sjöstrom replied. "Just as you were making your jump."

"Reopen it now," Walter barked, keeping his eyes peeled to the monitor.

Gillen and Samantha rejoined him at the workstation and watched the doppelgänger exit through the main corridor and into the airlock. There waiting for him, in a slightly smaller version of the enigmatic spacesuit, was Allaire.

"Where is he taking her?" Gillen asked, hoping anyone could offer a cogent response. The group remained silent for there was no logical answer. Outside of the habitat on Ortelius was nothing. Nothing but the vast, vacuum of space which would kill both of them in seconds should anything happen to their suits.

"Switch to the crow's nest camera," Samantha said.

"And why aren't the Hexagons unlocked?" Walter added.

Sjöstrom said, "He used the emergency shutdown lever on his side of the Hexagon to lock them. It takes sixty seconds for it to reset."

The screen blipped from the main corridor to reveal the outer perimeter of Ortelius. With only a minor adjustment, the view was corrected to point in the same direction as the airlock at the end of the corridor. The design of the exterior of the habitat prevented visual of the airlock itself, but granted a line of sight into where anyone exiting the premises might be heading. In a few seconds, Allaire and the imposter would be back in focus, an image for which Gillen both longed and dreaded to see.

"What is that?" Samantha asked, squinting at the screen.

"What is what?"

"That... just below our view, below the roof of the airlock."

Gillen leaned in, his face inches from Samantha's. "Looks like a wheel."

The glow from the screen burned into their irises as they tried to examine what could possibly look like a wheel just beyond the airlock's outer hatch. On the monitor the object was small, grainy, and was almost the same color as the lunar regolith on which it was resting. It's tread appeared to be metallic, titanium, and riveted into a chevron pattern. What else was connected to it was outside of their vantage point.

"It looks like..."

The wheel suddenly moved, and with it, created a deep indent into the lunar soil as three more appeared, all connected to a chassis on which two wire mesh seats were secured. In the back was some sort of retrofitted magneto, and in the front, a narrow column on which a steering wheel had been fastened, being operated by the abductor, and next to him, his passenger Allaire Rainer.

"Oh my God..." Samantha whispered, covering her mouth and gazing at Gillen.

A booming gearshift thud rang out into the laboratory.

"Go!" Walter demanded, shoving Gillen from his standing position at the workstation and toward the reopened Hexagon.

Gillen pounded the tile floor for as much speed as it could muster as he aimed himself accordingly and leapt into the reflective field pulsing within the heart of the Hexagon. In a single bound, he cleared the Alignment and landed on both feet on the floor of the lunar laboratory on Ortelius.

She was just here, Gillen thought to himself. With frantic glances he motioned forward into the lab, passing the workstation and the fractured swivel chair. Once inside the main corridor he saw the airlock at the end of the hall. A quick sprint brought him to the inner hatch of the airlock, its single porthole window giving a clear view of the rover steadily shrinking along the curvature of the lunar horizon.

The clicking of heels from down the corridor drew Gillen's attention from the hatch and toward Samantha as she closed the gap between them and pointed back down the hallway. "The EVA suits are in the utility closet. We can go after them in the tank."

◂ ◆ ● ● ● ● ◆ ▸

Walter Iselin stared at the monitor with the kind of expression one has when having been made witness to inexplicable horror. The old man stood at the workstation, leaning heavily against the desk on fists which acted as plinths for the columns of his arms. His shoulders sank forward, his cheeks gaunt, the color from his face having been drained and leaving behind only the ashen hue of a cadaverous body.

He appeared like a man trapped in a moment in time. The moment replayed itself in perpetuity both within the man and without. Even blinking offered no relief from the crushing waves of images assaulting his mind, images both present and past. So all encompassing was the sensation in his frame, that Walter suspected this was the very nature of Hell... a soul irrevocably absorbed inside a moment... possessed by the evil, obsessed with regret.

Oblivious to the actions of the engineer, Barry Sjöstrom, and the other team members moving about so as to occupy space and feel in control of the situation, Walter's inertia was a marked contrast and one he was utilizing by necessity, as if his strength alone could keep the forces beneath the desk at bay. His vision swam as Gillen and Samantha moved about the screen, trying to locate the rover, and yet his mind processed none of it. The only existence of which he felt hopelessly a part was his current one, a world without next steps, devoid of a backup plan.

There's nothing worse than loss, Walter said to himself.

Then a memory from much deeper in his past reminded him that there was.

◄ ◆ ● ● ● ● ◆ ►

"Where could they possibly be going?" Samantha asked, her voice crackling into her helmet microphone.

Marshaling forward into the desolate starkness of the moon's barren terrain, Gillen and Samantha sat side by side on a bench seat inside what the Iselin Amalgamate team had conveniently called "the tank". The makeshift cruiser was a six-seater chassis housed on top of a set of continuous track belts that sacrificed speed for versatility. Covering the cabin was an elongated dome of plexiglass giving the passengers a full panoramic view of their surroundings.

Samantha maneuvered the steering wheel and tiller bars with a finesse that wasn't reflected back to the cabin as the massive treads drove along the uneven lunar landscape. Gillen responded while trying to hold his binoculars steady against his faceplate, "I'd first like to know where he came from!"

"He must have breached the Alignment, stowed away like Allaire. Then screwed with the lunar Hexagon wiring, tampered with our controls, waiting for an opportunity."

Gillen pulled away from the binoculars looking unconvinced. When he had heard his other self declare that he had not arrived on Ortelius via the Alignment, for some inexplicable reason, Gillen had believed him.

"Damn that rover is fast," Samantha griped, trying her best to increase the speed of the tank by shifting gears.

Gillen nodded in the kind of agreement shown when desperately trying to distract oneself from the gravity of a situation. *This is not good...* he thought to himself after completing the mental algebra. The distance between the tank and the rover was expanding, and in all likelihood, the abductor and Allaire would reach their destination long before the tank did. *What kind of destination? A Soviet spaceship? A subterranean colony?*

The possibilities were absurd. Just as the Alignment had once been.

As they reached a crest along the highlands the rover ahead of them began a slight grade up a mound. The riveting wheels spun wildly, sending clouds of regolith down the slope. The porous dust and the depth of the soil caused considerable drag on the vehicle, and Gillen and Samantha watched from their view with renewed hope. Their tank was designed for hills like that.

"Come on... come on...." Samantha whispered, her gloves strangling the wheel.

The rover sputtered and fishtailed, sinking deeper into the mound the higher it climbed. The rear wheels vanished into a plume of powder, and for a second, Gillen and Samantha no longer had a visual on the target.

"That's right... keep revving that engine," Samantha chided.

Gillen leaned as far forward as the dashboard would allow and watched as the dust particles slowly settled around the rover. The vehicle had come to a complete standstill, its wheels almost entirely buried in the abrasive soil.

"A couple hundred feet to go," Gillen said, his eyes shifting between the rover and the odometer.

Ahead of them, the ebbing rays of sunlight cast the rover in a phosphorescent shroud, like a golden bubble waiting to be burst. The sphere remained intact for a moment as the rover sat stranded in the mound, seemingly unable to move forward or in reverse. Gillen watched with desperate eyes, wondering what the abductor's next move would be, and in a similar sense, what he and Samantha should do upon reaching the rover. Gillen did not consider himself a violent man, and a life of non-confrontation had thus far proven to be a beneficial strategy for survival. Yet whoever this imposter was, he had stolen the last remaining icon of joy left in Gillen's existence. For that action, every primitive fiber in his being was demanding a step beyond justice, and for the first time, he knew what it was to feel a burning desire for revenge.

Gillen stared daggers at the abductor as the man bounce-stepped out of the chassis and onto the mound. The tank had closed another hundred feet of distance and had crossed out of the shadows and into the light from the sun. The abductor looked over at them before rifling through a secured container next to the magneto and removing what appeared to be a shovel. The metal from its concave blade gleamed against the rays before the man plunged it into the regolith and began frantically digging out the wheels.

"Come on, Allaire," Samantha whispered like a prayer into the void. "Get out of that thing and run."

"She's not going to do that," Gillen whispered back into his helmet mic.

"Why not?"

"Because she thinks that man is me."

The tank leveled off onto the flat plane leading up toward the mound and steadily built speed. Gillen felt his gloves digging into his knees as he rhythmically began rocking himself back and forth in a metaphysical attempt to propel the tank. The abductor had cleared two wheels and was moving on to the third, a plume of dust still permeating the space around him. As he dug the shovel into the soil yet again, a quick glance backward acted as a course correction for the man. Bounce-stepping around the front of the rover, he tossed the shovel to the ground and reached his glove out for his passenger, gesturing for her to exit the seat. Her immediate compliance sent a crushing wave of reality through the beleaguered frames of Gillen and Samantha.

"How can Allaire not know who he is?" she asked incredulously. "Are the Soviet impersonators that good?"

Gillen remained silent as the tank charged the lunar mound with ease. Above them, the abductor and Allaire vanished over the crest of the hill, having abandoned the rover in the regolith and instead choosing to pursue their destination on foot. Gillen pushed his helmet against the plexiglass as they passed the rover, his eyes trying to identify any flags, emblems, or corporate logos emblazoned on the vehicle. Much like the imposter, their transport was incognito.

"Almost there," Samantha said as the tank reached the apex.

Even as Gillen's mind whirled with the possibilities of what they were about to see over the top of the hill, his vision caught glimpse of the glare beaming from off the rover's coating. The rays harkened back toward a point of origin, clearly viewable off in the distance with no firmament or atmospheric interference. Holding the farthest reaches of the solar system together from its singular position in space, the sun hovered within the expanse, blazing like a foundry furnace. Gillen watched it for a moment, purely awestruck, knowing full well that his helmet's visor was filtering out most of the blinding light from the star. The power it radiated was astounding, frightening, like taking a peek at the face of God. Yet it also seemed eternally distant despite its relative close proximity. The radiance it showered down from its throne appeared all encompassing within its realm, yet on the surface of the moon, the sunlight seemed limited, stretched thin, as if serving not to obliterate darkness but merely to illuminate it.

"What is that?" asked Samantha, drawing Gillen's attention back toward the horizon as the tank began the descent down the mound.

With two pairs of bootprints guiding their visual path, Gillen and Samantha spotted the abductor and

Allaire racing along the terrain toward a circular imprint laying flat on the lunar surface. The rune filled the window of the tank as they drove, its circumference stretching out across metal tubes linked along the ground at various intervals by compact titanium junctions. Situated next to the contraption was a small antenna cluster, on which a parabolic dish had been perched aiming back toward Ortelius. Inside the circle was nothing but soil, drawing the conclusion that this was either a remarkably simple piece of machinery, or else an elaborate work of art.

The abductor and Allaire were barreling straight for it, as if the depletion of any amount of energy or oxygen would be worth the effort. The tank closed in on the two as Samantha steadied the wheel. "Seriously, Gillen," she said, stealing a glance in his direction. "What the hell is that thing?"

"It's..." he paused, squinting at the shape and trying to count the junction points. "Not hexagonal," he whispered. "It has eight sides."

"Eight?"

"It's an octagon."

"But what does it do?"

The abductor was only a step ahead of Allaire as he pulled her past the edge of the octagon, triggering Gillen's hand toward the plexiglass panel latch and giving it a violent yank backward. Decoupling the lock from the chassis and opening the gullwing door, Gillen used the papillon design to his advantage and leapt from the rolling tank, his boots landing on the lunar soil in what would have taken a quarter of the time on earth. Gillen spread out his arms in an effort to balance himself, his head momentarily swimming from the foreign gravity of the moon. Through his faceplate, he spotted the abductor and Allaire, each having crossed the boundaries of the metal tube and seconds away from reaching its center.

The tank crawled to a stop next to him as Gillen bolted from his landing spot and bounce-jogged toward the horizontal octagon. His vision of the lunar surface jostled relentlessly as he maneuvered his spacesuit across the terrain, while his mind counted the steps he knew it would take before he was inside the circle with them.

At that moment, he understood his arrival would be too late.

"Allaire," he gasped, panting as he ran.

His daughter stopped at the center of the octagon and turned back to see what was happening. A single strand of auburn hair crossing her face was the last thing Gillen witnessed before the entirety of the octagon's central core pulsed with a rapid heat. Then, as if gazing at the scene through strained eyes, the blurred images of the abductor and Allaire shifted right, dragging their reflections behind them until the twisted reality uncoiled itself back to normal... without the presence of its occupants.

"Allaire!" Gillen screamed into his helmet, his eyes darting side to side as they welled with tears. The space within the octagon was completely empty, save for the bootprints leading up to the core, the last vestiges of evidence that Allaire Rainer had ever been on the moon.

Samantha reached the octagon a moment later and planted her glove on Gillen's shoulder, her labored breathing hissing into her mic. "Where did they go?"

Gillen gave no response because he had no words. The words had been stolen from him, syphoned into a void more isolating than the vacuum of space. Samantha was speaking to him, saying something, but to Gillen it was unintelligible. His senses dulled. His mental processing slowed. Even the abject desolation of the moon suddenly felt overwhelming. He perceived his eyes to be drawn downward toward the regolith, not because there was anything to see, but because he no longer possessed the physical strength to look up.

Samantha's voice was still chattering into his earpiece, a voice hollow of meaning, devoid of sound. He sensed his shoulders beginning to slump and his knees starting to buckle. The gravity of the moon was gaining on him and fighting to remain vertical now seemed too valiant a battle. Gillen watched as the angle of the ground began to shift toward his faceplate.

Cate jumped, you fool.

The lunar soil then jetted away from him, sending his vision spiraling outward toward the stars, the sun, and for the briefest of glimpses, the earth. He felt his body jostle within the spacesuit and wondered if he had become weightless. Shutting his eyes as he teetered on the precipice of unconsciousness, he sensed some of the welled up moisture in his eye overflow and form into a single teardrop that ran down his cheek.

Allaire...

"...Gil...len..."

The firm grip of a hand was wrapped around his arm, tugging at him, while Samantha's voice slowly registered within the recesses of his mind. It felt as though she was not so much trying to pull him back up, but pull him away from the octagon.

"We... have... to... get..."

Gillen's eyes opened and tried to orient themselves with the solar system.

"... out... of... here... now..."

He saw Samantha using the full force of her body to try and drag him back to the tank, condensation building up against her faceplate as she panted. Gillen wasn't certain if he was standing, or being pulled along the surface on one leg, but he did ascertain that Samantha had the look of a woman about to witness a murder.

"Please... Gil...len...!" he heard her plead.

As if observing the sequence through a series of glimpses, he saw her pull him to the open door of the tank, wrestle his dead weight up into the seat, bound around to the driver's side door, and then, suddenly, the gullwing doors had already closed and they were rapidly backing away from the octagon. Gillen blinked and wondered why they were driving backwards, why they had left the scene so frantically, and why Samantha was so visibly shaken that tears of exhaustion were streaming down her face.

A flash of light was followed by no sound as the runes and junctions of the octagon exploded into a halo of dust. So powerful were the bombs that rocked it that a circular wall of regolith shot up into the exosphere and erupted like a lunar volcano. The thick, gray ash spewed upward and outward in every direction, hurling pieces of shrapnel and crackling rock from its epicenter. Dings and pummels against the plexiglass caused Samantha to jerk with each ricochet as she struggled to wheel the tank. The abrasive soot wafted over the area like a storm cloud, obstructing her view and scratching the reinforced windshield with its angular shards.

The tank continued moving, in reverse, as it started back up the hill. Gillen watched the event without comment, without emotion, merely slumped in his seat, unresponsive, aphasic. Soon the inside of the tank had morphed into the chamber of the airlock, and he was standing, leaning against Samantha, who appeared to be holding him upright while trying to do the same for herself. He blinked again and he was out of his spacesuit, sitting in a swivel chair next to a workstation, whether on the lunar lab or on earth he couldn't tell, with a woolen blanket wrapped around him and a mug of tea in his hands. Samantha was seated next to him in similar fashion, sipping from a cup held by trembling fingers.

Gillen wanted to ask what had happened. Try to piece together the fragmented memories of the last hour. Attempt to construct a plan and a timeline for how they were going to get Allaire back. But he remained mute, with barely enough stamina to hold his tea. He scanned the laboratory and noticed they were the only ones still there. No Walter, no Barry Sjöstrom, none of the other brilliant minds who had helped restore contact with Ortelius.

The only one left was Samantha. The woman who had saved his life.

CHAPTER 10

PERMANENT INK

By all accounts, the home had been abandoned. Eighteen-year-old Gillen Rainer had stood on the sidewalk and looked up at the dilapidated two-story house with a restrained sense of reminiscence. He had neither seen nor heard from the love of his life for six months. His birthday had come and gone without her to share in it, and as the countless weeks stretched into a mounting case that their devotion had been mere verisimilitude, Gillen had awoken that Saturday morning and decided that his visit to the Hoyne residence was a long overdue, foregone conclusion.

He had prepared no script. No point-by-point summary as to the inanity of their actions. He arrived with no terms about which to bargain. There was nothing to negotiate. Gillen had granted the family the space and time they seemed to so desperately require in order to appease their deity, or rather, to appease their pastor, and when the day arrived that Gillen decided his self-sacrificing was over, that his needless suffering no longer served a purpose in protecting his love, he simply made up his mind in that instant and marched out his front door.

"You lookin' for the Hoynes?" a neighbor asked Gillen, standing where a fence would have gone if there had been enough space between the houses to post one.

"I suppose I'm not," Gillen responded.

The man sauntered onto the property and gave a hearty kick at the overgrown lawn. "Well, I'll tell you what... the mortgage company is sure as heck lookin' for 'em. Guy swung by here just yesterday asking around. I didn't tell him nothin' cuz it ain't none of my business. But between you and me, I saw them pack up that old pickup he had forever and haul outta here. Two weeks ago to be exact. Hoyne packed up the wife and kids, whatever junk they could fit into that truck, and you could tell... they were on their way and they were not comin' back."

Gillen nodded just once, taking in the condition of the house and knowing that it had been falling apart long before dereliction. "The children," he said, finally addressing the man. "How many children did Mr. Hoyne take with him?"

The neighbor rolled his eyes and tugged at his suspenders. "Umm... lemme think now. There was that little one... grade school aged. I forget her name. There was also a teenager... Gabrielle I think..."

"*Danielle*," Gillen corrected, curtly.

"Right... yeah, Danielle... and... another daughter between them two. Emily, maybe. Sickly sort of child."

"So three children?"

"Yeah."

"They all left two weeks ago with Mr. and Mrs. Hoyne?"

"Sure did."

Gillen hesitated before taking a step toward the porch. "Did they say anything before they left?"

The man chuckled. "Son, I'm a lousy sleeper. The only reason I know what I know is because I spotted them packin' up at one in the mornin'. They didn't say nothin' to nobody. Not that you couldn't tell what was goin' on just by lookin'. It'd been months since Hoyne found any steady work."

Gillen narrowed his eyes at the house. "You think I can get in there?"

The man shrugged, seeming not to care if it got ransacked. "I doubt it's locked. But the mortgage company already took any valuables, not that there was any."

Gillen thanked the neighbor and started up the porch steps. A yank at the screen door and a shove at the main one gave him entrance into the vacant living room in which he had always felt so unwelcome. Quick scans of the downstairs rooms confirmed the neighbor's story; it was as if the Hoynes had never lived there. Darting up the rickety stairwell, Gillen stopped at the landing and viewed the two doors on the second level. It would only be necessary to check one.

The girls' bedroom was farthest down the hallway and had the creakiest of hinges as Gillen pushed open the door and took his first step past the threshold. The room was utterly empty save for a mousetrap in the corner. A cursory search of the window seat, the closet, and behind the door left Gillen with an emotion to which he was not accustomed.

He felt foolish. Foolish for having wondered if there would be a note, a letter, a sign, something left behind to indicate where she was going and how to contact her, yet knowing full well that Danielle's actions were perfectly in line with the expectations of behavior within the Hoyne household. She had done exactly what she needed in order to remain a member in good standing. The lack of a note, call, or visit, was her act of self-sacrifice. One she hoped would result in a future reunion with her highest value.

Any other explanation of the immutable fact that Danielle Hoyne loved Gillen Rainer was not only unthinkable to him, but patently nonsensical. Gillen left the former Hoyne residence grounded in that belief as he walked home, waiting for the peace in his mind to begin the work of settling the agony in his heart.

◂ ◆ ● ● ● ● ◆ ▸

Gillen opened each eye separately and viewed his bedroom from his pillow. The emotions of his dream lingered even as he glanced down at his bed and saw that he was still in his clothes. He recalled Samantha having driven him home and helped him up the stairs where he then collapsed at the landing and buried his face into his hands to conceal a torrent of muffled sobs. Beyond that, his recollection of the previous day's events dissipated into a singularity.

Oh God... Allaire.

Pushing himself up from the bed with muscles that ached from surging adrenaline and shattering loss, Gillen rotated his shoulders back and forth in an effort to ease the radiating pain in his neck. His mind felt lost in a mist, one more dense than the foggiest of afternoons by the bay. The light from his window was overbearing and suggested that it was far past his usual rising time. His wristwatch agreed with that assessment. It was nearly eleven in the morning.

"Samantha?" he called out, his voice hoarse.

I need to talk to Walter, Gillen thought, *he'll know what to do next.*

The motions needed to shower, dress, pop two tablets of aspirin, and walk downstairs, movements that would have otherwise been automatic to a forty-year-old, required much more care as Gillen's body reacclimated to a desire for living. The hallway wafted of coffee and doughnuts, an aroma triggering an emotion that he quickly suppressed. At the kitchen table sat Samantha, reading the morning edition, appearing physically and mentally drained.

"They were on your counter," she said lackadaisically, "about to go stale. There's a few left in the box."

Gillen nodded as he stood in his own kitchen feeling lost. "Thank you. I'm not hungry."

Samantha pointed at the carafe. "There's coffee. And you received a telegram."

The tiny envelope sat on the kitchen table, unopened, addressed to Gillen Rainer from an anonymous sender. His curiosity piqued but then diverted back to Samantha. "Has anyone been in touch with Walter today?"

"I called Lisa. She arrived at the office about an hour ago and hasn't heard from him since he sent everyone home last night—I mean—this morning. I doubt anyone will show up until this afternoon. Then we can work on next steps."

Gillen pressed his hand against his forehead. After pouring himself some coffee, he sat down opposite Samantha at the kitchen table and sighed heavily. In the tone of a man who had succumbed to the tormentors and had signed the confession, he whispered, "Who was that man?"

Samantha shut her eyes and replied, "Someone who Allaire thought she knew."

"I can't get the moment she vanished out of my head. She turned back toward me as if she had an inkling of suspicion and then... just like that... gone. And then those thoughts handed me over to be tortured by other thoughts about what his intentions for her might be... and I just..."

"Those thoughts won't help us now, Gillen," Samantha said, as firmly as her enervated psyche could muster. "The only way we survive the next few hours, is to keep our minds focused on solutions."

He fell silent and slowly reached for a sugar packet but then abandoned the effort and simply drank his coffee black. After another moment of contemplation, he asked, "How did you know that thing was going to explode?"

"I saw a timer... installed into one of the junction boxes. It was still counting down after they had vanished, so I figured it must be a parting gift for us."

Gillen nodded distantly. "Lucky you saw that. I appreciate everything you did for me last night on the moon. You saved my life."

She smiled and took another sip from her mug. "'Never leave a man behind, even if he's a physicist.' I know you're not a physicist, but it was something my father used to say, which I think was, for whatever reason, funny to his colleagues."

"I've known you a long time. You never told me he used to say that. He was a professor, right?"

Samantha nodded slowly and then allowed herself a laugh. "Yep. Taught in Leipzig before visiting Hong Kong and meeting my mother. My parents were so cute together. My mother was 5'1" and my father was 6'3", so the fact that I made it to 5'5" is a testament to the miracle of genetics."

"You walk as if you're tall."

"That was my mother's training. She wanted me to be in films, become a child prodigy. I grew up watching starlets and dreaming about what kind of roles I would be good in. But since my father traveled frequently between Hong Kong and Germany, I developed a curiosity in what kind of work he did when he was away. That's what piqued my interest in science."

"Weren't you Allaire's age when you moved to the States?"

The question left her momentarily without reply, as she carefully untangled the present from the past. "I... suppose I was. My father... he was concerned... about what he was seeing in the German zeitgeist around that time, and my mother worried that collectivism might poison Hong Kong the same way it had some of the neighboring countries. Neither of them wanted those kinds of ideologies to destroy my individualist spirit. So my father secured a teaching position here and the rest is history."

Gillen traced the outline of the cup with his fingertip and said, "I assume your father's last name wasn't Leung."

"Technically, my parents were never married—for obvious reasons. So Samantha Leung I remained. But they were fiercely devoted to each other their whole lives, even if it had to be from a societally perceived distance."

"Were you an only child?"

Samantha curled the edges of her mouth. "My parents never admitted it, but I'm pretty sure I was an accident."

Gillen hesitated before saying, "You're anything but an accident."

For a moment, the kitchen was quiet again, as Samantha processed the compliment and Gillen processed the uncertainty that she would misinterpret it. Samantha smiled in kind and then tapped on the envelope. "You know how much willpower it took not to open that?"

A reach across the table had Gillen's fingers tearing open the seal and withdrawing the tiny beige card. In a single line the words stared back at him, without a shred of context, unwilling to be misread, demanding an answer to a question from an unidentified originator.

"'Can you see Sputnik from the moon?'" Gillen read, his eyes shifting up from the card to Samantha.

"That's it? That's all it says?"

He nodded suspiciously. "That's all."

"'Can you see Sputnik from the moon?'" Samantha repeated. "Who would send that to you? Walter?"

Gillen examined the envelope again before shaking his head. "Not Walter. He's never been the telegram type."

"Then who would be so cryptic?"

Gillen took another long sip from his mug before holding up the card and arching an eyebrow. "I bet I know who."

◄ ◆ ● ● ● ● ◆ ►

The main corridor of the psychiatric ward that led to the arboretum outside was resplendent with natural light. The stained glass ceiling windows bathed the white walls and floors in prismatic color, giving the entryway an aura of transcendence. Gillen quickly discovered that his perceptions of such places were challenged. He figured the visiting and rehabilitation areas of the ward might be less dreary than the medical rooms and dormitory. Any excuse to remind the patients that the world still existed outside of these walls was a benefit to sanity.

As he and Samantha approached the reception desk, a doctor passed them while guiding a patient along by the shoulders. The patient gazed up at them only briefly before readjusting his focus on being sure to step on only the white squares of the checkered floor.

"Who are you here to see?" the attendant asked.

"Jack DaLette," Gillen replied.

A short walk into the arboretum outside led Gillen and Samantha into a world of potted flowers, kempt shrubbery, and boxelder trees. Stationed at various points along the paved walkway were clinical staff either tending to their patients, or else taking a moment for themselves in the open air. Having been escorted in a wheelchair to dote over the chrysanthemums, one man hummed to himself while misting the flowers with a spray bottle. The tune in his head caught Gillen's attention as he and Samantha passed by toward a different man who was seated on a bench beneath a tree.

"Are you two here to deliver my pink slip?" the man joked.

Gillen and Samantha both flashed the weary smiles of those too exhausted to laugh but too deferential to ignore a friend's attempt at levity. "Hello, Jack," Gillen said while slapping him on the shoulder. "How are you?"

"Mad as a hatter," Jack replied with a wink. "But don't tell that nurse over there. I think she likes me and I'd hate to spoil the sexual tension."

Samantha remained standing as Gillen sat down next to Jack on the bench. Jack sat with his arm stretched along the back of the bench, his legs crossed, his body turned debonairly toward Gillen, reminding anyone watching that a little insanity now and again was no match for a suave nature. "Assuming you're not in fact here to hand deliver my walking papers, then to what do I owe this unexpected pleasure?"

Gillen fished the telegram out from his overcoat pocket and handed it to Jack. "Did you send this message?"

Jack's confused reaction to the envelope was the only answer Gillen needed, and as the man slowly reached for it and read its contents, Gillen was already feeling the pangs of having wasted precious time. Jack read, "'Can you see Sputnik from the moon?' That's a curious question."

"Isn't it."

"And you came all the way here to ask if I sent you this cryptogram?"

"Evidently."

Jack chuckled. "I wish I had."

"What do you mean?"

"I mean it's an interesting question. One that deserves an answer. Can we see Sputnik from the moon?"

Gillen exchanged glances with Samantha. She said, "I don't see why not. The telescope in the observatory on Ortelius is incredibly powerful. But we're more concerned as to who else would know that."

"Outside the company?"

Samantha nodded. "Precisely."

"You mean Walter didn't send this to you?"

Gillen cocked his head. "Why would Walter send me a telegram like that?"

"As a prank."

"I've known him a long time, and I promise you that Walter is anything but a prankster."

Jack nodded slowly and reexamined the message. "I guess that's true. I mean, the real prank is that I'm in this place instead of Walter."

This time Gillen chuckled as he reached for the telegram. "Why would you say that?"

"I mean, with everything that happened to him back in the day, what happened to his family... I'm not a sadist or anything, but it does seem like out of the two of us, he should have cracked up long before I did."

A long, quizzical stare from Gillen caught Jack's notice as the man reached into his pocket for a cigarette. "Either of you two have a light?"

Samantha withdrew hers from her purse and handed it to Jack as he said, "Why are you looking at me like I'm crazy, Gillen?"

Withholding a comment in the affirmative, Gillen steadied his nerves and patted Jack on the knee. "I'm sorry, but I'm not following you."

Jack looked up at Samantha and handed the lighter back. "You've known Walter the longest, Sam. I know he isn't one to talk much about his personal life, but surely he told you about what happened to his family."

Samantha nodded cautiously. "Of course. It was tragic."

Jack seemed reassured by that knowledge and then turned to Gillen. "Walter told you that story, right?"

"About how he lost his family? Yes, I know what happened. But I fail to see how—"

"You know they were murdered, right?"

Gillen felt a switch in his temperament of which he was unaccustomed. It was a fatigue induced irritation of listening to someone oblivious to the crisis at hand. This was not the day or the moment to be having a casual chat about losing loved ones, and Gillen prepared himself to calmly make that clear. "Jack... listen to me..."

"Walter told me that he had never told anyone, but even then I suspected he was full of it."

"Told anyone what?" asked Samantha, eyeing Gillen's simmering demeanor.

"How he lost his faith," Jack said nonchalantly, drawing in a puff from his cigarette.

211

We don't have time for this, Gillen thought to himself, and leaned forward to stand.

"I'm pretty sure that's what I had in mind when I wrote what I did on the wall, 'There's nothing worse than loss.' It's not that I was thinking about Danielle at that instant. I was thinking about Walter."

Gillen felt his thighs rebel against his mind's order to push his torso into a standing position. For a moment he hesitated on the edge of the bench, unable to leave, yet uncertain if he could bear to stay and listen to any more. It was at the moment he felt Samantha's hand come to rest on his shoulder as she took a step closer to where he was sitting. Articulating what Gillen could not, she said, "Go on."

Jack tapped the cigarette against the back of the bench and shook his head. "The only reason I know this story, the whole story of what happened to Walter's family, is because of that night you and Walter took me out to get hammered after Danielle left."

Gillen blinked, trying to readjust his brain to focus on an irrelevant memory. "I remember. You didn't stick around. We figured it was all just too much for you, so we paid the tab and left."

"No, you left, Gillen," Jack corrected. "Walter found me outside in the parking lot, sitting on the gravel next to my car, sobbing like a lunatic. He brought me back inside the bar and we got a booth. Next thing I know, Walter's more sloshed than I am, telling me about his goals for Ortelius, how he started the company, and what he was doing before he ever even thought about setting foot on the moon."

Gillen shifted his jaw. "I've only ever seen Walter drunk once, myself."

"I'm sure of that. Very out of character for him. But anyway, there we are, moving on to our next rounds, when all of a sudden, he starts waxing eloquent about technology, love, loss, faith, and being an overcomer."

"An overcomer?" Samantha clarified.

"Right. He starts babbling about his need to figure out the Alignment. To make the connection between the earth and moon stable, something our good buddy Gillen figured out with his Minreth-Hughes equation soon afterward. But I digress. He pulls out his notebook. You know, the little one he keeps in his pocket for moments of genius or what-have-you. He flips through the pages and shows me some diagrams, theorems, stuff he's been working on. He then hands it to me to flip through myself. I'm thinking, wow, this is like holding the Word of God, so I say that to Walter, hoping to cheer us both up.

"That man's expression changed instantly, and all of a sudden I'm being dragged from behind down Walter's own personal rabbit hole of diatribes and memories. More than I wanted to know for sure. He's going on about his upbringing, serving in the war, college, how he met his wife... and to be honest, I'm zoning in and out. I had just lost

Danielle and I was still processing my own personal hell. So as Walter goes on and on I'm flipping through his notebook, indiscriminately looking at a great mind at work, when suddenly, on the last page, and I mean, on the inside of the back of the binding, the part of the book that isn't paper... you know... at the end..."

Gillen and Samantha nodded in unison.

"He wrote out a single sentence. A question. Just like what you received in that telegram, Gillen. That's why it made me think of Walter. At the back of his little notebook, it read, 'Should I pursue A.I.?'"

"A.I.?" Gillen repeated. "Artificial intelligence?"

Jack snapped his fingers. "I'm impressed you know what that is."

"Well, Walter's alma mater, Dartmouth, just began that field of research a year or two ago. It's a branch of cybernetics and one of Walter's old colleagues is involved in the development."

"Correct," Jack continued. "Of course, I figured most of that out later, but then I'm thinking, why would Walter be interested in artificial intelligence? He's got enough irons on the fire with the Alignment. A.I. would be a waste of time."

Gillen's thoughts boomeranged back to the unconscionable image of his own face staring back at him in the workstation screen. His eyes darted away in an effort to rid his mind of the imposter's face, only to lock onto Samantha whose gaze was obviously registering the same memory.

"Anyway, all that aside," Jack said, "I hand the notebook back to him as he starts into his years working for the university, then the private sector, then he has some sort of wild epiphany and joins a non-governmental organization out of New York. After a few months they ship him and his wife—he showed me a photo of her incidentally, a lovely looking woman he met in Paris, a real *mademoiselle* if you know what I mean. Where was I? Oh... so they ship them and their five-year-old son, Lamar, out on a goodwill mission to one of those godforsaken countries."

Jack paused for a moment as if to collect his thoughts. "Well, things are going fine for a while, a year goes by, then, tensions start to rise in the city where he's teaching. Political tensions. Misunderstandings. Suspicions as to motives and alliances. Unrest begins and social order starts to unravel." After taking a long puff from the cigarette and flicking it to the ground, Jack added, "Perhaps it was a case of mistaken identity, or maybe it was a personal vendetta, I don't think Walter ever found out. But one night he's jumped by two men in an alleyway and a burlap bag is tossed over his head. Next thing he knows, he's in a basement somewhere being interrogated about who he works for and what his real purpose is in visiting the country. Walter had no idea who these jokers were, but it didn't really matter. Authoritarianism always breeds paranoia in its people. They needed a scapegoat for their grievances and Walter was their chosen victim. Only they didn't just stick with Walter."

"Jack," Gillen interrupted. "I hate to break up the story here, but we're trying to find out—"

"I'll spare you the grizzly details," Jack assured, "but let's just say that by morning, his wife and son were both dead. For whatever reason, they let Walter go free, and when he came back to the States, he was understandably messed up. Which is why I think there's some irony in the fact that I'm here in this nuthouse, after a simple divorce, and Walter is saving the world after what he went through. That's why I was thinking about that line the night I cracked up, and ended up writing it on the wall in... we'll call it *permanent ink*." Jack smirked at the morbidity of his pun. "Crazy stuff right there, isn't it, Gillen? But 'Can you see Sputnik from the moon?' I really can't help you there, except to state the obvious."

"And what's that?" asked Samantha.

"Somebody knows something that they shouldn't."

CHAPTER II

SEMBLANCE OF GRAVITY

"...continues to circle the globe every ninety-six minutes," the radio announcer said, his flawless elocution filling the speakers inside Samantha's car. Gillen leaned against the passenger door, his elbow up against the window, his hand massaging his forehead, his mind reeling from too many thoughts combating too many emotions. "...blame being hurled at American scientists, the military, and even the president, for being blindsided by the launch and success of mankind's first ever artificial satellite... by the Soviets."

Gillen reached for the volume knob and jerked it counterclockwise. "Did Walter mention any side projects to you?" he asked Samantha, without context into his line of thinking.

"Like artificial intelligence? He did not," she confirmed. "Honestly, Jack's story was the first I've heard about it. I wasn't even aware of Walter's participation in the Dartmouth study. He told you, though?"

"Briefly. He seemed ambivalent about his involvement at the time. We hadn't stabilized the Alignment yet."

"Nor had I heard the details about what happened to his family."

Gillen redirected his eyes back out the window and grimaced. "Yeah, it would seem that Walter is sometimes selective with whom he shares what."

The car sped along the interstate as a cloudless sky gave way to the midday sun. San Francisco was bathed in shimmer. The city almost looked celestial, as if humans had finally eschewed their petty differences and achieved ascension. The image was comforting to Gillen, even if it was a mirage, and reminded him of the first blueprint of Ortelius ever completed. It had been outlandish, preposterous, and idealistic. Two years later it was achieved.

The Iselin Amalgamate building appeared at the top of the hill as the car made its way to the mostly vacant parking lot. "Good," Gillen said upon spotting the other vehicle. "Walter's here."

The metal double doors granting access to the laboratory were already open as Gillen and Samantha entered the hallowed space. The swivel chair had been removed, along with all of the glass shards, and in place of the window pane was a single sheet of plywood, the kind that seemed to be manufactured for this exact sort of purpose. In the corner, various segments of machinery hummed contentedly next to the workstation and its intermittently blinking indicator lights. Diagonally opposing the workstation on the other side of the lab, the Hexagon occupied its own space, uninterested in the operations of the rest of the room.

Gillen looked up at it with the expression of acknowledging a friend who was now a foe. Above the Hexagon, a single bulb burned solid green. "Did you remember to lock the—"

"He's up there," Samantha said softly as she gazed at the console monitor. Gillen joined her at the workstation and observed the immovableness of Walter Iselin as he stood away from the camera, staring out the window wall of the embassy with his hands clutched behind his back. The observation room lights were off, casting his body as a silhouette against the exterior habitat lighting and the cobalt blue of their home planet.

Without rush, they casually walked across the lab and up to the Hexagon, and in tandem, stepped through the Alignment and onto the moon. The lunar laboratory was also dark, albeit pulsing with activity from control boards and germanium diodes, and the conference room chair and panel had been removed, yet a giant impact crater in the wall served as a lingering reminder of the effects of hubris.

Gillen and Samantha moved forward through the lab and into the main corridor leading to the entryway of the embassy's observation room. The recessed lights had indeed been dimmed, leaving Walter standing at the window wall like a projected image. The older man had removed his suit blazer and draped it over one of the conference chairs, and instinctively, Gillen did the same with his overcoat upon entering. A silence anomalous to even outer space saturated the room as Gillen stood on the other side of the circular conference table and awaited acknowledgment.

"Hello, Walter," Gillen said calmly.

Although the man didn't turn, he nodded toward the window so as to address Gillen through the reflection. "Hello, you two."

"Are you the only one here?"

"Quite," Walter said, his tone low and weak. "I sent Lisa home. She needed to rest."

Gillen nodded and then looked at Samantha who was already gazing at him with searching eyes. "Did you... send me a telegram this morning?"

Walter didn't move but Gillen could see through the reflection in the glass that he was listening. "No," was his anticlimactic reply.

Gillen parted his lips to speak when Samantha said, "We were just wondering because it contains proprietary information. If it didn't come from someone within the company, then we may have a security breach."

The news didn't seem to sway Walter. He simply stood staring out the window wall at earth. Gillen took a gradual step forward and slowly walked along the curvature of the conference table with Samantha toeing from behind.

"Do you want to know what it says?" Samantha asked.

Walter shrugged, and the action struck Gillen with the force of being disowned by a loved one. The man had been a stalwart in his life. A constant in a sea of tumultuous challenge. The gravity of what they were facing in finding out where Allaire had been taken, who abducted her, and by what portal access could be obtained was about as insurmountable as sending a man to the moon. Gillen cocked his head and furled his brows, trying to shake the level of insult and disrespect toward their situation that Walter's shrug had insinuated. He focused on that fact, that they were all under enormous stress at the moment, and one person's stress reaction tended to be a trigger for someone else's.

Clearing his throat, Gillen continued, "The telegram simply reads, 'Can you see Sputnik from the moon?' That's all. Can you think of anyone who would have sent that to me?"

Walter finally flinched, hanging his head forward as if chuckling to himself about a cosmic joke to which only he and the universe were privy. Gillen and Samantha had almost reached the old man by the time he turned to face them. The bags underneath his eyes were not as noticeable as the overall lifelessness of his expression. He was the manifestation of more than just insomnia. He was the archetype of the living dead.

With moist eyes, Walter began, "I don't know who sent you that telegram, but they are correct for asking."

Gillen tilted his head and stopped a few feet short of where Walter stood at the wall. "Asking what?"

Walter pointed toward the circular entryway with a hand suspended by an arm that could barely maintain the weight. "The telescope. It's right in the side room. Giant monstrosity that looks like an eyesore no matter where we put it. But it works wonders for space gazing. I was in that room all night. Everyone thought I'd gone home, but I didn't. I needed to think." Walter hesitated before saying, "I'm sorry you lost Allaire, Gillen. I too have lost a child... and it never really... the pain that is... goes away..."

"Walter," Gillen pressed. "What are you saying about the telescope? Can we use it to find Allaire?"

Walter exhaled loudly and shook his head. "We cannot."

"Why is that?" Gillen asked, trying not to seethe.

"Because we *can't* see Sputnik from the moon."

Samantha narrowed her eyes in challenge. "We should be able to. If it's set up properly."

"It is. But we cannot. And I should have known. It dawned on me the moment I saw your double in the spacesuit, Gillen. I knew in that instant, but had to come to the observatory to be certain."

"I'm not following you," Gillen said with exasperation. "What does Sputnik have to do with Allaire?"

Walter laughed the terrifying laughter of one keenly aware of danger and yet uncertain of the value in fighting. "Sputnik has nothing to do with Allaire herself, but everything to do with explaining where she is."

Gillen's eyes widened. "Where is she?"

"On earth." Walter pointed out the window. "Only that's not the earth, because this is not the moon."

Gillen and Samantha stared at him equally nonplussed, uncertain if the old man was cruelly toying with them or had joined Jack DaLette in achieving transcendence. Taking a moment to suppress his tension, Gillen rubbed his hand over his face and asked, "What are you talking about?"

"I'm talking about the Alignment," Walter replied. "You see, the three of us, and the whole rest of the company, we've never been to the moon. The Alignment that we built, connects earth, our home planet, to an alternate moon orbiting an alternate earth that resides in an alternate solar system... one closely mirroring our own, but not exactly."

Gillen laughed, but this laugh was different from the one he had exhibited on his porch steps in front of Mr. Hoyne. That laugh had been one of derision. This laugh was merely a delay tactic, used to push his sudden spike in terror into the confines of the next moment. With a crooked smile, he said, "Walter, just because you missed Sputnik's flyby doesn't mean—"

"I was watching for it all night, Gillen," Walter countered. "I should have seen it multiple times. Never appeared. So then I installed the last of the antenna components that Richard and Barry had brought up. Took a couple of hours to assemble, but when I was done, I tuned to Sputnik's frequency. Radio silence, as they say. Yet coming from the workstation tuner which is linked to the receiver down on earth, our earth, there she is... pinging away."

"Then you must have been getting radiation interference. Maybe a solar flare knocked out transmissions for a bit."

"I already told you, I could hear Sputnik from the earth-based console, but not from the lunar antenna."

"Then you assembled it incorrectly, or they damaged it in transport."

Walter again pointed out the window. "Doesn't change the fact that *visually*, that satellite is not orbiting that blue planet."

Gillen shook his head in vexation, flashed a glare at Samantha whose silence now felt like betrayal, and then reaffixed his gaze toward the man he idolized. "This... can't be..."

"I'm sorry, Gillen, but it is."

"An alternate earth? Are you serious?"

"It's in line with superposition and parallel universe theory. It's basic astrophysics."

"It's insane."

"So was the Alignment. But here we are."

"Then who was the man who kidnapped my daughter?" Gillen snapped.

Walter's pause bore an uncomfortable resemblance to the sympathetic expression Gillen loathed, and Gillen's countenance showed it. Walter said, "That man... in the spacesuit, that man was you. The Gillen Rainer from the alternate earth—"

"No."

"Which explains why Allaire trusted him so."

"That's not possible."

"Why not?"

"*Because a daughter knows her father!*" Gillen exclaimed, his voice echoing throughout the room.

Walter fell silent as he stared at Gillen. The two men stood in the shadows, against the window wall, against the backdrop of the magnificent desolation of the lunar surface, the unmistakable glory of a distant earth, and the dawning realization that from their vantage point, they had never witnessed either.

Samantha stood off center, her arms crossed against her chest, her head slightly downward, and with a look of imputed pain on her face. "Everything," she whispered. "All that we built... all that we accomplished..."

Walter nodded slowly in confirmation. "It's not what we thought it was."

Gillen felt his hands run through his hair and down his neck as his mind raced. "So where does that leave us?" he asked intensely.

Walter glanced at him with genuine curiosity. "What do you mean?"

"I mean with finding Allaire. If the other me abducted her and took her to an alternate earth, where is it and how do I get there?"

The old man parted his frail lips yet could offer no words. They simply trembled, log jammed by a torrent of emotions dammed up against the immutable laws of reality. His eyes searched the darkened corners of the room, hopelessly lost to find any response that didn't remotely sound like a betrayal. Instead, the well-meaning platitudes of those in his past assaulted Walter's memory, spiraling into his vision with the traumatic power of the present. The endless condolences, the promises of redemption, even the candor of those who assumed they could relate, all of it coiled within Walter's being, chaining him to the images of that torturous room, of his son and of his wife, and of the night that would forever alter his perception of the world.

"I can't live here anymore," he had once said to himself. With determination, he had plotted a course to leave. Now, standing inside the very embassy intended for ambassadors to hash out a better way of life for planet earth from the safety and viewpoint of the moon, a stark realization struck him with the fury of approaching thunder.

"Dear God," Walter pleaded, "I never escaped."

This time Gillen fell silent as Walter scanned the room with distant eyes. The old man struggled to find his footing for an instant, but then began walking away from Gillen and Samantha around the other end of the massive mahogany table. With trance-like motions, he headed for the exit only to be called out by Gillen who took a step forward in outraged protest.

"Walter!" he demanded, trying to pry an answer from the man but instead forming a different question. "What do we...? How... how do we...?"

The man continued walking away from them, stopping only when Gillen shouted into the void, "Does any of this have to do with artificial intelligence?"

Walter hovered at the threshold to the room, seeming unwilling to stop yet unable to continue. The three individuals remained in fixed positions like pieces on a chessboard in which the game had ended in a stalemate. From behind, Gillen watched as Walter began the efforts necessary to turn his body back toward them, but then in midmotion he abandoned the attempt and resumed his exit strategy.

Bewildered and on the verge of panic, Gillen struggled to comprehend what he had just heard, what he had just seen, and why somehow, all of it had the unconscionable connection to a thirteen-year-old girl from planet earth. "Samantha," he mumbled, pressing his hands to his temples and turning toward her. "What do we do? How do we get her back?"

The light from outside the window wall cast a gossamer ray against her face, highlighting both the glint in her eyes and the uncertainty of her agape mouth. Samantha looked down at the floor and then back up at Gillen who appeared seconds away from scaling the walls. The conference room suddenly seemed to be closing in on them and

Samantha instantly knew why. If Walter was correct, this was not the moon, and the blackness behind the stars cocooned something that was not the earth. They were standing nonchalantly inside the borders of another solar system within another universe, and no matter how similar the parallel seemed to be, one fact could not be ignored.

They were aliens in this universe, and that truth was beginning to terrify her. "Gillen, can we go, please?"

"What?"

"I want to leave. I want to be back on earth. Our earth. Let's work this out down there. Not here. I don't feel safe here anymore."

Gillen gave the room a quick scan before nodding and reaching for his overcoat. "Let's go then. We'll head back down to the lab."

Samantha shook her head with fervor. "Not the lab. I don't wanna be anywhere near this place right now. I need a drink. Can we go get a drink?"

◄ ◆ ● ● ● ● ◆ ►

The terrestrial laboratory was still empty when Gillen and Samantha walked through the Alignment and stepped foot back on earth. Walter was nowhere to be found, and his vehicle had vanished from the parking lot, leaving them to suspect that he had taken what was left of his sanity and gone home. Following his lead, they got into Samantha's car and traveled the few blocks back to Gillen's residence, where a shuffle up the front steps and into the foyer left them unusually spent for a midafternoon.

"Whiskey sour, right?" Gillen asked wearily as they stood in the den.

"Yes, please."

After fixing her drink, he poured some scotch over a pair of ice cubes and gave the tumbler a swirl. He raised his glass toward her with a mocking poise as if to punctuate the fact that there was nothing to celebrate. Samantha nodded and continued nursing her drink as she sat on the edge of the divan.

"I'm so sorry, Gillen."

He took a step forward from the cart and sat down next to her. "I can't imagine for what. You saved my life."

Samantha gazed into her drink. "The day I agreed to help Walter build this thing, create a team, go to the moon, I thought about all of the challenges, frustrations, and even peril we would be up against. I knew the odds were against us but believed in the mission. I believed in the..." Drawing a blank, she took another sip from her glass and then continued, "But I never saw this coming. Not once did the possibility of something like this even cross my mind. That we were building in the wrong place, gazing back at the wrong planet... never once. If I had, none of this would have happened and Allaire would still be safe with you."

"That kind of retrospective is pointless and you know it," Gillen challenged. "Okay, so you didn't think of it. Neither did Walter, Barry, Richard, Cate, or Frank in accounting." Gillen then rested his hand on Samantha's wrist and gave it a gentle squeeze. "Neither did I."

Samantha briefly smiled before returning to her drink. "We have to figure out who sent that telegram. They were on to it before we were and that might lead us to Allaire."

Gillen shifted his gaze toward Samantha as if to scold her for not thinking through the possibilities. After a moment, he whispered, "They detonated that octagon for a reason. Unless there's another entryway somewhere on *their* moon or our earth, the only other way we get to Allaire is building a rocket ship on their moon that can land on their earth. And even then, we have to figure out some way home."

"There must be another portal. An Octagon like our Hexagon."

"On their moon?"

"Perhaps. Or maybe here on earth."

"One that bypasses the moons altogether and is a direct link between the two earths?" Gillen gyrated his glass anxiously and shook his head. "If they have that capability then why go through all the trouble of trapping her on the moon? Why not just abduct her from one planet to the other?"

"Placing Allaire in a perilous situation and then showing up as a rescuer is a much more effective tactic for building trust than is showing up with... I don't know... a chloroform rag and duct tape."

"Well, it worked. She trusted him all right."

Samantha said, "It would seem counterproductive to sever your only tie to another dimension just to evade a rescue attempt by us. There must be another entry point, and I'm guessing it's here on earth. Our earth. Probably right here in San Francisco. And whoever sent that telegram knows where it is."

"You think there's another Octagon hiding somewhere in San Francisco?"

"It's possible."

"Where? Where the hell would one hide it?"

"I don't know, Gillen. I'm just thinking out loud. I'm just trying to save your daughter."

Gillen removed his hand from her wrist and looked away. As he took another sip, his vision began to swim, and it was at that point he realized that he had not eaten anything in nearly a day.

"Gillen, that's not what I meant. I didn't mean it like that."

Leaning forward, he responded, "I know."

Samantha also leaned forward and rested her hand on his shoulder. "I only meant that I'm trying to do my part too. Trying to assuage this enormous guilt I feel for what happened to her, and what's happening... to you." The last two words barely made it past her lips before a tear escaped from her eye. Covering her mouth with her hand, Samantha choked back the emotions that threatened to overtake the moment. She had always prided herself on her ability to maintain composure in stressful situations.

This situation was a step beyond that.

"Oh, Gillen," she whispered, gripping the polyester of his white button-down shirt. "What are we going to do?"

The arm sleeve wrinkled under the pressure of Cate's grasp as the pain settled in. Gillen blinked and tried to resist the memory, manifested most often in times of extreme exhaustion on his own part. In that way, the memory was as merciless as its subject matter.

"I've got you," Gillen had spoken to Cate in tones of soft reassurance. They were still in their evening wear, having ungracefully left Walter's dinner party during the meal.

"I'm so sorry, Walter," she had said, hugging her abdomen as streaks of pain radiated throughout her torso.

"Never mind, darling," he had said, ignoring the other guests at the table and helping Gillen escort Cate out the front door. "Take care of her, Gillen," Walter had asked.

By the time Gillen had assisted Cate into their bedroom, she could barely stand on her own. The intensity of her muscle pain seemed to be directly proportional to the amount of movement in which she was engaged. A vicious cycle when still in heels and a dress.

Her attempt at unzipping the dress was unsuccessful. "I've got you," Gillen repeated, working the stubborn zipper down her spine. As he gently slipped her arms through the straps, the black dress fell to the floor and bunched together at her feet. The skin of her naked back glistened in the dim twilight of the room and gave Gillen a strobe-flash image of their last intimate encounter. The tiny beads of sweat on her skin had once been so erotic to him, and had been the tangible evidence of their abilities to summon incredible amounts of pleasure from each other. The flashback faded, however, as she removed her panties and stood before him, trembling. These beads of sweat had nothing to do with sexual energy and everything to do with a physical response to suffering.

"I'll draw the bath," he had whispered, and when the tub was sufficiently full, helped lower her into the scalding water.

Cate gasped, winced, and then quickly settled into a lethargy of submission to both the pain and the caressing warmth. "Thank you."

"Of course," he had replied, kneeling next to the tub on the tile floor, his suit pants absorbing trace amounts of bathwater, his hands touching any part of her body that was tolerable, and their eyes locked onto one another in solidarity.

"I love you, Cate," he had said.

"I love you, Gillen," she had answered.

I think we both meant it, Gillen pondered to himself, as Samantha loosened her grasp of his arm.

"When was the last time you've eaten?" Samantha asked. "Because I'm famished."

A nod got them off the divan and into the kitchen. Mindless motions of reaching for cupboard handles, stirring a saucepan, and pouring wine, left them both somewhat surprised when they discovered that they were sitting at the dining room table eating hastily prepared spaghetti and jarred pasta sauce. Lifting their forks from the plates to their lips seemed an almost cruel form of manual labor as they sank into their chairs, but it was the only way to offset the hunger induced nausea and clear the way for more alcohol.

Gillen chewed slowly, purposefully, having no concept of what he was tasting yet being grateful for the actions of normalcy. Samantha did the same, periodically looking at Gillen and expressing an entire conversation within a single stare.

When they had finished eating, they left the dishes at the table and finished their wine in the den. The fact that dusk was rapidly approaching left them dazed and bewildered, begging the question if anyone had come into the laboratory today, and also, if anyone had a lead on the whereabouts of Walter.

"You haven't seen him all night?" Gillen confirmed as he held the sleek handset up to his ear. "Well, would you have him call me the second he gets in? Thank you." The phone let out an off-key chime as he hung up the receiver. "The concierge at Walter's condominium hasn't seen him since yesterday. But he said there are several messages waiting for him."

"No one has any idea how to handle this," Samantha muttered. "We need Walter in on these discussions. Is there someplace he typically goes when depressed?"

"He's more of a homebody outside of work, so who knows? A bar...a park...maybe he built an Alignment to Venus."

Samantha and Gillen paced the den, passing each other every few seconds as they walked, feeling the crackling waves of heat from the fireplace as the embers burned. "Do you think Richard Kaine sent you that telegram?" she asked midstride.

Gillen shrugged. "As an act of penance? Who knows? He's crazier than Jack will ever be. If he did, there's no way to reach him. He's on his way to New York."

"Is there a way we could reconfigure the Hexagons to access their earth instead of their moon?"

"We would need a frame of reference in order to define the Alignment's trajectory. We have a point of origin, the lab, but we really don't have a fixed destination because we have no idea where in the universe that planet actually exists."

Samantha bit her lower lip and smirked. "I guess the Minreth-Hughes equation can't fix everything."

Gillen matched her smirk with an arched eyebrow and reached to tap her arm as they passed, but inadvertently instead slid his fingers along the length of her exposed forearm sending goosebumps up her tender skin. "Sorry," he corrected, not turning back to see her face.

Samantha continued pacing, absorbing the momentary sensation and preventing the smirk from forming into a smile. "Don't worry about it."

The grandfather clock in the corner made its hourly chime, subtly announcing the start of evening. Outside the window panes the skies were already gray, as if they had been well prepared for darkness for some time. Gillen broke pace with Samantha and walked over to the sill, gazing out at what little of the world he could see. He imagined the moon as a giant searchlight swaying over the landscape of earth, shining as a beacon to guide distraught parents back to their lost children. The impression then faltered upon a sobering realization. Every parent who had ever gone through this had one thing in common. They had known that their missing child was at least on the same planet.

The haunting truth found words as Gillen bowed his face before the window. *If I had access to all the moonlight on earth, I still couldn't find Allaire.*

With coercive subtlety, a memory triggered an emotion, and before he knew what he was doing, he heard himself hum the nine notes from Allaire's song. His palms acted reflexively and pushed his body away from the window. *No. Not right now. Work the problem.*

Turning back toward Samantha, he slapped his hands together and tried to repurpose his mental energy on the few options available. "Until we hear back from Walter, I suggest we rally up the team and begin digging into the binders at the lab."

Samantha nodded but then paused. "What good will that do, exactly?"

"Not the ones for the Hexagon. I mean the early stuff. What you, me, Walter, and Jack worked out when we first discovered the Alignment. The rudimentary calculations and projection models that led us to that alternate dimension in the first place. You were correct a moment ago. If we randomly stumbled upon a parallel moon, maybe it wouldn't be too hard to align it with their parallel earth."

"Oh my God," Samantha gasped, her brown eyes capturing Gillen's attention. "Jack."

"What? What about him?"

"I should have thought of this earlier, when we were talking to Jack, when he was talking about Danielle. It was her, Gillen! Danielle must have sent the telegram!"

The certainty of her words lingered as Gillen formed a rebuttal. When he parted his lips to state it, his argument failed before it left his mind. "Of course," he whispered, taking a step toward Samantha. "The Danielle we saw on the train—"

"Wasn't her. At least, not the one you knew."

"It was the Danielle from the alternate earth."

"Which is why what Jack told you was the truth," Samantha added, softening her tone ever so slightly. "Your Danielle... I mean... Jack's Danielle... really did die last year."

Gillen nodded methodically, his eyes wandering, his pulse galloping. "Yeah."

Samantha noticed and tried to quickly reel him in. "I'm sorry, Gillen. But at least we know someone who might be able to help us."

"But... how did she get here?" he asked. "From their lunar Octagon and onto Ortelius?"

"Doubtful. I think this instead proves my theory. There's a terrestrial Octagon on earth, probably right here in San Francisco, and the other Danielle Hoyne knows where it is."

Gillen spun around on his heels and was hit by an instance of vertigo. Inhaling before taking a steadied next step, he said, "Assuming all of that is true, what makes you think she's still here? We chased her for a mile. She obviously doesn't want to talk."

"Not in person. But maybe she's trying to communicate in other ways." Samantha swiped the telegram from off the credenza. "Step one." Her eyes then scanned the den before marching out of the room and into the hallway. Gillen followed her curiously as they entered the foyer. A suspicious glare etched Samantha's facial lines as she clipped the telegram between her front teeth and unlatched the panel of the house mailbox. Several days worth of mail fell into her hands along with a small package in brown wrapping paper.

Gillen examined the box first before tossing it aside and splitting the envelope stack with Samantha. Invoices, solicitations, and industry related mail comprised Gillen's half, while more invoices, advertisements, and a religious pamphlet took up the space in Samantha's hands. Their eyes met in reserved disappointment as the last piece of mail dropped to the floor.

"Damn," Samantha mouthed through the telegram in her teeth.

"Wait. What is that?" Gillen asked, belying his sudden hope.

Wedged at an angle between the aluminum inner lining of the box and the latch which kept it shut was a single white envelope that seemed to defy gravity. Having been crushed underneath the weight of incoming mail, an accordion-like crease ran the length of it's seal — which mattered little to Gillen, and on its face, the lack of a postage stamp or address line meant that the sender had dropped it in the box themselves — which mattered far more to him.

A paralysis of hesitation rendered his arms and hands inert. Gillen stood transfixed, a man conflicted between two worlds. In one existence, this was the letter he had been waiting for since he was eighteen. The one explaining the what's and why's and delving into her life experiences with enough details to bore an interloper. In the other existence, this was a letter from a woman he had never before met.

The dissonance wreaked havoc with his motor skills as Samantha watched him reach forward only to twitch away. With the compassionate touch of one tethered to another's fate, a fate seeming to toe the line between despair and euphoria, she carefully removed the envelope from the box, straightened it, and offered it to Gillen without looking at the single word penned in cursive over the recipient line.

"Is that her handwriting?" Samantha asked, finally removing the telegram from her lips.

Gillen gazed down at his own name and slowly shook his head. "I honestly don't know."

As the envelope graced the tips of his fingers, he carefully examined the letters of his name for much more time than would be necessary, and then flipped the envelope over, sliding his thumb underneath the seal.

"Remember, Gillen," Samantha warned, her lips smiling, her eyes as reflective as the opening of the Hexagon. "This might not be everything you're hoping for."

The statement rang true within the recesses of Gillen's mind as he slowly removed the letter from the envelope and suppressed an adolescent scold from his younger self that he was indeed opening someone else's mail.

CHAPTER 12

OCTAGON

The letter, contained on a single sheet of white stationary, had been written in the kind of cursive that denoted a thoughtful penmanship. Although his mind internally vocalized each word, the voice was entirely hers.

Dearest Gillen,

I've long believed that life saves the cruelest of fates for those least equipped to handle them. Well, this is mine. My spirit breaks for all that you do not know, and rages that the responsibility to show you has fallen upon me. I never asked for this, but here we are.

Yes, I am angry. Incensed that the tools of torture have been placed in my hands. That out of a world — no, two worlds — filled with people who delight in inflicting misery, I am the one who must now watch you suffer. When you spotted me on the train, I panicked. I had been the one following you but when the tables were turned I bolted, half in hopes that running could delay the inevitable, half in fear that it would.

You see, I came here to your world to prevent a tragedy, but I was too late. The plan to kidnap Allaire had already been set in motion by the time I arrived, and before I could determine how to intercept, they got her. I could blame myself or I could blame human nature, but none of that matters now. There may still be time to rescue her, but not much. I've held back those who have the power to subvert us for as long as I could, but soon those gates will be forced open by a battering ram that no one can stop.

Meet me at dawn at the Palace of Fine Arts. I'll be waiting for you in the rotunda.

Universally Yours,
Danielle

P.S. — Please come alone.

Gillen gradually handed the letter to Samantha and then turned to walk away. As her eyes graced the words and the meaning between the lines of ink, her lips retained tight control over the thoughts percolating inside her mind. She locked onto Gillen's stare from down the hallway as he thrust his hands into his pockets and took each step with painstaking measure. He was obviously working something out, and Samantha determined not to be the one to break the silence.

"Who would want to kidnap Allaire?" Gillen finally asked, more incredulously than intended.

Samantha's blunt response had a soft edge. "You."

Gillen squared his jaw and gazed intensely at the floor. His mind churned with the kind of aggravation from mulling over a problem just a little too long. "She can get me into the other world," he whispered, yet not as a complete thought.

Samantha nodded, unable to withhold the look of terror from her own face. "She certainly can."

Breathing heavily, he said, "This is good. I'll... I'll just go with her... I'll find my other self... and... I'll bring Allaire back home."

"Right."

"Shouldn't take long at all."

Samantha's voice cracked. "Danielle knows the layout. She should be able to protect you."

Gillen felt himself lean back against the wainscoting and slowly slide down to the floor. From outside, the streetlamp cast a narrow ray through the stained glass sidelight next to the door, bathing him in a dim radiance, but to Gillen, it felt like a searchlight. Crossing his arms over his knees, he tipped his forehead down against his wrists and tried to remember what his life had been like two days prior.

"I can do this," came Gillen's muffled words.

"Yes, you can," came Samantha's tender reply. "But it's all right to be scared."

"Poor Allaire," he said, deflecting. "She must feel so alone."

Samantha, with Danielle's letter in hand, walked over to where Gillen was sitting and knelt down next to him on the floor. After setting the letter on the wood grain panels with the care of a priestess touching holy writ, she leaned herself against Gillen's shoulder and slid her hand into the crevice between his arm and torso. The two sat silently for an hour listening to nothing but the occasional passing car and the rhythms of their heartbeats assuring them that they were still alive.

A near nodding off on Gillen's part finally prompted a return to their upright positions. Without discussion, he offered Samantha his hand and they gingerly climbed the stairs together, feeling the weight of gravity as never before. The winding of the alarm clock was the last thing Gillen did before collapsing on top of his linen sheets and absorbing a slight bounce from Samantha doing the same.

"Goodnight, Samantha," he whispered, edging unconsciousness.

"Goodnight, Gillen," she responded, awash in a fierce and unexpectedly frenetic wave of sorrow.

◄ ◆ ● ● ● ● ● ◆ ►

The nighttime sky was just starting to suggest that dawn was approaching. Off in the distance, streaks of pink and purple were seeping through the darkness above a halo of daylight. From the quiet city streets below, the early risers of San Francisco could now scarcely distinguish the outlines of clouds against the backdrop of space. Even the plants and trees seemed to exude an opaque glow from the ethereal first light of the new day.

The fog-shrouded Golden Gate Bridge was quite a ways from the Palace of Fine Arts, yet the slow, intermittent pulse of its strobe lights could be seen from across the bay. Gillen's vision hadn't yet processed the dissonance between the towering bridge hidden within the waves of ascending mist and the behemoth of domed architecture standing before him. The complex was in some parts a homage to ancient Roman landmarks, and in other parts, a fully functioning exhibition center for works of art and trade fairs. The designers had positioned the massive rotunda front and center against a semicircle of colonnades that led to the exhibit halls, and on the other side, an artificial lagoon reflected the resplendent ruins of the palace for all to see.

Ambient light from within the rotunda made the monument glow with an amber hue, and for an instant, Gillen squinted his eyes to better determine the origin. Samantha came around her vehicle and methodically metered each step as she took her place next to Gillen. The sidewalk on which they stood ran parallel to the lagoon before disappearing into a treed pathway that led back around to the rotunda. He glanced over at the walkway before giving the rim of his hat a firm tug and turning to face Samantha.

"Thanks for dropping me off."

"Of course."

The tail end of her silk scarf flapped a little in the crisp morning breeze, aiming toward the pathway and seeming to insist that Gillen should not delay. The moment between them was somber, albeit not in the way it should be between friends. Samantha gazed up into his eyes with realization that so much had been left unsaid, and Gillen reciprocated in acknowledgment. Without prompting, he opened his arms to her and she reached around him for an all encompassing embrace. Gillen felt her exhale into his shoulder, and decompress into his arms, and for the first time noticed that what he presumed to be her regular perfume was that of lilac.

As she hesitantly pulled away, she stopped to take one final visual inventory of his readiness for the journey, only noticing an instant later that he had not yet removed his grasp from around her waist. The two held their stances, locked onto each other's countenances and attuned to the uncertainty of their impulses.

Samantha finally said, "I hadn't even considered this until right now, but I wonder if I'll be there? Another me, in the other world."

Gillen nodded to that and so many other unstated things. "Perhaps. And if so, I wonder if she'll be there for me the same way you always have." The two sensed another breeze and perceived that the horizon was indeed shining. "I should go."

Samantha agreed even as she maintained her grasp of his coat sleeve. Gillen looked down at her hand before covering it with his own. He said, "I'll be back soon."

"I..." she whispered, knowing full well she would never be able to summon the alternate words, "... look forward to that."

A tender kiss on her cheek was the last thing Gillen did before sliding his hands into his pockets and walking briskly toward the pathway. The air brushed against his face as he moved, drawing his attention to the fact that he was no longer standing idle. The fact that he now had a course of action only slightly offset the sense of internal dread that threatened to slow his pace.

He looked up at the trees that lined the walkway as he entered the grove, a grove that quickly gave way to a curved path flanked by towering Corinthian columns. The colonnade stretched the distance up to the gargantuan rotunda, with gossamer rays of early morning light peaking through the shrubs and foliage along the lagoon. The totemic columns had deteriorated over time, but the essence of their former glory remained, granting those who walked the path an awareness that they might be approaching a caesar.

Gillen followed along the curve as the open rotunda overtook his view. The entablature panels featured a frieze depicting allegorical scenes of virtue from ancient culture. The octagonal, domed structure was the kind of monument that upon entry, made men of stature feel like peons. Through the wide-open space, the colonnade could be seen continuing around to the other side, where atop a cluster of columns was a concrete sculpture of four weeping women with their backs to the observer. The box against which their heads were leaning was lavishly ornamented at the crown, with layers of ruffled hem from the four women's himations at its base. The image struck Gillen as his eyes wandered the vista. He had never visited the palace at dawn, and he found its otherworldly atmosphere a fitting threshold to the entrance of an alternate earth.

His steps slowed as he reached the rotunda, not out of reverence, but out of recognition. A woman stood next to one of the columns inside the structure, her features obscured by the shadows but distinguishable by outline. Gillen felt his pulse quicken as he watched her. The inside of the rotunda was vast, making the distance between them seem even greater than it actually was. Each step emitted a delayed echo off the celestial dome, and as he reached the middle of the monument, the woman took a brief glance at her surroundings before starting forward to meet him.

There she is, thought Gillen.

She walked toward him with purpose but without effort. Her gait was appropriate for someone of her height yet her heels seemed to click at twice the speed. Gillen watched as she paced, as she ran, sailing across the expanse of open space and entering the light at the precise moment that she reached the center of the rotunda. Without introduction, without question, they opened their arms to each other and formed into an embrace of retrofitted perfection.

Gillen buried his face into her neck as she pulled down on his shoulders. He wasn't at all certain if this reaction was justified, only that the surrealism of once again holding Danielle Hoyne, any Danielle Hoyne, was a force outside of his control. As her fingers slid up to his neck, he pulled away for the briefest of moments to gaze into her hazel eyes. The shock and disbelief was steadily waning against a desire to unequivocally accept who he was holding, and who was also holding him.

Feeling a mounting weight to be absolutely certain, Gillen finally stammered out, "Do... do you know who I... am?"

Danielle's crooked smirk complimented her upturned eyes, a countenance whose full expression was that of a single response. "Of course, silly." And with that she drew his lips to hers, and in doing so, caused both of them a moment of reprieve from the memory of evil.

Like interwoven fabric their lips twined, familiar in the way one would kiss after a day instead of a lifetime. Gillen lost track of his hands, finding them pressed onto her back, then into her hair, and finally, cupping the silky skin of her neglected cheeks. Danielle had yet to let go of the back of his head, the tips of her fingers absorbing the sensation of the nape of his hairline. Neither gasped for air, or even felt the necessity of breath, imagining themselves reborn into entities impervious to anything but the need of their own carnality. The clock was no longer ticking against them. The years had not been stolen. They had been transported back to their first embrace, their first kiss, and the first time they had discovered that pleasure was not guilt.

Underneath the canopy of the domed rotunda they rekindled something that both were sure had always existed, even if it had been in alternate worlds. Gillen was no longer certain he was even on earth. Perhaps they had already stepped through the Alignment and were now in a place unreachable by the horrors of the past. Maybe this was where he had once lived, or else, was now destined to be.

"Danielle," he whispered, touching his forehead to hers. "How did you find me here? How did you get here without the lunar Octagon?"

She smiled and nodded, a thousand words bubbling up to her tongue at once. "I always knew you had to exist outside my world. I never gave up looking. Searching for the Gillen Rainer who used to love me. Who used to remember what we went through to be with each other. I knew you were here. And I knew once I found you, that the moment would be just like this."

"But how? How did you get here?"

"I'll show you," she said.

Stepping out of the center of the rotunda, Danielle led Gillen by the hand over to one of the colossal columns upholding the dome above their heads. The side of the column had deteriorated with age and was noticeable in its distinction from the others only upon close inspection. A small chunk of marble had been created to cover a hole in the column. When Danielle removed the piece, the hole was backlit by a watertight panel. Gillen watched as she carefully removed a key from her overcoat pocket, unlocked the panel, and proceeded to flip a sequence of switches.

The result was silence interrupted by a lone thud and subsequent echo of the Alignment's portal being opened. Gillen gazed up and around him, slowly piecing together what was happening and how the apparatus from the other world worked. "This is the Octagon," he said, dumbfounded.

Danielle locked the panel and replaced the marble decoy. "That's right."

"But who built it? How did it get here?"

"You built it, the other you, at Walter's request, the other Walter that is. See, we needed someplace inconspicuous that we wouldn't have to monitor too closely. You came up with the idea of placing the components inside the rotunda columns and using its octagonal shape to our advantage."

Gillen shook his head. "Is that why the one on the moon was an Octagon? Why did they, or... I... change it from a Hexagon? And also... you work with the Iselin Amalgamate team?"

Danielle reached for his hand again and stared for a moment with her glistening glare. Her eyes shimmered from more than just the dawn. They sparkled from the onset of emotion. "There's so much to tell you, Gillen, and unfortunately, you'll need to know all of it before we can rescue Allaire. But we can't talk here. We must proceed back to earth."

"You mean back to the alternate earth?" he said with a grin.

The two walked to the center of the rotunda and held each other as the atmosphere within the dome began to change. Gillen felt a moderate weight start to press down on his shoulders, and after a few seconds, even his eyes and sinuses began to feel the strain.

"It's brief, but intense," Danielle warned, resting her head against his chest and closing her eyes.

"Okay," Gillen gasped, trying to calm his galloping heart rate. The air surrounding them began to warm, slowly at first, then with increasing velocity, coming to a radiating point of almost unbearable heat. The torrid effect reminded him of being up on the moon, sensing the blast furnace slamming into him like a wall at the moment Allaire had vanished into the Octagon.

A second thud bolted out from some unknown origin and into the vast open space of the rotunda, thundering back down on them from the dome. Gillen felt his eyes shut and his mouth grimace as the roaring in his ears reached a pinnacle. The ground beneath their feet suddenly shifted, and for an instant, Gillen was certain that he and Danielle were about to tumble backwards. But the sensation proved to be a trick of the mind as the sole of his shoe cautiously twisted sideways against the cement flooring and confirmed their vertical positioning.

All too rapidly to be some naturally occurring phenomenon, the artificial heat was gone, as was the anvil-like pressure on top of their frames. The environment into which Gillen and Danielle opened their eyes was serene, unmoved by either breeze or world-hopping. It was still the Palace of Fine Arts, still the rotunda and the colonnade, still the lagoon, and still dawn... only on another planet.

"Did we make it?" he asked quietly against the crooning of a black swan.

Danielle looked up at Gillen with the most conflicted expression of fear and hope that he had ever seen. She again drew his lips to hers, driving her hands into his hair and taking from the action the strength she would need to continue. Only when she pulled away were her lips finally ready to answer.

"Yes, we made it."

The first few steps out of the rotunda were seminal for Gillen as his body adjusted to the infinitesimally higher concentration of gravity on the planet. He smiled as he thought of the almost weightless stride Danielle had displayed on earth and how this had ended up being the reason. The gradual build up to a normal pace gave Gillen time to examine his surroundings. Everything appeared to be the same as on earth. Around the vista and back to the sidewalk at which Gillen had bid Samantha farewell offered a panoramic of the Palace complex. The similarities were striking enough that he struggled to identify even a single alteration.

"I thought there would be something that was dissimilar," Gillen said.

Danielle hesitated before taking his hand and leading him over to her car. As she drove, the city came into vivid focus. Over the hill stood the Golden Gate Bridge, now bathed orange in morning sunshine. The residential streets passed by, lined with the same row houses Gillen had been accustomed to witnessing. Down a steep road was his favorite bookstore, and across the street, the coffee shop at which he frequented. The vehicle slowed at a red light as a cable car came to a halt, dropping off passengers and picking up new ones, only to sound its gong before clearing the intersection and continuing its trek down the graded hill. Danielle hit the gas pedal and the city once again picked up speed.

"Where are we going?" he finally asked.

"To get the worst of it over with," she replied.

Gillen had innumerable more questions but discovered that his anxiety was tranquilized when with Danielle. He had no idea what she needed to show him or tell him, but the very fact that she again existed was enough for him to recall that patience was a virtue.

At the crest of a knoll, Gillen momentarily spotted the Iselin Amalgamate building off in the distance. The utilitarian rectangle appeared just as lacking in charm as ever, albeit with slightly more dilapidation. It almost seemed vacant and was the first differentiator he noticed, a crack in the mirror-image world.

The street signs flew by sequentially as the bay came in and out of view. The periwinkle sky was the only constant as the neighborhoods changed. Gillen found himself shifting focus between the cityscape and Danielle, awestruck that she was seated next to him, elated that not an iota of chemistry had been lost. Without hesitation he reached his hand across the gearshift pedestal and rested it on her exposed knee. Danielle glanced down at the gesture before flashing her trademark smirk back at Gillen. The smirk lasted only an instant, however, before reverting back to a face desperately withholding the furls of dread.

Gillen knew he should be worried, concerned about whatever was concerning her, yet the trepidation he had felt walking up to the rotunda had all but vanished. Confidence in the power of their reunion was the driving force inside his veins. Allaire would be found, rescued, and returned unharmed by the same determination that had tethered two hearts across the multiverse.

"Thank you for this," he said to Danielle, giving her knee a squeeze. "I could never have found this place without you."

Her response was interrupted by the most fleeting of looks that caught itself in the center of her eyes before fading away. Gillen barely noticed it before glancing out the windshield and seeing the Bay Bridge stretched out in front of them. The impact was immediate and harsh. With the momentum of a freight train, the bridge brought several memories to the forefront of Gillen's mind, all of which culminated into a solitary realization.

"Oh my God... Cate is here."

Danielle's grip on the steering wheel tightened as she nodded. Gillen's periphery picked up on the acknowledgement as his attention remained transfixed on the landmark which, to him, had become a symbol of death.

"Sorry..." Gillen blurted, trying to stay calm. "I just... hadn't thought of that."

"It's all right," she replied softly. "I knew you would eventually. And that's important."

If the presence of some sinister poltergeist had suddenly made itself known within the confines of Danielle's car, Gillen could not have felt more horripilation. The implied meaning of her last words was painfully clear, and suddenly, all of his initial panic began to return.

"Why are we going to see Cate?" Gillen asked, his tone vacillating between anger and confusion.

"Because we can't rescue Allaire without doing so."

Gillen was about to protest but found himself mute. Nothing about Cate's reemergence was he ready to face, born from a well of unprocessed emotions and a consistent lack of coming to terms. Her death was still shrouded in mystery, yet the most likely answer was the one he worked diligently at making certain never to hear.

"What does Cate have to do with this?" he asked Danielle, his voice pleading for a way out.

She wheeled the car to the left and continued down a residential street until coming to a stop along the curb of a two-story house at the end of the block. Its exterior was unfamiliar to Gillen. White paint, picket fence, a small patch of lawn on both sides of the walkway. The bow window stood out from the others in the neighborhood, but aside from that, the home was dismissible. There could be no reason for them to be here save for one.

"I brought you here to rescue Allaire," Danielle said, her eyes searching for permission to cry. "This is the first step, and for that... I am so very sorry."

CHAPTER 13

ANTIMERIDIAN

"She's absolutely stunning," Jack DaLette had once said while stirring his daiquiri with a swizzle stick. "What a dish! You have to go up and talk to her. Just introduce yourself and say something profound."

Gillen had sighed heavily and leaned further onto the table. The nightclub was packed but subdued, filled with the kind of lighting and music for sophisticated singles with questionable dancing abilities. Seated next to Jack was his interim girlfriend, Nicolette.

"I don't know, Jack," Gillen had griped. "I'm not really good at the whole... approach tactic."

Jack rolled his eyes and then jammed his finger on the table. "Look, I almost invited Barry, but then I realized that I could bring a square or I could bring you. In any event, she looks like that woman... that one actress—from that really famous movie—you know what I'm talking about?"

"As usual, I do not."

Jack grimaced and took a sip from his drink. "Take me and Nikki here for instance. I spotted her from across the room and never thought twice. Now it's been four months!"

"Three weeks," Nicolette corrected.

"No way? Seems like so much longer."

Gillen stood up from the table. "Okay, I'm going to go get another drink while you two figure that out."

The short walk provided enough time for Gillen to eye the woman leaning with her back to the crowded bar. Her maroon cocktail dress had a v-neckline centering initial attention at her empire waist. Accessorized with black heels and a clutch purse, with icy blonde hair pulled through a clip and the softest touch of makeup on her cherubic face, the woman seemed to exist within her own sphere, to some — an emblem of timeless beauty, to Gillen — in the way of the bartender.

"Pardon me," he said graciously, tumbler in hand.

"Of course," she whispered, pushing herself from the bar with some effort. It was that moment at which Gillen had noticed her limp. She moved forward a few feet before hesitating, appearing uncertain as to where to go. After setting his empty glass down on the bar, Gillen ignored the bartender and took a few steps toward her.

"Are you all right?"

She turned back quickly, not so much startled as perpetually used to being in people's way. "Don't worry about me," she laughed, a little too forcibly. "I just need to find another place to sit down. I came up to get a drink and another couple took my table."

"I hope it wasn't that table," Gillen asked, pointing at Jack and Nicolette. "Or that couple."

"No-no," she smiled. "Anyway, it's all right. I'll be fine."

"Fair enough. However I must tell you that my friends are hoping I ask you to join our little group. You see, they have this belief that they are gifted with the powers of matchmaking. Something I find highly unlikely insomuch as they've only been together a month and are already showing all of the hallmarks of contempt."

The woman burst out into a laugh, this time genuine, while also doing her best to remain upright. Gillen outstretched his hand. "If you happen to care... I'm Gillen."

"I'm Cate," she said, sliding her limp hand into his. Gillen wondered if that was how she had been taught to handshake or if she was really in that much discomfort.

"I welcome you to join our table if you'd like."

Cate's hesitation seemed less connected to the presence of a possible setup, and more related to if she would make it across the room. With a nod she smiled at Gillen and he offered his arm.

Jack smirked gleefully, his hazel eyes sparkling. "Well... who might this be?"

"Shut up. Cate, this is Jack and Nicolette. You both... this is Cate."

"Lovely to meet you," Jack said as Cate sat down in the seat opposite Nicolette. "I knew it. The moment I saw you over at the bar, I said to Gillen... you gotta go over and talk to her. You gotta go over and introduce yourself. I mean, and I'm sure you've heard this before, but you look just like that one actress. From that movie everyone saw a couple years ago."

Cate's emerald eyes widened ever so slightly. "Oh, I'm not sure."

"I forget the name of it. Do you remember, Nikki?"

"The name of the movie or the name of the actress?"

"Either. Cause she looks just like her, doesn't she? It's uncanny. Anyway, I don't mean to put you on the spot. I'm usually better at remembering these things. Isn't that right, Gillen?"

"Yeah, Jack's mind is a steel trap. Would you like me to freshen up your drink?" Gillen asked Cate.

Sitting next to her allowed Gillen to notice her pearl earrings and pearl necklace, chosen for their reliable elegance. It rested along unblemished skin that revealed how thin and fragile she was, like in the way one would be if a body was working against itself.

"I'm okay for now, but thank you," she responded.

"Of course," Gillen said, gazing.

The evening had progressed without much incident. The nightclub had begun to filter out,

Jack and Nicolette had continued to misalign, and Gillan and Cate had discovered that their primary mode of communication seemed to be banter. The laughter from their table was raucous, a combination of poking fun at others mixed with self-deprecating humor, and by the time they were ready to leave, all were surprised by what little they had had to drink.

"I'll get the check," Jack said.

Gillen walked Cate out to her car as Jack and Nicolette argued about which song the band was playing. "So let me make sure I have all of this correct," Gillen said as Cate kept pace next to him. She was now moving without a limp, yet had still chosen to wrap her arm around his. "You've lived in San Francisco all your life. You have no siblings, no parents, and basically just one girlfriend who ditched you early on this evening after meeting the man of her dreams. Am I good so far?"

"So far."

Gillen smirked as he continued. "At the ripe old age of nine you decided you wanted to work at city hall because you thought the building looked like a palace, which led to a subsequent career as an administrator at the mayor's office, which you did up until last year... why was that again?"

"The mayor lost his bid for a third term and I didn't like the new one."

"Gotcha. So you gave up serving your community over political affiliations" — Cate jabbed Gillen in the ribs as he continued —"only to find yourself as an administrator at a local non-profit, which is equally impressive, yet this all leaves me with one remaining question."

"And what might that be?"

"What exactly is an administrator? Is it like being a bureaucrat?"

Cate turned to face Gillen as they reached her car. "I could spend our last few seconds together explaining that... or I could kiss you. Your choice."

"I would really like to know what an administrator does."

Cate playfully bit her lower lip and pulled Gillen's head down to hers. The kiss started off with the intensity of the often analogized fireworks moment, slowly mellowing out into a lingering tug-of-war between lips. When Cate finally pulled away, Gillen needed to catch his breath.

"Thanks for a pleasant evening, Gillen."

"Likewise. May I see you again some time?"

"You've got my number."

"Do I?"

Cate chuckled to herself as Gillen chivalrously opened her car door. "Jack made sure to ask for it when you were in the bathroom."

"Stealthy bastard, isn't he?"

The narrowest of smiles warmed the edges of his face for only an instant as the memory faded into the shadows. Gillen looked up from his seat and noticed that Danielle had already opened the passenger door and was waiting for him to exit the vehicle. The morning sun had cleared the atmosphere of any filters and had warmed the temperature to the degree that Gillen no longer desired his hat or overcoat. After tossing them into the back seat, he turned to Danielle and sighed anxiously. "All right then."

The steps leading up to the fence were askew but leveled out closer to the porch. As Gillen and Danielle made it to the landing they took notice of the wooden railings covered in flower pots evenly spaced between the balusters. Over the door, a small beetle inched its way along the lintel as Gillen's hand hovered over the knocker.

"I just can't believe this..." he whispered.

Danielle reached around his torso and drew him into a side hug. "Gillen," she mouthed, seeming to add emphasis to each syllable. "Listen to me. There's only one thing that matters. You and I found each other. Remember that."

Gillen looked down at Danielle with more concern than before. Squaring his jaw, he bristled as his fingers made contact with the knocker and heard the clanking of its bronze plate. The sound dissipated and left him standing with Danielle in as much hope that Cate wouldn't answer as fear that she would.

What the hell am I going to say to her? She wouldn't even know about the crash... or would she? Either way, this isn't the same woman I married... so just...

Danielle had pushed open the door without hesitation. "It's usually unlocked. Let's just go on in."

Gillen stood alone on the porch, stunned. If Danielle was part of the Iselin team, then it would be no wonder that she and Cate could have struck up a friendship. Perhaps even a close one. Her nonchalant attitude at simply barging into Cate's house left Gillen feeling orbitally adrift. Nothing about this moment was congruous with his world, but trusting Danielle to guide him to Allaire was his only option, and according to her, walking over that threshold was the next step.

Upon entering the foyer and inhaling, Gillen felt his face begin to flush. "Oh wow," he said in a hushed tone. "Her perfume... my God, I'd forgotten."

Danielle's face turned back toward him with the expression of a single purpose. She was determined not to cry. Clenched teeth and worry lines worked hard to maintain that composure as she reached back for his hand. Gillen looked up at the ceiling, the walls, then the coat rack and floor. He wasn't certain what he was hoping to see, but whatever it was, it wasn't there. After another centering breath, he nodded slowly and took ahold of her hand.

They moved deeper into the house. As they passed a wall mounted mirror, he spotted their reflection — Gillen and Danielle, a couple again. What would have been a thrilling image outside the context of the house was now nothing short of disorienting. Gillen forced his eyes straight ahead.

"Cate!" Danielle called out from the hallway.

"Cate... are you all right?" Gillen had asked, lying next to her in bed.

The night had been their second date, and had ended in the penultimate action of bringing her back to his place. After a nightcap and more playful bantering, Gillen had found himself underneath his satin sheets with a goddess. The lovemaking had been intense, almost athletic in its primal motions. She had known and had asked for exactly what she wanted, and Gillen had been all too willing to please. It had been mechanically physical, and at the moment of climax, he felt washing over him a kind of disappointment that he had never before experienced. As their chests rose and fell in waves, he glanced over at her and she at him. They lain flat on their backs, gazing up at the slow whirl of the ceiling fan blades. It had been at that moment when Cate burst into tears.

She had assured him it was nothing. She had promised it was just a fleeting emotion. Her tears were merely his ability to unlock her pent up trauma, she had said. A fragmented childhood was always the foundation for a good post-coital cry, and for the moment, Gillen had believed her.

Their subsequent escapades added subtext to her reactions. Cate herself began to understand and even anticipate the oncoming torrent of emotions and would prepare Gillen seconds in advance that her weeping was a testament to his devotion.

Then, sometime during their second month together, Cate had been unable to get up from Gillen's bed. A misguided joke about his sexual prowess sobered him to the realization that she was serious. She was physically unable to move her muscles without excruciating pain. Panicking, Gillen had groped for his telephone but was halted by Cate's pleas.

"This has happened before. Just give me a few minutes."

"Being temporarily paralyzed?" Gillen exclaimed.

Cate then dove into the story of how this mysterious wave of pain would cripple her body from time to time, without prompt or explanation. She had never mentioned it to him because it so rarely affected her.

"Is that why you were limping at the nightclub?" he asked.

"Yes. And why I accepted your offer to join your table."

"Because you were in this much pain?"

"Because you were kind."

True to her word, the wave soon passed leaving her mobile but spent. Still just as naked as Cate was, Gillen had helped her out of the bed, and step by cautious step, held onto her as she maneuvered her way into his tub. That had been the first time he had drawn a bath for her, but certainly not the last.

"This could end up being a taxing relationship for you, Gillen," Jack had said to him six months later, after Cate had missed yet another get-together.

"I know, but I make her happy, and she deserves some happiness after all she's been through. Plus, I enjoy being there for her. Makes me feel needed."

Jack paused before glancing down at his beer and hoping his face wouldn't betray his uneasiness. "Are you sure that's a good reason to be with someone?"

Gillen arched an eyebrow and grinned. "The playboy of San Francisco is giving me relationship advice?"

An awkward nod and a lengthy chug from his beer had ended the discussion.

"Cate?" Danielle called out again as they entered the kitchen. The countertops and cabinets were white, accented by chrome fixtures and a teal backsplash. A mug of coffee having long since cooled sat on the table next to a plate with a half-eaten danish. "Let's check upstairs."

Gillen reached the stairwell first but took a step back to let Danielle ascend. As her fingers circled the newel post, a strobe-flash of nostalgia flooded his senses with pleasant memories of their first sexual encounter. The thought vanished as quickly as it had materialized, yet the juxtaposition stalked his every step up toward the second level of the house.

At the landing, he stopped to examine a pair of framed photographs hanging on the wall. One was of Cate at a party looking unusually happy, almost vibrant, while standing next to, who Gillen knew to be, his other self, along with Danielle, Jack, a few other unidentified persons, and Walter. All had champagne flutes and were captured as if in midtoast. The second picture had been shot inside the terrestrial laboratory in front of a more meager looking workstation console. Several members of the team could be seen in the background, while Cate, Walter, the other Gillen, and Jack stood in the foreground holding up a crucial component of what would years later become the Hexagon. Gillen's eyes narrowed in on the device, then on the goofy faces they were making, and finally on how Jack and Walter both had an arm around Cate, who seemed to be central to not only the photo, but the entire team ecosystem.

"Where's Samantha?" Gillen whispered.

"Who?"

"Samantha Leung. I very clearly remember that night. We'd just made our first breakthrough with what would eventually become the Alignment. Walter threw a party for everyone. Samantha was certainly there. Was she never part of the project in this world?"

Danielle shook her head slowly, oblivious to the name. Gillen shifted his eyes away from the pictures and up toward Danielle, who was again reaching for his hand, leading him to a particular destination. The upper level of the home was quiet, tranquil, having all of the distinctions of thoughtful living. The drapes danced with a gentle breeze as the daylight bathed the hardwood floors in warmth. More photos lined the walls and Gillen's eyes started to wander, but a tug from Danielle repurposed his vision toward the room they needed to enter.

"Why are we going in there?" he asked tepidly.

"Because we have to," she replied, without looking back.

The door to Cate's bedroom was open, giving the space a feeling of having nothing to hide. The wooden sleigh bed in the corner tied all of the other furniture pieces together in both arrangement and style. Gillen again spotted their reflection in the armoire mirror and caught a side view of Danielle as they walked. Her gaze was fixed, narrowed in on the farthest wall.

"Congratulations, Gillen," Walter had once said, slapping him on the shoulder of his black tuxedo.

"Thanks, Walter."

"You too, darling," Walter said to Cate, leaning in for an embrace. "I love you."

"Thank you, Walter. I love you too."

"It was a beautiful wedding for sure," Jack added, standing next to his plus one, Olivia. "You know, Livy, I actually introduced these two."

Gillen smirked. "Well, you and Nicolette. Wasn't that her name?"

Olivia shot a glance at Jack who had shrugged his shoulders innocently. "That was a long time ago, Livy. Nikki and I are through. Anyway, we only went out for what... three weeks?"

"Four months."

Gillen had his arm tightly around Cate's torso, both from excitement and from visual cues that she was starting to feel weak. Her wedding dress had layers of crystal sequin fabric leading up to a reasonably sized train, the hem of which Gillen always seemed to be standing on. After planting another enthusiastic kiss on Cate's cheek, Gillen turned back to Jack and said, "So when are you gonna get hitched, Mr. Bachelor?"

Jack had shook his head, leaned in toward Gillen, and whispered, "When your best friend finds platinum, everything else is just gold."

The chirping of a cardinal brought Gillen back to Cate's bedroom. He was still walking with Danielle toward a wall covered in photo frames. The photographs, as opposed to the ones elsewhere in the house, were much more candid. No signs of booze or parties, no poses or formalwear, just the landmark moments of everyday family life. As Gillen stepped up to the wall, he felt like the photos were staring back at him, a series of eyewitnesses to something, a jury of his peers.

Danielle was no longer facing him. Having turned away, she placed her hand over her mouth and looked in any direction but Gillen's.

Her reaction fueled his curiosity and he focused in on each image, each face, and the story that the photos were apparently trying to tell. Cate was in almost all of them. Happy, carefree, at times in obvious pain, but seemingly disconnected from it. She was a woman living life within the boundaries of an illness, and her countenance projected the potential limitlessness of that existence. Gillen felt a smile etch the corners of his face as he observed her in the den, the kitchen, outside in the yard, at a park, and at a diner eating soft serve. She was just a human, but she was very much alive.

It was not until his eyes had ceased focusing solely on Cate that he noticed who else was in all of the photos with her... next to her. Gillen tilted his head as his mind slowly absorbed the indicators. The holding of hands. The wrap of an arm. The kisses on cheeks and the kisses on lips.

"Walter?" Gillen said, so hushed that he wasn't even sure he had heard himself say it.

His boss, mentor, and friend appeared with Cate in most of the photos, unashamedly caught up in the whirlwind of love and romance. She unreservedly reciprocated. On this planet, within the confines of this version of Cate and Walter, a love affair appeared to have blossomed that eclipsed anything Gillen and Cate had ever known.

He nodded slowly while his mind and his emotions fought for supremacy. In his reality, in his world, this didn't amount to much except for shedding more light on a marriage that had faltered. If this Cate and the other Gillen had never fallen in love, and Walter had filled that emotional gap, then he had no reason but to feel satisfaction for her.

The photographs on the wall were a depiction of a period of time. In his periphery, Gillen noticed that there were other pictures hanging on the connected wall, ones that seemed to indicate a different time, which also featured Walter and Cate. "Who else is that?" Gillen whispered to himself as he turned to look.

As a sequence of events, the photographs moved forward in time. First was taken at a hospital, upon the birth of a child. The baby was swaddled in pink and was being held by a euphoric Cate. The next few frames displayed the child growing into a toddler, interacting with Walter and Cate, taking her first steps, and even covered in cake frosting. The toddler continued growing into a child. With fearless energy she seemed to confront the world, each picture more bombastic than the last.

Then finally, nearing the end of the row of photographs, the child had turned into a teenager, one with long wavy hair — the color of amber, and dark haunting eyes — the color of mocha. The girl had all of the qualities of both Walter and Cate. She was so clearly and distinctly an emblem of love between the two, such a perfect representation of their union, and without question, their genetic offspring, that any outside observer would have immediately identified the girl as Walter and Cate's daughter.

She was precious and lovely in every way... and she was identical to Allaire.

"Dear... God..." Gillen murmured. He took an instinctive step away from the wall which only made the collage more pronounced. The crisp whiteness of the paint suddenly seemed blinding, as did the light from the windows, as did any direction in which he looked. Like the excessive widening of an aperture, Gillen's irises took in every visual image, even as his mind processed none of it. For his concentration had narrowed down to one indisputable and inescapable truth.

I'm not Allaire's father.

Gillen gasped, pressing his palms against his temples. He spun around on his heels only to stop when his eyes locked glances with Danielle. She stood before him, distraught at her own helplessness toward his plight, and livid that she had needed to take on the role of tormentor.

"Oh, Gillen," she whispered, her face streaked with tears. "I'm so, so sorry..."

Gillen darted his eyes from her and zeroed in on the bed, only to dart from that visual as well. His vision jostled back and forth along the carpeted floor, unable to find a fixed point, uncertain as to what imagery would assuage the burning realization from his mind's eye. Clenching his eyes shut, Gillen opened them again only to discover that his depth perception was gone. He held out his hand before him, a hand trembling from a shockwave of emotions that his body had yet to compartmentalize, and felt a surge of panic wash over his torso. Taking a cautious step toward the armoire, he placed his hands firmly against its hardwood surface and gazed into the mirror.

"I can't... see..." he stammered.

Danielle reached for him and firmly took hold of both of his shoulders. "Sit down. Please... just for a moment."

Despite her best intentions, Danielle was unprepared for his level of disorientation as he tumbled backward against the side of the bed frame and slid down to a sitting position on the floor. She knelt next to him and wrapped her arms around his chest as he shook.

"Oh my God," he said, pressing his palms against his eyes and trying to readjust to the overbearing brightness of the room.

"Just breathe, Gillen. In and out. Slowly."

"This can't be..."

"I'm so sorry..."

A wave of physical pain passed through his body without origin or exit. It settled in the center of his chest and radiated with the kind of agony that made him wish to scream. The eventual relenting of his tunnel vision only heightened his other senses, and the pounding in his ears sounded like footsteps.

Danielle glanced toward the door. "Someone's coming up. It's probably Cate."

Gillen grit his teeth and held tighter to Danielle's hand. "I...can't... I can't see... her right now."

"It's not her, Gillen. You must remember that! She's a different Cate who had nothing to do with this!"

"No..."

"Gillen... please..."

The threshold creaked as a man turned the corner and entered the bedroom. Gillen had first glanced at Danielle, whose face registered the kind of terror known only to the damned, and then directly at himself... into the face of the Gillen Rainer who had abducted Allaire.

The other Gillen hesitated before parting his lips, but he never uttered a word. With the force of a man disinterested in facing tomorrow, Gillen bolted up from the bedroom floor and body slammed his other self into the wall. Photo frames clattered to the ground as Gillen tightened both hands around the fabric of the other Gillen's collar. "Where's Allaire!?" he seethed, inches from his own face.

The other Gillen, although identical in physical appearance, was about an inch taller than his counterpart. Yet the strength and level of aggression which was being administered at him made the height difference irrelevant. "Hey... just calm down..." he said in a shaky tone. "Listen, I can explain."

"Too late!" Gillen hissed, and kneed his other self in the abdomen before tossing him across the room and into the armoire.

"Wait!" Danielle cried as the other Gillen slumped down to the ground next to the fractured mirror. She arose and placed her hands on Gillen's chest, hoping to slow him down long enough to tolerate diplomacy, but her efforts were futile as he pushed past her and reached down to his alternate.

"She'll tell you..." the man said, eyes wide in fear. "Ask her... she'll explain everything!"

"She already did! You forced her to be the one to show me! You coward!" Gillen had no idea what he was doing, for he had lost control of his limbs. All he knew for certain was that what he was witnessing was his own fists pummeling down against any exposed flesh with which he could make contact. The other Gillen flailed in an attempt to stop the onslaught, his motions the reflexes of panic and desperation. Pulses of twisting pain shot up Gillen's knuckles and wrists as each punch landed against muscle. The discomfort was beginning to trigger a semi-lucid awareness of what he was doing, the fact that Danielle was tugging against his vest, and the dawning realization that he had never before so much as hit another human being.

Within the spiderweb cracks of mirrored glass Gillen spotted his reflection, fragmented and splintered. The image gazed back at him unadulterated by soft lighting or angle. It was the raw, jarring reflection of a man unrecognizable. A man who had lost reason, who had succumbed to primal rage, and who had discovered a side of himself that he had always feared.

He was gasping, almost panting for oxygen as he pushed himself away from the other Gillen and leaned against the armoire. In horror he gazed down at his other self lying on the ground, moaning in pain, having turned away from Danielle who had knelt down to help. Gillen looked at his own hands and wondered if his knuckles were broken. His next thought was also a wonder.

Could I have killed him?

He then glanced at Danielle who was gently caressing the other's head while trying to suppress her instinct for sympathy. She tried to coddle him, coax him into a sitting position. In response, he twitched away from her in a way which reminded Gillen not so much of pain, but of irritation, of contempt. It was the contempt of familiarity.

Massaging his knuckles within his palms, Gillen slowly nodded while staring at Danielle. He then asked, gravely, "How long have you both been together?"

She shook her head, appearing wholly lost in the present situation. "I was going to tell you that too. I swear it."

"How long?"

"Twenty-two years."

Gillen felt himself lean a little more sideways. "Married?"

"Yes," she whispered. "But we began a separation last year."

The silence was again pierced by the moans of the other Gillen as he writhed along the floor. Gillen ignored it and inched his way across the carpet until he was kneeling next to Danielle.

"That means," he said, "either your family never left that night, or else..."

"I didn't go with them."

The memories threatened to overtake the moment and he pushed them back with the full force of his concentration. Fading into the corridors of his mind was a manufactured image of a youthful Gillen and Danielle starting a life together in abject poverty and happiness.

"Why?" he asked, barely a whisper.

Danielle removed her hands from her husband and set them squarely on the sides of Gillen's face. "Because I loved you then, and later... I knew I still loved you."

"Later? After what?"

"After the accident."

Gillen felt the last remaining remnants of warmth leave his body. "What accident?"

Danielle's stare lingered before her response was offered. As her hands slipped away from his cheeks, she said, "You—I mean—he... started to have feelings... long ago... for Cate. I knew it even before he did. His relationship with Walter became less about work and more about an excuse to see her. Any reason to come over to this house, to interact, to fantasize about another life..."

Danielle's voice cracked as she continued. It was a pain simmering beneath a filter, one she had installed not to protect herself, but to protect the other Gillen. "Then one day... one afternoon... he offered to go pick up Allaire from the skating rink."

"Oh no..." Gillen said, shutting his eyes to a narrative to which he already knew the ending.

"It had just stopped raining, and Cate and Walter weren't going to be home for a while. So he offered to drive Allaire... to her favorite confectionary. On the way..."

The other Gillen moaned again, this time placing his hands over his ears. Danielle continued, "His car slid out of the lane and hit an embankment along the Bay Bridge. Allaire... was—"

"Stop."

"Ejected from her seat—"

"I said stop."

Danielle gazed at Gillen through watery eyes which blocked her view. "He never forgave himself. I don't know if Cate ever forgave him either."

Gillen's head leaned forward on shoulders that could no longer hold him up. "Now it all makes sense."

"He did the math. Over and over again. He and Jack both. They knew what was probable, what was possible. They didn't expect Allaire to be identical in your world, only similar. Then they connected with your Richard Kaine, who filled us in on the details of your life and work. That's when we made the discovery of Cate and Walter's infidelity. And when Walter left the project to focus on the Dartmouth study, he and Jack came up with the plan to... to... well..."

"Replace Allaire."

Danielle nodded in disgust. "Yes."

Walter's notebook... A.I. ... Artificial intelligence or Allaire Iselin?

The air in the bedroom seemed as if it had been syphoned into the other world, leaving nothing for Gillen to inhale but the effervescent scent wafting from Cate's perfume bottle. A wave of nausea cascaded down his frame, leaving him flushed and dizzy. As he tried to center his disorientation, his counterpart leaned over onto his back and sighed, his eyes bloodshot from pain and tears. "I'm so sorry, Gillen... but you have to understand—"

"Burn in Hell," Gillen replied, and stumbled out of the bedroom.

CHAPTER 14

SIMULACRA

Cate jumped, and I knew it all along.

The water rushing over his bruised knuckles offered little relief from the swelling pain of betrayal surging throughout his body at random and terrifying intervals. Gillen watched his hands shake underneath the porcelain fixtures of the kitchen faucet. As the drain swallowed the runoff, his eyes gazed into the hole with a frightening attentiveness.

"Let me explain," Danielle said, entering the kitchen but speaking from afar.

"I bet I know when their affair began," Gillen said, reflectively, "and it would have been the same on both planets." The sequence played itself out in his mind like scenes from a movie in which he himself was playing the unsuspecting victim. On one side was the moment Gillen had introduced them, mere months after joining Walter's production lab — back when it was a struggling company experimenting with semiconductors and selling the research results for profit. Walter had become a close friend. Cate had enjoyed his camaraderie. The three quickly become inseparable.

On the alternate planet, he pictured the other Gillen and Danielle happily married, leaving Jack DaLette free to pursue the woman at the bar with whom he had been so instantaneously enamored. Cate would have inevitably agreed to date him, up until the moment when Jack would have brought her to a work function in order to show off his latest romantic conquest. That's when she would have met Walter for the first time.

"The night we finished our little side project... the component... the first step to building the Alignment... in that photo I showed you... that night would have been the same on both worlds. We all celebrated as if the future belonged solely to us. What an evening it was. Cate became tired early and had asked me to drive her home. Rather uncharacteristically, I refused. I told her to take a cab. I wanted to stay. Walter offered to drive her, and for once, I was relieved to relinquish the duty. That's probably when it happened. That's probably where it happened. In the alternate world — on Walter's bed, and on planet earth — on my bed."

Drying his hands with a towel, he shook his head slowly as the irony festered into his muscles. He then turned to Danielle and asked, "What's your stake in all of this?"

"My stake?"

"Sure. After all, your husband gets a salve for his wretched conscience, plus a shot at wooing another woman. Jack gets to step into Walter's shoes and finish what the old man left behind. So where does that leave you? What does kidnapping my—" Gillen nearly choked as his tongue retracted the word from his lips. "Kidnapping Allaire do for you, in this world?"

Danielle stared directly at him and offered no reply, which gave him the bulk of the answer.

"Good God," he spat, and turned back toward the sink.

"For a moment, for an instant," she pleaded. "I thought about you. The fact that you might exist in the other world and be a better version of Gillen. A better man. Yes, even a better husband. But I was never on board with abducting Allaire. And once Jack and Gillen set things in motion, I tried to stop them."

Gillen shook his head and leaned heavily against the marble countertop. "Yeah, you made that crystal clear in your letter. How you're the victim in all of this. How awful this has been for you. How you're my only ally in a scheme nobody but you fully understands."

"It's true! Why else would I risk bringing you here?"

Gillen turned around. "To do the same damn thing your husband was trying to do. Replace a human being that didn't work out with what you hope would be a better working model."

"How dare you..." Danielle whispered. "I'm the one who knew what kind of torture this would be for you. I wrestled with this for days before I summoned the courage to lock them out of the Palace Octagon. And then once I saw you on that train, I lost my nerve again. Forcing you to see the lie that woman made you live... the enormous responsibility of raising a child who wasn't yours.... of all the senseless exhaustion and pain that she put you through in caring for a spouse who didn't really love you. You think those horrible truths weren't at the forefront of my mind?"

"Then why do it?" Gillen demanded, taking a step closer to her. "Why put me through any of it? Why not leave me in my ignorance? Is the situation in which I find myself now any better than believing Allaire was my daughter? That my marriage to Cate wasn't a complete farce? Why? What good did any of this actually do but destroy my illusions?"

"Because those illusions could destroy everything, Gillen. That's why I brought you here. Okay... I admit it. Was there a small part of me that hoped things between us might work out? That I could be the reawakening of your adolescent dream and that you could be the restoration of the man my Gillen once was? Yes... I admit that was a driving hope in my actions. And for that... I have no regrets. Condemn me if you will. I'll accept that damnation for bringing you into the light. But listen to me when I say the kidnapping of Allaire... the creation of the Octagons... Walter choosing to leave the project... all of this has much farther reaching ramifications than just you and your family."

The kitchen no longer seemed as bright as it had when Gillen first entered. He suspected that his vision was slowly beginning to revert back to normal as his surging blood pressure waned. A constant wave of physical pain continued to attack his muscles, the waves riding in on the emotional tides of his volatility. After taking another step forward, he leaned back against one of the breakfast bar stools and took a lengthy exhale of both his breath and of the moment.

"What ramifications?"

Danielle closed the distance between them and rested her hand on Gillen's arm. "The plan to kidnap Allaire is about more than just the resurrection of a lost child. It's so much worse than that."

Her next words were halted by the sound of hardwood floorboards creaking underneath the weight of walking. The sound was above them. Their eyes followed the movements from upstairs as the noise drifted toward the stairwell. With slow, painfully systematic steps, the other Gillen worked his way down to the first level and limped into the kitchen.

"Oh God," Danielle whispered upon witnessing the totality of bruises on the other Gillen's face.

"Would you get me some ice, darling?"

Danielle seemed to wince at hearing his term of endearment for her. With an uncomfortable pause she headed over to the icebox and then returned with a hand towel twisted into a knot. The other Gillen nodded appreciatively before setting the damp towel on the side of his face and smarting at the sensation.

"I'm sorry, Gillen," the other said wearily. "I had no right to take Allaire from your world."

Gillen could sense Danielle staring at him but maintained eye contact solely with his doppelgänger. "Swapping out one child for another..." he said, exhaling into his syllables. "Did you really think Cate would accept her?"

"I did, and I still do," he replied.

"You're insane," Gillen said with a laugh, pointing an incriminating finger into the space between them. "What do you think is going to happen? Cate's just going to arbitrarily accept this carbon copy daughter as a suitable replacement for the one you killed? That her love and affection will just automatically transfer to a replicant? A girl who, mind you, has her own will, ambitions, talents, ideas, and personality traits that may not exactly align with her predecessor's characteristics."

"Gillen—"

"Did you know *my* Allaire is an ice skater? A very talented one at that. Won numerous awards. Wants to go to the Olympics some day. How about the one you killed? Did she skate? Or maybe she's an artist like mine? Allaire is one hell of a sketcher. Almost unlimited artistic abilities. Dabbles in watercolors, acrylics, you name it. Her room is a cornucopia of creation. How about yours?"

"I was aware there would be differences—"

"Well that's a load off my mind. At least you're giving Cate's maternal instincts a fighting chance.

But what about Allaire herself? Did you not think she would rebel against this madness the moment she figured out she was on the wrong planet? Or did you assume she has no agency?"

"If you'd just let me explain—"

"Because if you think for a moment that Allaire is just going to cozy up to the replacement mother you resurrected for her... that she isn't going to fight this at every step of the way... then you obviously have no idea who the child I raised really is."

The other Gillen hesitated before saying, "You didn't know who she really was either."

Silence fell over the kitchen as the two men stared into each other's eyes. Standing between them, Danielle occupied her space in isolation, her presence acting as the repelling poles of two magnets. No one spoke despite each having a volley of words ready to fire at the slightest provocation. A shifted glance one direction and a lingering stare toward another could lead to a new instigation, and despite their collective tempers, lassitude seemed to be winning out.

After several minutes of unbroken silence, the other Gillen sat down on a stool and spoke with a moderated tone. "I need to explain what's going on here, because you need to know. Will you do that? Will you let me explain?"

The other side of the breakfast bar had Gillen leaning slightly askew against the marble countertop with a fist supporting his jaw. He bit his lower lip as he exchanged glances between his other self and Danielle, all the while cognizant of the fact that no one had yet informed him of Allaire's whereabouts.

"Very well," he said flatly. "Go ahead and explain. Explain how you built that Octagon on the moon, contacted Richard Kaine through our communications system, used him to gain control of the lunar Hexagon, and then trapped Allaire so that she would be obliged to trust you and blindly follow you on to an alternate earth. Please explain all of that. I'm eager to listen. But before you do, clarify one thing for me." Gillen asked the question to himself but never deviated his gaze from Danielle. "How could you *possibly* desire Cate?"

Only Gillen noticed that his alternate had sunk ever so slightly into his seat. Danielle had missed the moment for she had not been looking at her husband. She had been looking at her ideal.

The other Gillen sighed heavily and moved the towel knot up from his jawline to his temple, making it more difficult for his periphery to see his wife. "I love Danielle. I have since the moment I met her at the coffee shop. That first instant, watching her from afar, wondering—"

"I don't need the walk down memory lane," Gillen irritably interjected. "I was there. I remember."

The other Gillen nodded. "Then you must also remember what it was like when you first laid eyes on Cate."

"No," he countered. "I remember what it was like to give up on the woman I loved and settle. Cate was second best. The runner-up. She was my shot at happiness and fulfillment in spite of being haunted by the phantom of what could have been. A phantom who chased me since I was eighteen. A phantom whose mere existence was predicated on the actions of those outside of our relationship and solidified by their ideology."

"What do you mean?"

"I mean Danielle and I were never given a chance to decide what our futures would be, therefore, we never got closure."

"Closure..." the other said. "If that's what you're looking for, go right ahead. She's standing right here."

"She's not the same woman," Gillen replied, with terse inflection.

"Nevertheless, she's as close as you're ever going to get. Maybe finally saying what's been on your mind all these years will help you process the closure you need to move on."

Gillen's mouth was agape as he listened to words that sounded like his own. The audacity of the idea was only eclipsed by the person who had suggested it. If Gillen was certain of anything, on this planet or any other, it was that he and his alternate had remarkably little in common. "What did you do with Allaire?"

◄ ◆ ● ● ● ● ● ◆ ►

"Allaire is safe," the other Gillen said as the three of them ambled into a study in the back of the house. "She's with Jack DaLette in New York."

"New York?" Gillen asked incredulously, suddenly feeling even more detached from her than he did when it was just a planetary hop through the Alignment. "Neither that city nor that man backs up your claim of her supposed safety."

"Jack will cause her no harm, I assure you. He desperately needs her. For now."

"Needs her for what?"

The study was small, encased by wrap-around bookshelves that had zero vacancy. The wood floors and wood furniture were accompanied by what Gillen could only suspect was a wooden desk, for he could not see it. The notepads, schematics, manuals, and loose pages all coalesced around the arc light of a lamp that hunched over the desk and seemed to give illumination to the levitating sprawl. Behind the desk was a cubbyhole framed into where two more shelves would have otherwise been. Inside the opening was a small chalkboard affixed to the wall covered in mathematical formulas and equations.

Unsurprisingly, Gillen's eyes wandered there first. It only took a few motions to sidestep behind the desk, and as his finger followed the lines from one end of the chalkboard to the other, he soon hesitated above a particular cluster of numbers and tapped at it with intention. Turning his head back toward the other two, he said, "This is *not* the Minreth-Hughes equation."

"No, it's not," confirmed the other Gillen, pressing the damp knot harder against his skull. "But it is the one that gave us the Octagons. This is Walter's study. I mean... it was."

"Was?"

The other Gillen's reaction was one of momentary confusion usurped by instant realization of a truth. Doing his best to feign contrition for an event which no longer gave him any emotion, he nodded slowly before saying, "Walter—our Walter—is dead."

Gillen stared blankly, with the same expression one would have gazing at an abacus. "Suicide?"

"Yeah."

"How?"

"Overdose. After what happened to his first wife, and his son Lamar years ago, then also losing Allaire... it was all just too much for him."

Utter silence filled the study as Gillen turned away from the chalkboard and leaned over the desk. His shadow projected back against the wall from the lamp's light casting an omnipresent pall over the tiny room. As he flipped through a manual that happened to be open, he rested his other hand against the edge of the desk and enunciated his words with care. "Now... Allaire. Jack needs her for what?"

The other Gillen and Danielle exchanged glances. His stare reflected an unknowable fear. Her stare projected an unconscionable rage. With the sigh of one exhaling a series of regretful actions, the other Gillen faced the man behind Walter's desk. "We couldn't get the Alignment to stay open. Walter and Jack couldn't do it. I couldn't do it. God only knows why, but none of the equations worked—not even Minreth-Hughes. The farthest we ever got was a momentary exposure, a single transport between two locations. Teleportation be damned, we wanted to go to the moon. Eventually, I discovered the key to long distance teleportation, via the Octagons. Our arrival spot on the lunar surface being a few miles away from Ortelius was mere coincidence. We didn't even know your base was there." He then added with a huff, "We thought we were pioneers."

Gillen continued listening to his other self while zeroing in on anything on the desk that interested him. "Go on."

"The initial trip through was disastrous. Walter and Barry were the first two on the moon via the Octagonal Alignment. They had spacesuits on with reserve oxygen supplies and emergency rations. Immediately upon their jump, we sent the components they would need for the return, case by case. It took about thirty minutes, but we sent all of the necessary items through for them to build the return Octagon on the moon. An hour later, only Walter returned. Barry had accidentally severed his air hose just as they were installing the last component. He suffocated before Walter could assist."

Gillen looked up from the desk. "Dear God..."

"That incident put a chilling effect on the whole team. Richard Kaine left the company. The investors backed out. Barry's death weighed over everything. Walter was devastated. We all were, but it hit Walter especially hard. I saw the fire go out, so to speak. He lost all interest in the project, and having been on the fence about joining his old friend from Dartmouth on a new field of study, he shut down Iselin Amalgamate and transferred ownership of the intellectual property to me and Jack."

"Walter abandoned the project?" Gillen asked, confirming what he had heard.

"And not a moment too soon, it appears. From what we can tell of the sequence of events on your planet, Walter's taking of that role prevented someone else from getting it, which altered the course of events leading up to the launch of Sputnik. Walter's decision seems to be the lynchpin in preventing, or more likely—just delaying, the world's first artificial satellite."

Sputnik, Gillen scoffed. His eyes slowly scanned the architectural lines of the Octagon schematic, each page more detailed than the last. It was unnerving to witness the product of someone else's mind in his own handwriting. In the margins were copious notes, some his own, some from Jack, most from Walter, until the last few pages when Walter's involvement had obviously dissipated. Pushing the blueprints away from the center of the desk, Gillen reached for another binder and nodded for his other to continue.

"Anyway, Jack and I continued perfecting the Octagons for the next several months. But then, Jack started to... obsess. Not just about the project, but about everything. It's as if he was trying to figure out the whole of the universe in a single sitting. I tried to inquire as to what was bothering him, but he was either unwilling or unable to discuss it. That is, until last month."

Gillen looked up from the desk as shadows ran the length of his cheekbones. "What happened last month?"

"Jack had been gone for several weeks, claiming to be on business in New York. Upon his return, he sat Danielle and I down and explained... an idea. One that would turn the world upside down. A plan that would finally turn the tide on the endless waves of human loss."

The bloodstained wall assaulted Gillen's memory as the image strobe-flashed from the recesses of his mind. "What about it?"

The other Gillen and Danielle each took a step closer toward the desk. "Jack said that there was an opportunity for us to build the concept of the Octagons, secure the funding we needed to grow the company, and provide another daughter for Walter and Cate."

"Danielle already told me this," Gillen said. "So you decided to kidnap Allaire and offer her as a replacement for the last one. I understand how she helps you, but of what value can she be to Jack?"

Whether it was the dim lighting of the windowless study, or just the exhaustion from intergalactic travel wearing down his senses, Gillen narrowed his focus in on his alternate as the man appeared to be doing two things at once: rallying up the courage to utter the words on his lips and trying desperately not to become physically ill.

"Jack..." the other Gillen gasped, "didn't just want to replace Allaire. He wants the ability to replace anyone."

The shadow on the wall shifted as Gillen straightened his posture. "You mean... anyone who has died?"

The reply came from dark, distant eyes. "Yes. But not just those who died. Even those... who... in someone's subjective estimation... deserve to be replaced by their alternate."

Gillen felt an overwhelming temptation to shoot a glance at Danielle, but resisted in order to keep his other talking. "What you're describing is madness. It's..." Gillen struggled for the word, for the concept he needed to convey the magnitude of what was being proposed. Then it dawned on him. "It's cross-dimensional human trafficking."

"Not to Jack," Danielle said, speaking through a quivering lower lip. "To him, it's picking up where God seems to have failed. Restoring order to the universe. Creating equilibrium."

"How is cherry-picking the best humanity from one planet for the sole benefit of another equilibrium?"

She answered, eyes wide in terror, "Because some other universe is probably already doing the same thing to us."

Gillen turned his face ever so slightly. "Oh my God..." As his line of sight sank back down to the desk, the scribbles, theorems, and equations all of a sudden looked like hieroglyphs. Gone were the reasons for the years of toil and miscalculations, for the emotional sacrifices and delayed dreams. Nothing within the lines of text justified what he vaguely recalled to be his virtuous aim when he envisioned a city on the moon. It had morphed into something unrecognizable. Darker than his worst fears. More perverse than the cruelest of fates.

Gillen... don't do this...

Cate's words seared into his consciousness. The look of horror on her face upon witnessing the lunar embassy had only been dwarfed by her overwhelming countenance of sorrow. A sorrow birthed from a vision of the future that was so outlandish, it had become verbally non-transferable. Only the look in her eyes had conveyed a morsel of the meaning that night, a meaning that her suicide removed any chance of decoding.

How could she have known? Gillen wondered, still gazing at the iniquity before him. *How could she have foreseen this?*

"Jack's already done this once before," the other Gillen continued. "That was how he convinced your Richard Kaine to sabotage the Hexagon. By contacting him on the radio—like I did to Allaire. Only instead of offering to rescue him, he made him a business proposition. In exchange for installing that cable, Jack offered Richard the son he and his wife were never able to have on your earth. The son... who belonged to the Richard Kaine of this planet. A young boy, named Morley."

Richard was heading to New York... Gillen suddenly remembered. *That's what he was referring to on the train. Wondering if the other me was telling him the truth. The truth about... whether his payment... would be awaiting him in New York. His son... from the other world.*

Gillen recoiled in horror.

"That's why Jack needs Allaire before he gives her back to me," the other Gillen said with a shutter. "Tonight is the meeting for which he's been working all this time. Seven o'clock. The Silver Lining Club room on the sixty-eighth floor of the Chrysler Building in New York. We'll both be there giving a pitch to an elite group of investors. It's the chance to obtain the funding we—he...needs in order to bring this idea to fruition. Allaire is the final touch. Proof that replacement is possible. An alternate in the flesh."

"No one is going to believe that," Gillen objected, trying desperately to fend off doubts of his own. "He could show them the newspapers of the crash, a copy of her death certificate, but even the most cockamamie bunch would demand more proof than one teenage girl."

"Cate will be at that meeting too. In fact she's already in New York. Jack had me send her through this morning."

Gillen leaned forward a bit, as if the solid wood table had just lost some of its footing. "Cate?"

"And she has no idea about Allaire."

From across the desk, Gillen looked over at Danielle. He had nothing to say to her, he just needed the reassurance of having one ally in the room.

"Can you picture it?" the other Gillen recited. "Jack's charisma, followed by the introduction of Allaire, ending with the emotional reunion of a mother and daughter? It's going to be a powerful image."

"Only if Cate falls for it."

"Falls for what? Biologically, Allaire is her actual daughter. It's no different really than if she'd grown up abroad and was just now coming home to meet her once distant parents."

"Nice advertising. Did Jack put that line into the pitch or did you?"

"It's true, and you know it."

"I don't know it. You're not giving Cate enough ethical credit."

"And you're giving her far too much. Okay, give her a tumultuous night of sleep, one where she wrestles with this opportunity against the pushback of her moral compass. By tomorrow morning, we both know she'd be back in Jack's office begging him to grant her custody of Allaire. And you know how I know that? Because it's the exact same thing I would do if I were in her circumstance... and furthermore, Gillen Rainer, we both know that you would too."

Gillen moved swiftly from around Walter's desk and marched toward the door when his alternate grabbed his arm. "I admit that I've had mixed emotions about all of this, and while I now see the danger in where the Alignment could take us as a human race, I still believe that Cate deserves a second chance with Allaire."

Gillen turned around and shoved his other a step back. "It's only you who is looking for a second chance, an act of penance, a hope for absolution. You will not be going to New York this evening," he stated. "Because by seven o'clock, you will have filled me in on every detail I need in order to convince Jack DaLette that I am the Gillen Rainer of this world."

CHAPTER 15

DESTROYER OF WORLDS

"Are we hoping for a boy or a girl?" the doctor had asked.

The delivery room had been temperate, yet Gillen had sweated right through his dress shirt and into his wool vest. Although uncustomary for husbands to be seated next to their wives during labor, Cate's precarious health had left him little choice in the matter. The hours of agony compounded with the fact that the symptoms of her mysterious illness had been in full force at the start of her contractions, placed her in an already weakened state by the time they reached the hospital.

"Is it normal for it to take this long?" Gillen had privately asked the doctor.

"It's only been a few hours, Mr. Rainer," the doctor had said. "These things can take time. The best work for you to do is try and keep your wife calm. She's not a well woman, but I do believe that she's capable."

"What if there's complications?"

The doctor shook his head and smiled. "One step at a time. Women have been doing this quite literally since the dawn of man. Your wife is having a baby. This isn't the end of the world."

Dusk gave way to dawn and Cate was becoming lethargic. The nurse brought her some bone broth and ice chips, along with a suggestion to try rotating into different positions in between contractions. The advice offered only temporary relief, and soon, Cate was again unconsolable.

"You're doing great," Gillen whispered, exchanging one hand for the other as she squeezed the color from it.

"I'm sorry, Gillen," Cate had replied, the sparkle having long since drained from her eyes. "I'm really trying. I don't know why I can't do this."

"These things can take time," Gillen reassured her, feigning expertise. "Maybe our little one is just a bit stubborn."

Cate tried to smile. "Probably gets it from me."

By midmorning, Cate had managed a few minutes of sleep. Gillen returned from the washroom and requested a newspaper from one of the nurses. Despite asking for it again later, it never came.

The hour hand pressed on as the doctor checked her vital signs and announced, "My guess is that this baby will be along soon."

Cate shook her head. "I can't do it. I have no more strength to push."

"You must push, Mrs. Rainer. Your child's life depends on it."

Cate turned to Gillen, her eyes pleading for him to grant her a vicarious power. Gillen caressed her forehead with a rag while unable to think of anything more to say than the hopeful platitudes he had been offering for sixteen hours. The truth was, he was terrified that she was correct. She had always been so slender and frail. So easily prone to exhaustion. Fitted with a body uncooperative for daily living and recalcitrant as to the reasons. They had known that pregnancy would be a challenge for her, and with that knowledge brought a hesitancy on Gillen's part, a hesitancy often exhibited in their bedroom. A once fiery copulance tamed, then diminished, leaving behind something metered and void of spontaneity.

Cate's desire to be ravished and Gillen's fear of causing her harm led to misunderstandings and frustrations which eventually settled into a mutually understood complacency. Their intercourse continued, but could hardly be categorized as sex. It brought neither satisfaction nor fear of the future. What it did do for them, was provide an alibi for their longings.

The day Cate told Gillen she was with child, the couple was ecstatic — for the afternoon. By that night, an unshakable trepidation had fallen over them like the news of a terminal illness. Jack had come over to the house to offer congratulations and had poured himself and Gillen a drink. Jack drank to celebrate. Gillen drank to forget. The guilt steadily wore on him that night as he laid in bed next to Cate, his mind chastising his desire for her as lascivious, thoughtless, and irresponsible.

The months that followed took a toll. Gillen ran himself ragged in order to ease her ongoing distress and Cate had no choice but to let him. As the trimesters progressed, and the due date approached, a realization slowly made itself known to first Cate, and then much later to Gillen. If Cate died in childbirth, Gillen would be a widower with a newborn. While that fact was not a novel concept in the history of civilization, it was a startling terror to the Rainers.

"Just a little more now," the doctor had said from below the stirrups.

She's not gonna make it, Gillen had thought to himself. "You can do it, darling. You're almost there."

Cate had stopped screaming hours earlier, not because she wasn't in agony but because her voice was gone. Seeming to teeter in and out of consciousness, she would find a particle of inner strength and push with tremendous effort, only to have nothing to show for it, before shutting her eyes listlessly and having to be gently reawakened by Gillen's clammy palm.

"She's crowning," said the doctor.

She's dying... and it's all my fault.

"One more giant push, Mrs. Rainer, don't give up on me now."

As Cate heaved, Gillen suddenly felt faint. The arc light over the delivery bed blazed down over them and the room began to whirl. Sitting back down on the arm of the chair, Gillen continued holding Cate's hand as he heard the doctor ask for yet another push. Cate did not respond to the command.

"One more push, Mrs. Rainer. We're almost there."

Cate gazed up into Gillen's eyes as if paralytic. She had not fainted, but she was no longer pushing. It was as if the motor in her fragile body had given out after having been throttled too far. In helplessness, she looked up from the bed with the kind of remorse that pleaded for lenience. Gillen bent over and kissed her forehead, knowing that she still needed to push, and understanding that if she could, she would.

"Mrs. Rainer?"

"She can't do any more," Gillen said defensively. "There must be something we can do instead."

The doctor proceeded to adjust the height and position of both of the stirrups holding Cate's legs in order to account for the baby's shoulder dystocia. A metallic tool was quickly removed from the tray next to the bed, leaving Gillen to scold himself for not noticing which tool it had been. Silence then ensued for several more minutes, with nothing but the occasional noises of the stirrup hinges to pull Gillen from his unease. He glanced down again at Cate, caressing her face, trying to offer encouragement within a moment devoid of certainty. She had stared back not quite catatonically, but seemed to crest on the verge of dissociation.

"Doctor?" Gillen asked.

"Stay close, Mr. Rainer."

Stay close?

The nurse pulled away from the delivery table and opened a manilla folder on the other side of the room. Gillen watched with insistent eyes. "Mr. Rainer, your chart says that you're O negative blood type. Is that correct?"

Gillen did not remember answering, but simply bobbing his head and being reclined next to Cate separated only by a bloodline. The transfusion was rapid. The actions of the clinicians were more so. Before long, with little more than a bandage applied to his arm, he found himself standing on wobbly legs next to the bed where Cate was cradling their newborn daughter.

"You did it," he had said, landing a kiss on Cate's parched lips.

"Is she all right?" Cate had asked, still reeling from the delivery.

"She's perfect. She has your face, and apparently my broad shoulders. Sorry about that."

The baby was then handed to Gillen. His first inclination was to tighten the gap between his arms. He was astounded at how tiny the little human was. The next realization was more sobering.

This girl is partially me.

"Amazing," he whispered.

"What's that?" asked Cate.

"She's half of you and half of me. It's funny, but I'm just now coming to terms with that. This little person is another version of us."

The razor thin smile on Cate's face vanished.

"You have a visitor," said the nurse. "He says he's the grandfather."

Walter Iselin had entered the room while humming to himself, even as a giant smile pushed back a look of concern from his face. He walked directly up to Gillen and gave him a hug, at which time he whispered, "Keep the radio off and confiscate any newspapers lying around."

For a moment, Gillen wondered if Walter was being serious, yet a side glance back in his direction as he motioned toward Cate's bed was all the confirmation necessary that he was. Gillen excused himself and left the room. After hunting down a newspaper in the lobby, whatever fragile grip on his emotions he had obtained in the hour since Allaire's birth was lost in the span of a single headline.

First Atomic Bomb Dropped on Japan.

"Mother of God..." he had muttered, uncertain as to whether he meant it as a prayer or a profanity. The newspaper shook in his hands as the black ink stained his sweaty fingertips. When he was finally able to tear his eyes from the horrific wording, he tossed the newspaper into the trash and returned to Cate's room. There he saw Walter holding Allaire, cooing to her, babbling nonsensically, exhibiting all of the hallmarks of grandfatherly adoration.

"The world needs cheerfulness, now more than ever," Walter had stated. After soaking in another impression of the baby girl in his arms, he had turned to Cate and said, "*Allaire* would be a lovely choice. It's French for cheerful."

Gillen had tried to smile, but could not, his mind still trying to suppress the news of the day. Yet much later, years later, as he knelt down on the carpeted floor of the alternate Cate's bedroom and carefully disposed of the shards of shattered mirror, the memory now seemed ever more disturbing. A truth seeped into his physical frame and made his muscles ache. At first it was hard to accept. The incongruity between the Cate he had envisioned and the Cate she seemed to be wrestled for supremacy. Like some ghastly carousel his mind spun out example after example of his devotion to her. Of his myriad of sacrifices, both physical and mental. The countless hours by her side, comforting her in her nameless, faceless, causeless distress, setting behind him any notion of his own wellbeing. Then eventually, as a reaction to that existence, he grew to need her reliance on him, extracting a haggard fulfillment from a marriage having long since deteriorated into a codependency of staggering proportions.

Poor Allaire...

Allaire. Victim to it all from the moment of conception. Her very life had been predicated on the truth that was just now unfolding before him — one he had yet to volitionally accept. Her years of fruitless attempts at becoming closer with Cate now made sense. For Cate, Allaire had been an ever-present emblem of a choice she only partially regretted, made in conjunction with a man whom she could never marry. In lieu of motherly affection, Cate had channeled that energy into supporting Allaire's successes. Allaire had picked up on that token and internalized it, motivating her subconscious into recalling a time when Cate actually had demonstrated the kind of love she desperately sought... early on, during Allaire's most formative years, when Walter could still be around, when Cate had still been happy, when the three of them could pretend to be a family.

Gillen blinked and brushed the last of the pieces into a dustpan. The truth would be retained no longer as it broke through the guardrails of his conscience. *Cate wanted to have a baby, she just didn't want to have one with me.*

Setting the dustpan down on the armoire, Gillen slowly rose to his feet and wondered why his body felt pulverized. He exhaled loudly and gazed about the room. What he saw brought nothing of any value to mind. Instead, his conscience continued to simmer, believing that one good confession was worth another.

No, he protested, *that was not the same thing.*

"I can't believe it's really you," Gillen had once said.

"It's really me," Danielle had replied.

The two couples had left the restaurant and headed back to the Rainer's home for a superfluous nightcap. Allaire had been away for the evening at a sleepover, leaving the adults in the house to be kids. Gillen poured their drinks silently, still mostly sober despite the bottles of wine they had all finished, and astounded as to who was standing in his den. Danielle Hoyne, after all those years, being displayed underneath Jack DaLette's outstretched arm like she was some sort of costume jewelry.

"You two... are so cute together," opined Cate with a bit of a slur.

"Yeah," said Jack. "Dani and I are gonna be all the rage. I really feel something special with this one."

Gillen downed his glass and excused himself from the den. With his pulse pounding into his ears, he marched upstairs and began pacing the bedroom. He did not know whether what he was experiencing was the onset of jealousy or the pangs of regret, but whatever the emotion, he knew he needed to speak privately with Danielle.

That opportunity was abandoned as Danielle found her way upstairs. She had needed no guise for going to powder her nose, as Jack and Cate had each passed out on the divan and recliner respectively, their glasses mostly drained of cognac, while Danielle's glass sat on the coaster nearly untouched. As her cerulean dress brushed against the side of the door, she smiled at Gillen who was standing in the corner of the unlit bedroom with his hands thrust irritably into his pockets. He gazed at her in wordless awe, volleying questions toward her simply by the longing in his eyes and the broadening of his shoulders.

"I can't believe it's really you," he finally gasped.

"It's really me," she whispered, removing the linen gloves from her hands.

Gillen remembered the feeling of his hand closing the wooden door behind her and that the thrill was not in the action itself but in the look she bestowed upon him when he did. Without explanation or directive, he had her back up against the bedroom wall, his lips pressed to hers, his hands reclaiming lost territory, his emotions seeming to have absconded with his ethics. Danielle leaned into him and clenched the back of his shirt between her fingers. Their breathing synchronized and turned from exhaling to panting. This was what he had longed for since their last and only encounter. The sensation only Danielle had ever given him. The full perceptual awakening to life as it could be.

She ran her fingers into his hair before zigzagging them down to his collar and unbuttoning the line of white dots along his shirt. As he found the zipper to her dress and began to work it skillfully down the seam, he could feel the fabric begin to slip off her body, and knew that when it did, they would have mutually reached the point of no return. Her hypnotic upturned eyes flashed their hazel spell while her smirk confirmed the message with vivid clarity.

Danielle's dress fell to the carpet the instant they heard a clatter from downstairs followed by an exclamation from Cate. The sound reverberated through them like a shockwave. Gillen pulled away and stared at the door for a moment. He then looked at Danielle who stood at the wall as if the recipient of a strip search.

"Wait here," he said, "I'll check."

"Gillen!" Danielle said, grabbing his arm. "Your shirt buttons."

Putting himself back together on his way out of the bedroom, he dashed down the stairwell and back into the den where a snifter glass had shattered onto the floor. Next to it, Cate was crawling on hands and knees, cursing herself for having been clumsy. When she saw Gillen standing before her, she gazed up at him and flashed an inebriated smile. "Silly me," she mumbled. "Too drunk to even drink."

Gillen stared at her as she crawled, the sapphire pendant he had recently purchased for her dangling from her neck, only partially blocking the droop in her cocktail dress from which far too much cleavage was emerging. He pressed his palm up to his forehead and sighed heavily into his wrist while a tsunami of impulses and anger churned within.

"Don't, you'll cut yourself," Gillen said to Cate as he knelt down. "Let me."

Cate nodded and leaned back against the legs of the end table. She watched the cognac trickle away from the epicenter of the spill as Gillen collected the fragmented glassware in his hand. After a trip to the kitchen, he returned with a towel and sopped up the pool of liquid and then went after what had seeped into the wood grain.

"Thanks, dear..." Cate whispered. "I'm sorry."

"No harm done," he said, continuing to scrub.

"You... you're such a... nice man."

Gillen mumbled a reply which prompted Cate to lean forward until she was inches from his face. "No, I mean it. You're... a good person, Gillen. You're... so much... better than me."

"Babe, you're drunk. Let me finish—"

Cate wrapped an arm around his shoulders and tried to kiss him but he firmly pulled away. "That should be good. Not even a stain left."

"I'm sorry, Gillen..."

"Don't worry about it."

"But... I'm sorry..."

Gillen lifted Cate up to her feet and maneuvered her back onto the divan. "Sleep it off. You'll feel better in the morning."

Cate blinked and then smiled. "You do look... so beautiful."

"So do you, Cate," Danielle responded from the hallway.

Gillen jerked upon seeing her standing before them, back in her cerulean dress, hair mostly re-styled, pearl gloves running up to her elbows. She was addressing Cate with the kindness one offers a hostess after overstaying a welcome. "Did you... find the powder room okay?" Gillen asked.

Danielle motioned something akin to a nod before looking over at the recliner. "Jack," she said. "I've called us a cab. It should be here any minute."

"Oh, there's no need to... I mean, you're both welcome to stay."

"This has been great, but we should go. Jack?"

Jack's slumber seemed to linger even as he waved toward Danielle in agreement and slowly patted Gillen on the back. "You've got the best cellar in San Francisco," he chuckled.

Words jumbled up on the bridge of Gillen's mouth as Jack donned his hat and offered Danielle a hand with her evening wrap. Before he could process what had occurred in the last hour, they were gone, leaving behind nothing but a memory which had exhumed the coffin of his first love — a coffin he had thought had been successfully buried. If there had been even a shred of hope that this reunion was to rekindle a dormant romance between him and his first love, Gillen was sorely mistaken, as after the events of that evening, he never again saw her.

Jack was helpless to explain it. She had had nothing but positive things to say about their visit. Yet she had been adamant that their small wedding be just family. Then she declined dinner invitations, or attendance at any social gathering where she might run into either Rainer. So inexplicable was her shunning of them that Jack's embarrassment grew to frustration. It had been the first nail in a doomed marriage. Jack had blamed Danielle. Cate, as always, blamed herself. Gillen ignored blaming altogether and instead reburied those emotions in the graveyard of the unknown. He stopped jockeying to see her. He resigned the past to the realm of antiquity. He focused solely on his future with Cate, a woman he loved, and to an unhealthy degree, desperately needed.

And it was in that moment, as Gillen watched the broken pieces of armoire mirror slide out of the dustpan and into the garbage bin, that he fully comprehended the horrible, suffocating, merciless power that guilt had played in systematically destroying Cate's life. For her sins, she was subsequently sentenced to eternity in her own personal hell, never to forget her lover, her daughter, or her caretaker, all of whom she had betrayed.

Cate... he thought to himself, shaking his head slowly. *Why? Why do it? Why do it to... yourself? What could have possessed you? You and Walter... it makes no sense. What was it about him that so captured your heart and mind? If you were here, that's what I would ask you.*

Yet she was not there, leaving Gillen with only the limits of his imagination to conjure up a response to his questions. For although there were enough pieces of her left in his heart to hear her voice, what her actual words would be left him wanting.

Gillen would never know that Cate had felt an instant attraction to Walter the first time they had all met for lunch at the red delicatessen. Nor would he have had any knowledge of the time Walter had partaken in a few too many drinks at a party and had solemnly confided in Cate the horrific story of his past. Her silence following the end of his confessional had been correctly interpreted by

Walter, who watched as tears of empathy streamed down her face. The moment was sobering for him, and revealing for her. Two people, acquainted with suffering, now acquainted with each other.

"Please take me home, Gillen," she had asked, almost trembling.

Gillen, for the first time in their marriage, had shot her a glance which bordered on detest. "If you're not feeling well, just take a cab. I'm gonna stay."

Please don't be that way... not tonight, Gillen, her mind had pleaded. *Can't you see it in my eyes? I need you to stop me from what I'm about to do.*

"Don't worry," Walter had said, placing his hand on Gillen's shoulder, "I'll drive her home."

Gillen had smiled in relief. "Thanks, Walter. I'll owe you one."

Never would Cate be able to share with him the moment that a thousand accusations from her conscience had finally formed into a course of action. The catalyst had been a single transmission, sent from the lunar Octagon to Ortelius, almost a year before Richard Kaine had ever heard the voice of the other Jack DaLette come through the workstation speakers.

Cate had been alone on the habitat. As the other members of the team busied themselves with preparations for the investors' walk-through that evening, she had offered to tidy up loose paperwork on the Ortelius lab — something of minimal physical exertion, and a way to eschew her increasing sense of disconnect from Gillen's coworkers.

"Greetings to whoever is listening..." came a familiar voice.

Imagining the call to be a prank, Cate had flipped the microphone switch and responded with, "This new pitchman isn't nearly as funny as the old one."

"This is Jack DaLette of planet earth. To whom am I speaking?"

"This is Cate Rainer of planet earth. Are you all done down there already?"

The long stretch of silence that followed eventually broke through into a terrifying conversation.

"That's the only way this is possible," Jack had emphatically stated. "We're each from alternate universes, but you all inadvertently built your base on our moon instead of your own."

Cate didn't care about that. None of the technological, political, or astrophysical ramifications so much as graced her mind's eye save for one — the image of Gillen's face upon discovering her secret.

"What does she look like?" Cate's quivering lips had asked, her emerald eyes wide with horror.

"Who?"

"Walter's and my daughter. You said we have a child together. What... what does... she look like?"

Jack's description was cursory, yet it was all the physical features Cate needed in order to seal her own destiny.

"There's so much to tell you all." Jack had added, "And so much for us to learn. We must introduce our teams and begin—"

"No," Cate had whispered, from a voice hoarse with emotion.

"I'm sorry?"

"We do not wish to hear from any of you further. Do not contact us again." And with that, Cate had flipped the microphone switch to the off position, knowing that the motion was futile, and knowing instead what was to be her only way out.

I'm sorry, Gillen. I can't be here to see you go through this, Cate had said to herself in the dawning hours of the next morning. After having carefully applied her mascara, blush, and lipstick, she studied herself in the mirror for more than a minute, examining her dress, her hair, and the utter lack of trepidation she thought she should be having.

Her countenance displayed a resolved peace as she left the powder room and peeked in on Allaire. The twelve-year-old slept peacefully, her positioning in the bed strangely idyllic. Without feeling the need to extract any reminiscence from the moment, Cate silently bent forward to kiss her daughter on the cheek and offer one final smile to the child who had never seemed to notice them.

"Just know..." she mouthed breathlessly. "You were so very loved."

Some time later that day, Cate jumped. The event had left Gillen hopelessly lost, perplexed to despair. And even as the light from her past shed new insight into the woman he barely knew, there would always be portions of her life shielded from his sight. Cate was an equation without a sum, and his fruitless attempts to solve it had left him with an infuriating truth.

In some worlds, certain equations just didn't work.

Gazing into the garbage bin, Gillen sighed heavily and then slowly arose from off the floor. *I just don't understand. Why Walter? Why not me? I did everything I could for you. I loved you more than I loved...*

The memory of Danielle brought an icy blow to his chest.

... anyone.

CHAPTER 16

SPIRE

Allaire awoke from her nap in a fetal position. She was instantly aware of two things: That she was in an unfamiliar bedroom and that she had been humming. The cotton sheets wrinkled around her body as she turned over to see the clock on the nightstand. Beams of midafternoon light found their way through the window blinds and cast slanted rays against the furniture in the room. The bustling sounds of the city that never slept reminded Allaire of her change in locale. Her bedroom was inside an apartment which was nestled along a row of buildings encompassing a burrow of New York.

The residence belonged to a friend of her father's, a man named Jack, who was to watch over her until her father's return later that night, a time at which they would head over to the skyscraper that looked like a sunburst peaking over the other buildings and attend some sort of small gathering... perhaps a party. Her excitement was instantly palpable. It was going to be a fun evening.

With a yawn and a stretch, Allaire arose from the bed and stood in front of a mirror. After putting her auburn hair into a pony-tail, she slipped on her pair of black-and-white saddle shoes and adjusted the cuff on each leg of her mauve pedal pushers. Her white, sleeveless blouse needed a bit of tucking in places, and with a quick twist of the bow on her collar, she gave herself a reassuring nod and marched out of the bedroom.

"Dad?" she spoke into the apartment. The hallway was lined with impressionistic artwork, some depicting imagery from San Francisco, others of Times Square and the Brooklyn Bridge. Allaire slowed to observe one piece in particular. Hanging on the wall in an exquisite frame, the canvas displayed a dreamlike amalgamation of a bustling city street, a cloudy sky, and peaking through the very same clouds was the Chrysler Building and its art deco spire. Her eyes followed the painting as she walked by, wondering if the reality was just as beautiful as the depiction.

"Mr. DaLette?" she said, cautiously entering the living room. The space was vacant and gave her the feeling that it would still seem empty even if someone had been there. She moved into the kitchen, then back into the hallway, and after determining from a series of gentle knocks on the second bedroom door that the room was also vacant, Allaire decided that she was alone in the apartment.

"Nifty," she said with a smile.

The radio pulsed with energy as Allaire maneuvered around the kitchen while preparing a sandwich. Her ponytail bobbed as she shimmied to the music, with an occasional pirouette finding its way into the motions. Despite being almost three thousand miles from home, she was slowly settling back into a state of calm, normalcy, of being back on planet earth. Her harrowing voyage from the moon had been as draining as it had been wondrous, but her subsequent day and a half of rest had rejuvenated the teenager to the point that an evening out on the town sounded like a splendid treat.

No one at school is going to believe what happened, she thought to herself while firmly pressing the sandwich together and taking an enormous bite. The jump through the Alignment had been intense. They almost hadn't made it. Her father had told her that they could no longer use the Hexagons and needed to utilize an alternate method, but their window of opportunity to use it was short. The trek across the lunar terrain had been heart-pounding, but one she would never forget. When the lunar module got stuck in the sand, their race to the Octagon was nearly their undoing. But within the frame of the last possible second, they had arrived, and in the blink of an instant, the moon was once again the earth.

She had later asked Gillen who it was that she had seen behind them, but he had assured her that it was merely a spacetime distortion. And quite a distortion it had been, as the illusory image running toward them had appeared to be a replica of her father. The memory haunted her even as she tried to let it go.

The music on the radio broke for station identification and top-of-the-hour news. As the announcer droned on, Allaire discovered that she was relieved to hear nothing more about Sputnik. Everyone had been as equally depressed as obsessed by the thing and she was glad that it was no longer news.

With crumbs left on her plate, she rinsed the dish and walked back to the living room where a window overlooked the city street below. The sidewalks were bathed in sunlight as pedestrians hurried by. Each face responded to the warmth with a subtle appreciation, one that transcended their predicaments or individual lots in life. As Allaire's eyes followed the current of people, she noticed a man walking out of a bookstore carrying what appeared to be a lengthy novel. His hand cupped the book tightly to his chest as he disappeared around the street corner. She then caught sight of a small group of teenage girls exhibiting an adolescent glee as they approached a small shop. Allaire's vision lost focus of the girls and instead shifted to the bold lettering on the shop's window.

A record store... she thought, while tapping her fingers on the sill. Her instructions had been clear. She was to stay inside the apartment until Mr. DaLette's return. Yet the tantalizing lure of the vinyl just across the street in a brand new city on such a beautiful day in the middle of the afternoon having just survived being stranded on the moon seemed to be of minimal risk.

After dashing down the stairwell, Allaire yanked open the apartment door and breathed in the exotic air of Manhattan. She knew what it was to feel small as she stepped out onto the sidewalk and observed the rows of brick buildings that were themselves dwarfed by the monumental towers of the New York skyline. The moment gave her pause as she considered heading back into the apartment, but as her eyes narrowed in on the record store, a quick inhale and a clenching of her fists propelled her cautious dart across the street.

Her heart pounded with excitement as she reached for the shop door. A bell announced her entrance as she walked inside and gazed at the countless records lining boxes and shelves throughout the small store. Affixed to the walls were posters of the current heartthrobs topping the music charts, and in the back corner, a booth had been set up where patrons could audition their selections through headsets. Allaire watched as the teenagers she had spotted bopped and grooved to the tunes only they could hear, all as more seasoned audiophiles stood by while awaiting an open player.

Allaire slowly walked along the aisles, peering into boxes with records demarcated by artist or genre, some in shellac, most in vinyl. Many of the albums she recognized by title, others by artwork. The joy of being surrounded by something that was so intrinsically happy made her wonder just how long of a trip this might end up being.

"Anything I can help you find, young lady?"

Allaire turned to see a middle-aged woman standing behind one of the tables while reorganizing a box of albums that had begun to defy alphabetization. The woman was tall and had beaded lanyards hanging from her glasses which extended around her neck.

"I've never been here before," Allaire said with a twinge of uncertainty in her voice.

"To a record store?" the woman asked with a smirk.

"Not in New York City," Allaire said. "I mean, we have these in California, but there's something really neat about being in this one."

The woman nodded. "I like to think we're pretty neat. Where are you from?"

"San Francisco."

The woman placed her hand against her chest. "Oh, I've never been. Would love to some day. I hear it's gorgeous all the time, although, I'm certain there's a bit of hyperbole in that statement."

"It is gorgeous, most of the time. And I've always wanted to visit New York City... and here I am."

"Here you are," the woman chimed. "Although if you'll forgive my impertinence, there's really no need to add the city to the name... just New York will suffice. But then again, I was once corrected by someone who told me that certain residents of San Francisco consider it a pejorative to hear their beloved town referred to as Frisco. Who would have thought?"

Allaire crinkled her nose and laughed. "Yeah, I don't really care either way."

"What's your name, sweetie?"

"Allaire."

"Well, Allaire, I'm Stacey, and I run this store with my husband. He's in the back accepting a new shipment. So getting back to my original question, anything I can help you find?"

Allaire's eyes wandered while taking in the overwhelming selection of albums and wondering, by some extreme random chance, if Stacey might happen to recognize an elusive tune. "If I hummed a few notes from this song I'm looking for... do you think you would know it?"

The woman adjusted her glasses and straightened her posture. "Well, that depends. I've been known to blow the socks off the occasional customer by identifying a song from just the bridge, and sometimes the tail end of a chorus. The opener can be just as easy as it can be impossible. But I'll do my best. Is this a newer song?"

Allaire shook her head. "No, I don't think so."

"Do you know the artist, band, style?"

Allaire's mocha eyes gazed into the box of vinyl records and tried to shut out the noise of the store. The first few notes were always there, just teetering within the bounds of her reach. It began as a woman's voice, with low, comforting chords of dynamic humming. The sound had been once carried by instruments as well, the ones she had heard over the console speakers on Ortelius. Flutes and violins playing off of each other in a soft aria that introduced the vocal hums. Hums that began with nine lovely notes.

Shifting her gaze back toward Stacey, Allaire inhaled and hummed what she knew, her voice lilting between the staccato of each note. When she finished, Allaire noticed that the woman seemed momentarily lost in the sound, reflecting on its beauty, daunted by the simplicity of its arrangement. Her eyes then darted over toward the jukebox as if to reassure herself that she was still inside the store.

"That's lovely," she said, furling her eyebrows behind the frame of her glasses. "It sounds classical to me. Symphonic. Did you hear this while attending an orchestra?"

"I don't think so."

"Perhaps on the radio then? Or on an album?"

Allaire shrugged. "Maybe. It was a long time ago."

"How long? A few years, or more than that?"

"I think more than that."

The woman smiled. "It almost sounds to me like it's the opening to a lullaby."

Allaire's lips parted ever so slightly. The word lullaby triggered an emotion which in turn recalled a memory. The image was of her mother singing to her when Allaire was very young. She wasn't certain exactly how young, but whatever her age, she remembered gazing up from her bed, nestled underneath layers of bedsheets, as her mother's soft hand gently caressed the contours of Allaire's face. Cate's expression had been partially hidden in shadows and partially revealed by the gossamer light coming in from the hallway. As the memory sharpened, Allaire recalled the humming that had drifted her little self to sleep. There had been music, coming from a record player in her bedroom, and those unforgettable first few notes accompanying the flutes and violins which were so ethereal in their beauty.

Allaire blinked as the bedroom, the humming, and the angelic face of her mother gradually faded, leaving her confident in only one thing. Her mother had not been the one singing to her. The lullaby had only ever been sung to her by her father. *He must have been in the room too... why can't Dad remember?*

"Did your mother used to sing it to you?" Stacey asked gingerly.

Allaire shook her head and tried to laugh off the moment. "Maybe so. I'm not really sure. Anyway, thanks for trying."

"You've piqued my curiosity. If I come across it, I'll be sure to give you a call. Where can you be reached in San Francisco?"

After Allaire jotted the Rainer phone number down on a notepad, the woman tucked it away behind the cash register and walked her to the door. "Feel free to come back anytime during your stay in New York. We'll have the new records out on the floor by tomorrow."

"Swell. It was nice to chat with you, especially about something other than Sputnik."

Stacey flashed a crooked grin. "Is that something out in San Francisco?"

Allaire hesitated. "Oh... Sputnik... the satellite the Soviets just launched." Stacey nodded obliviously. Allaire added, "It's all anyone's been talking about. Seems like the whole world is in a panic."

"Perhaps I've been too deep in these records to hear about it. This place keeps us pretty busy. Too busy to worry about what the Commies are up to."

Along with Stacey, Allaire laughed while utterly amazed to find someone unfamiliar with the planet's biggest story. Particularly a New Yorker. It was as much an astonishment as it was a relief.

Stacey then said, "By the way, if you have some time this afternoon, the Bryant Park Art Festival is underway. There's always some neat stuff to see there."

"Art festival? Where?"

Stacey chuckled. "Silly me, thinking you'd know where Bryant Park is. Just go out this door, make a right, go down a block and then make another right, and you're there. Can't miss it."

Allaire thanked the woman again before leaving the store and standing idle on the sidewalk, exchanging glances between Jack DaLette's apartment building across the street and the right turn at the end of the block. There were still several hours before she would need to leave for the party, and attending a local art exhibit might give her something intelligent to talk about with the local New Yorkers as they sipped their champagne — and Allaire her ginger ale.

Without another moment's consideration, she marched down to the end of the corner and turned right, all the while musing to herself on finding the one person in the civilized world who had not heard of Sputnik.

◄ ◆ ● ● ● ● ● ◆ ►

A few miles away from Bryant Park, on the north end of a narrow island in the middle of the East River, a building complex stood in a state of abandonment. The brick structure occupied the site with abject stillness, comprised of two perpendicular buildings more than on their way to ruin, meeting at an apex of shapely significance. The five-story building at the corner of the right angle was topped with a modest rotunda and built from gneiss stone quarried from the island, giving the exterior a bluish-gray tint.

The exterior was eight sided.

Within the octagonal structure was a grand lobby that opened all the way up into the rotunda above. Circling the lobby was a spiraling staircase that hugged the walls on each level, every step now a showcase for the growing accumulation of dust and chips of fallen plaster. The open floor plan was supported all around by Corinthian columns holding up the circular balcony of each level, an architectural element repeated from the top story all the way down to the, no longer illuminated, glass brick floor.

The Octagon was lifeless, yet held within its wooden beams and beveled railings were the moments that once occurred inside the complex, moments experienced by the living who had wished they were dead. That was the environment into which Gillen and Danielle suddenly found themselves, as the whole of the lobby's invisible matter stretched and twisted and then returned to normal.

The two stood inert in the center of the entrance while wrapped in each other's arms. Their eyes slowly opened and adjusted to the darkness of their surroundings. A single ray of sunlight was split apart by the cracked window pane, allowing for periodic glimpses of dust particles that drifted hauntingly from the rafters. Gillen's eyes followed the spiraling staircase all the way to the rotunda above, yet he was startled by how much of the room's design seemed to convey a sense of descent.

"Where the hell are we?"

Danielle took hold of his hand. "This is the Octagon, the entrance to what used to be the New York City Lunatic Asylum. Don't worry, it's been abandoned."

Gillen nodded slowly. "That's comforting."

"The whole complex is pre-Civil War, part penitentiary, part hospital. This island is where smallpox victims would come to be quarantined. It's only been a couple years since Metropolitan Hospital left the island, leaving all of this to crumble."

"When did Jack get his hands on it?"

"He doesn't, actually. Like with the Palace of Fine Arts, he just installed the components into the Octagon and no one is the wiser."

Gillen chuckled to himself as he surveyed the dilapidation. "Jack must be insane in every universe."

Danielle kept in lockstep with Gillen as they approached the entryway. The weatherworn doors groaned as Gillen opened them, giving way to fresh air and eliminating the astringent taste from his tongue. "It's hard to believe we're on an island," he said stepping out onto the wrap-around porch. His eyes followed the landscape over to the river and then up toward the Queensboro Bridge that stretched over the island above their heads; its cantilevered design reminding him of another bridge, one that was emotive yet void of nostalgia.

"The Welfare Island Bridge is over there," Danielle pointed. "That will get us to Astoria. From there we can catch a cab to Manhattan."

"Let's try not running into Jack in the process."

The short walk over the bridge was quiet, leaving the two of them with their thoughts. Each step of leather against iron confirmed to Gillen the reality of what was going on, where he was, and with whom he was sharing these crucial moments. His mind reeled as he stole a glance at her. Danielle Hoyne... in a manner of speaking... resurrected. He blinked and looked away, uncertain as to if the human mind was truly ready for this new paradigm.

"Taxi!" he called out as they stood at a street corner while an aging neon sign blinked madly above their heads.

"Where to?" the cabbie asked.

"The Empire State Building."

The city of New York enveloped them as the taxicab entered Manhattan. Sailing through green lights eventually turned to gridlock as they approached the business hubs, the late afternoon traffic crawling and halting in sporadic jolts. Gillen and Danielle gazed out their individual windows while watching nothing of importance. The faces walking parallel to them on the sidewalks offered no answers, just reminders that there were still questions. Gillen in particular wrestled with the gnawing unease of indecision, of ambiguity, and once again, of closure. He had no concept of who this woman actually was, or who she could become. She was not his teenage dream. She was a parallel to that person. She was married to his other self, a man she either despised but had learned to live with, or else a man from whom she sought emancipation yet dreaded to lose.

Gillen wondered about his alternate's stake in all of this. The allure of Cate was powerful, perhaps inescapable, but in comparison to Danielle, also inexplicable. Why his other self didn't recognize the tether by which he and this woman were linked was baffling. In this world, had he not been summoned by divinity, struck with fire, felt the earth wobble off its axis upon meeting Danielle? She was the embodiment of every virtue he could utter and the promise of ones for which no words had been invented. She was his endless obsession. His highest value.

At least, at one time she had been.

Gillen sighed heavily as he thought about her death, and how a piece of him had felt like it had died with her. That chapter of his life had not so much been closed as it had been forcibly torn asunder, and as with the moment when she had been pulled away by a belief system at the foot of his front porch, so did illness snatch her away from him again — this time permanently — leaving him always without closure.

I love you, Danielle, he had once told her.

I love you, Gillen, she had once replied.

Biting his lower lip, Gillen felt himself begin to lean against the passenger window when all of a sudden he felt the unmistakable warmth of human skin on his hand. As he turned back toward Danielle, he felt her hand wrap around his fingers with gentle reassurance. All of his questions and concerns lost their clarity within the force of her touch as she leaned into the gap between them and pressed her lips to his.

This isn't real... Gillen reminded himself, as he cupped her face in his hands, his mouth crossing over to her cheek and neck before returning to her lips in starvation. The streets beyond their windows moved by without their notice, creating a stark contrast of the couple in the back of the taxi. Even the cabbie arched an eyebrow at the rearview mirror, musing to himself about the lovers lost in a dream inside the city that never slept.

With the taste of her perfume still fresh on his tongue, Gillen finally managed to pull away from her while maintaining some semblance of breath. Danielle gazed back at him with those hazel eyes and searched not for answers, but for why those questions had no meaning when wrapped in his arms. She turned her head with the slightest tilt and ran her finger along the length of his jawline.

"Oh, Gillen," she whispered. "Why do we torment each other? Why must we obsess over the things which only wish to keep us apart? It's always been you and me, in this world and any other. If my husband wants the life you once lived, let him have it. What do I care when I have you? It's like Jack said. Equilibrium at last. A chance to shape one's life ideally with the person who you knew just had to exist beyond the horizon. Please, Gillen... let's not reject the gift of life itself. I'm not her... you're not him... but let's love each other anyway."

Off in the distance, the spire of the Empire State Building came into view. The red strobe lights affixed to its pinnacle had only begun to pulse as the setting sun peeked through the shimmering glass and metal of the downtown skyscrapers. The tower stood as a totem, a structure built from girders that acknowledged gravity but would not yield to it. The emblem of the city had been commercialized, vilified, worshipped, and even ignored, yet standing it remained.

Gillen could not help but notice it as they approached. His eyes followed the straight lines of the building from the base all the way to its zenith before realizing that the moon had already made its evening appearance... just above the spire.

I miss earth, he thought to himself, and after a hesitation, wondered if that was a complete statement.

Turning back toward Danielle, he whispered, "Let's grab a drink and go over the plan once more."

Danielle nodded without agreement and nearly gasped for what little oxygen was left in her lungs. "Of course."

◄ ◆ ● ● ● ● ● ◆ ►

The Bryant Park Art Festival was so crowded with exhibitors and attendees that upon entering the grounds, Allaire lost sight of the street almost immediately. Hastily constructed booths, tables, and pegboard stands displayed art of all kinds, the amateur artists busy either chatting with prospective buyers or else attempting to lure foot traffic closer to their exhibits.

The color was overwhelming. Oils, acrylics, some on canvas, some on plates and pottery, some on materials Allaire couldn't identify. Her eyes darted wildly from one booth to the next. She could imagine herself here one day. Showcasing her latest work. Making a name for herself. All achievable after winning a gold medal at the Olympics.

As she weaved through the crowd, none of the exhibitors addressed her, for the odds were slim that she had any money. Allaire gave it no thought. She was here to absorb some New York culture before the party. To perhaps bring back a story to share with fancy people doing fancy things.

Deeper into the festival was a small, circular open area where several families were seeking momentary refuge from the teeming throngs. Men sat on benches next to their dates while trying to appear suave as parents with pram strollers walked by, attempting to quiet whatever lurked beneath the edges of the bassinet. Allaire smiled at the scene as her vision wandered up toward the buildings that surrounded the park, and beyond them, the top of the Chrysler Building reflecting the late afternoon sunlight from its ornamental gargoyles and eagles.

So beautiful...

Allaire's eyes drifted back down to the fair grounds where a single stare focused her attention on a man in a plaid blazer. The man's eyes were a shade of piercing blue, and he was slowly — yet attentively — coming her way.

CHAPTER 17

ANY MOMENT

"What'll you have?" the waiter asked Gillen, who was seated across from Danielle in a red leather booth. The lounge bar sat a half-level down from the street, allowing for patrons to view pedestrians on the sidewalk, and for pedestrians to peer down into the ground-level windows as they passed by.

"Scotch on the rocks," Gillen replied, and then began to order a whiskey sour for Danielle. "Oh... I mean..."

"Gimlet, please," she told the waiter directly.

Once alone, the two stared at each other silently while the voice of a female soloist crooned to a jazz standard from inside a jukebox. Their silence ensued until the drinks arrived, with Gillen then saying, "How are you feeling about this?"

The look on Danielle's face told Gillen that she was uncertain as to which topic he was referring: the one at hand or the one left unfinished. After a sip from her gin, she nodded slowly and set the highball glass back on the table. "I'll be fine. I have the key to Jack's office here in my purse. I'll wait until just before the start time of the presentation to assure there aren't any surprise visits from Jack grabbing a last minute folder. Then I'll go up to the fiftieth floor, install the red bulb, destroy all documents about the Octagons, and then flip the office lights on and off for sixty seconds to indicate that I'm done."

Gillen sipped slowly as she spoke, picturing the sequence in his mind. "I sure hope I can see that light from the Silver Lining Club room at the Chrysler Building."

"Gillen said he was able to."

"Do you remember where he said the files are stored?"

"The desk drawer and the safe. He gave me the combination. There's a metal wastepaper bin next to Jack's credenza that I can use to burn the files."

Gillen nodded. "Meanwhile, I'll intercept Allaire at the meeting as soon as I see your signal and then join you back at the Octagon, where Gillen should have already programmed the control panel for our final jump."

Danielle's eyes widened only for an instant before she took another sip. "Yes."

"Everything else will then be sorted out back at the house."

Again, Danielle stared into space. "Yes."

Gillen took a slightly larger gulp than intended and choked back the excess scotch. Coughing into his sleeve, he glanced up at Danielle who had cracked a smirk... her trademark smirk, the one that Gillen remembered as being indelibly part of her face yet more pronounced in moments like these.

"Down the hatch," she quipped.

"Yeah," he said, coughing again. He stole a glance at his wristwatch as the jukebox played the next track on the album. "We've got a few more minutes."

"I feel a bit jittery," said Danielle.

"So do I."

"No, I mean, just sitting here, waiting."

"Did you eat anything today?"

"It's not that. I just don't want to sit. Can we go for a walk outside?"

The tune from the next track on the album caught Gillen's attention as the melody swelled. "Ooh..." he breathed. "I've been hearing this song on the radio lately."

Danielle's eyes shifted over toward the direction of the music as if she could see it. Her countenance melted into the sway of the rhythm. It was a swooning, jazzy sort of arrangement, with the female singer describing a pair of lovers either too broke or too vexed with the idea of a getaway. So they decided to make the most of the simple pleasures of their neighborhood in old Manhattan. Danielle suspected that some of the song was sung in jest, with references most appreciated by locals, yet the nonchalance with which it was presented flooded her with warmth, nostalgia, and an unwelcome dose of ennui.

"May I?" Gillen asked, already in a standing position.

Danielle blinked and shot her eyes up at Gillen before noticing his hand extended to within her reach. "What's this?"

The gesture needed no further explanation. The hand remained outstretched as Danielle examined the look on Gillen's face. The overture was not intended as an interpretation of anything but two people stumbling upon a moment. That fact both relieved and saddened her.

"Why, yes," she replied, taking his hand. "I'd love to."

The open floor space was limited so Gillen led them in a basic waltz. Before she knew what was happening, the lounge began to twirl and the lights began to blur. Danielle straightened her posture as she felt Gillen's hand plant gently against her back, his other hand suspending hers in midair like a torch. As they swayed across the floor, her hand on his shoulder, she became aware of the fabric of his suit coat. The sensation reminded her of the woolen suits worn by her husband, of the way he moved within them when they used to go dancing, and of the sense of relief she had once felt believing that their love was unbreakable.

Danielle looked up into Gillen's gray eyes and mused to herself that in some strange way, she had been right.

The floor beneath his feet shifted without effort as Gillen gently guided Danielle in the simple, swaying motions of the simple, impromptu dance. The act of moving his body heightened his awareness of his surroundings, which only led back to the woman with the upturned eyes. Time had left them unaltered. They ensnared him with the same hypnotic force as when she was sixteen. The soft skin of her hand pressed up against his palm and made him conspicuously aware that he was leading her in every turn. It was the natural order of things reduced to a societal ritual.

The two continued to waltz until they realized that the song had already come to an end. A solitary patron clapped for them in the background as Gillen and Danielle gazed at each other. Apprehension kept them within each other's grasp. It was the dawning recognition of yet another moment.

"The music stopped," Danielle whispered tearfully.

Gillen nodded, trying desperately to maintain eye contact with her. "I suppose that's it then."

The statement lingered for as long as they did, begging for clarity. Danielle set her cheek against Gillen's chest and leaned into him with exhaling resignation. His hands found her shoulders as they continued to stand in the center of a room completely lost to recognition. Within Gillen's mind, the bar had been converted into the bayside park from his youth, its glistening water electrifying the scene while the swaying branches of the trees cast shape-shifting shadows of light against the grassy knoll. Beneath his arm was a girl. His first love. His first lover. The woman who had added texture to the gradients of his existence.

Danielle's mind also drifted from the lounge and resurrected the day of her wedding. The chapel had been filled with flowers, every aisle, every pew, bedecked with pink and white peonies. Satin drapery covered the chancel and pulpit. The attendance had been small, mostly Gillen's side of the family and a few of her close friends. His father had walked her down the aisle. A nineteen-year-old Gillen had stood there in his passable-black suit and had taken her hands in his. His eyes had appeared lost, uncertain as to where to gaze first, drinking in her flowing white dress, her tasseled hair, and the trademark smirk smiling back at him through her veil.

"I now pronounce you husband and wife," the officiant had said. "You may kiss the bride."

And then... life had continued, and continued, until the day they met Cate. The Iselins were such a wonderful couple together, yet Danielle had sensed an immediate sadness settle into her husband after each interaction with them. It was the sort of deflating one has after a celebration when the reasons for celebrating were no longer vivid. Not wanting to place a wedge between Walter and Cate, Gillen had redoubled his focus and affection on Danielle for a time. Their second honeymoon period had been a whirlwind, if not also somewhat artificial.

It was not until Allaire's death that everything changed. Guilt mixed with unprocessed emotions for Cate drove Gillen into an erratic depression, one propelled in finding a solution for a complex problem. Obsession replaced reason, and soon, Danielle could barely remember the man who had once wooed her, fought for her, married her, and had devoted his love to the single pursuit of their fidelity.

In a way, the day Allaire had died... she had also lost Gillen.

"I miss him so much," Danielle finally said, a single tear crossing the bridge of her nose, running the length of her other eyelid, and then disappearing into the fabric of Gillen's suit.

At the point when he could have offered tender words of reassurance, or refocused her attention on a more pleasant memory, Gillen simply chose to hold her, silently, and acknowledge the pain that his other self had inflicted upon her. Gone was the shimmering bay, the fluttering shadows, the park bench. The peonies vanished along with the pews. And all that remained was a tiny bar on Thirty-Fourth Street in the center of a city on another planet.

In methodical steps, Danielle gradually pulled herself away from Gillen. She stood before him on her own two feet, suddenly leaving him to feel an instance of instability. After dabbing her fingertip at the corners of her eyes, Danielle drew in a breath and gave him a salute-like nod. "Is it time?"

Gillen gazed at her for a minute longer, knowing that if there was ever a reason to memorize an image, this was it. Without glancing at his wristwatch, he responded, "Yes, it's time."

◄ ◆ ● ● ● ● ● ◆ ►

"Allaire?"

Even if the voice had not known her name, the tone in which he spoke was one of familiarity. The man in the plaid blazer steadily approached her, his eyes never wavering as he weaved through the crowd.

Allaire recognized the man. His height, build, and facial features were not as much the giveaway as the sterling blue of his piercing eyes. She had witnessed the man recently, in an unusual setting, the face whom she would swear had made eye contact with her seconds before stepping through the Alignment and locking the Hexagon behind him.

He was that engineer on the moon.

The dawning realization left her with little time other than to acknowledge his presence as Richard Kaine towered next to her.

"Hello," she said cautiously.

The man's face was ashen. His trembling lips fumbled his words. It was not so much the witnessing of a man seeing a ghost, but of witnessing a man trying desperately to deny his own senses. "You..." he muttered, "can't be real."

Allaire took a step back only to have the distance immediately closed by Kaine who took another step forward. She said, "I'm... I'm sorry?"

"You're... you... are... supposed to be dead."

Despite the gravity of the assumption, Allaire couldn't help but crack a smile at the man's obvious error. "Oh, no-no. You must have me mistaken for somebody else. My name is Allaire Rainer."

"Allaire... *Rainer?*" Kaine emphasized. "Certainly you mean Allaire Iselin?"

Iselin? wondered Allaire, as the seriousness in Kaine's expression melted the smile from her mouth. Despite the masses of bodies teeming about them, Allaire suddenly felt isolated. Leaving Jack's apartment now felt enormously foolhardy. "Umm... I just came to walk around for a bit. But I should be heading back now."

"There was a funeral for you," he continued. "I was there."

"Again... I..."

"Are you here alone?"

"No," she blurted. "I mean... at the fair... yes. But I'm not in New York alone."

"Where's your mother?" Kaine asked, his question seasoned with a hint of hostility.

Allaire's eyes widened. "My... mother?"

"Yeah, your mother's name is Cate, isn't it?" Then, through a clenched jaw, Kaine posed his real inquiry. "On second thought, where's Jack?"

The surging rush of adrenaline that pulsed through Allaire's veins drained her mind of clarity even as it tightened the muscles in her ankles. "Umm... who?"

"Jack... DaLette..." Kaine mouthed. "Do you know where he lives? Is he here with you? Or is it just Gillen Ra—" The rest of the surname left his lips without the element of sound. Kaine glanced down at the grass beneath their feet before slowly working his eyes back up to an increasingly uneasy Allaire. "Why did you say your name is Rainer?"

"Because it is."

Kaine's agitation was steadily turning into determination. "Your last name is Iselin. Your father was Walter Iselin. Your mother is Cate Iselin. And Gillen Rainer is supposedly the man who accidentally killed you."

As her vision began to swim, Allaire suddenly realized that she hadn't drawn a breath in nearly a minute. "My mother is Cate Rainer... and she died last year."

Kaine grimaced as one decoding an enigma. "My dear, I saw your mother an hour ago at Rockefeller Plaza, and let me assure you that she was very much alive. So either you're lying to me, or someone is playing a diabolical trick on us both."

Allaire felt her knees struggling to maintain her torso. The man with whom she was speaking had to be disturbed, his facts jumbled, his emotions unstable. Yet the authority of his demeanor and his unwavering interest in the topic left Allaire questioning her own judgment. In a shaky voice, she replied, "My mother is dead."

"I'm terribly sorry you think so," Kaine responded gravely. "Now, where is Jack?"

"I don't know. My... my father is... coming to get me."

"Your father is dead, Allaire."

She shook her head forcefully. "No... he'll... be here soon. You'll see."

"Walter Iselin is going to come out from under his tombstone just like you did?"

"My father is Gillen Rainer."

The sudden modicum of sympathy in Kaine's voice caught her off guard. "Allaire, you don't even look like Gillen Rainer."

◄ ◆ ● ● ● ● ◆ ►

There's nothing worse than loss.

The memory of Jack's blood-stained message was whispered into the masses as Gillen marshaled along the busy streets of New York. Hands in his pockets, hat curved toward his face, Gillen suppressed the image while wondering if this version of Jack DaLette would believe what his eyes were seeing — his friend and business partner, Gillen Rainer.

Fifth Avenue stretched for blocks. Gillen noted each block as a line of demarcation, indicative of how soon he would have to breach the curtain, enter from stage right, and play the role of himself.

The Empire State Building vanished behind him as the Chrysler Building periodically made appearances through the city skyline. Gillen gritted his teeth and ran through what his persona knew, did not know, and what his level of emotion should be upon interacting with Allaire. Too much emotion and he would be a dead giveaway as an imposter. Too little emotion and he would raise Jack's suspicions of a foible in their plan.

Once those office lights flicker, grab Allaire and run.

As Fortieth Street came into view, Gillen's eyes diverted from the right turn he would need to make at the intersection, and instead focused on a man walking briskly toward an art fair in the middle of Bryant Park. The man appeared frantic.

He looks like Jack. What's he doing here?

Quickening his pace, Gillen crossed the intersection diagonally and entered the park a few steps ahead of Jack who had disappeared into the bustle of people. Gillen spotted him again around a row of booths but kept his distance. Jack seemed to be searching for someone, his head bobbing up and down with the passing of each attendee. His movements were sharp and his face was the color of rage.

Gillen followed him deeper into the fairgrounds, all the while dodging the occasional oblong work of art protruding from the edges of a pegboard. A deftness was moving Jack's legs forward as a panic drove his eyes.

"Excuse me, sir!" shouted an exhibitor holding a whittled figurine. Jack paid him not so much as a glance while continuing his hunt. To him, in that moment, the whittler did not exist on the planet.

Another row of booths diverted Gillen's attention. By the time he navigated around them, no one in the crowd was Jack DaLette. Gillen's vision shifted wildly from person to person, knowing one of them would eventually manifest into his target. His eyeline scanned a panoramic of the park until it stopped at a person standing near the benches. The manifestation was not of Jack, but of someone who had the power to evaporate every other concern from Gillen's mind. In an instant, the park was completely vacant, save for the frightened teenage girl in a foreign universe.

"Allaire," he gasped.

His next thought was tethered to an action. Each step forward was faster than his last, for he knew that his opportunity would be gone in seconds. If he could capture Allaire's attention, even for a moment, he could convey the reality of her situation and the assurance of his rescue plan before Jack could intercept the scene. A few moments alone with Allaire was all he would need, and judging by how close Jack had been at the last sighting, a few moments was all Gillen had.

Allaire appeared to be gazing directly at him as he approached, yet her lack of enthusiasm proved otherwise. Gillen tried to subversively wave, hoping to gain her attention from afar and save precious seconds of reunion for the desperate information he needed to share.

A final cluster of people blocked his entry into the family area of the park. Weaving through them with all of the courtesy of a bulldozer, he broke through into the circular knoll and found himself stunned that Allaire was finally within reach. Suppressing the overwhelming impulse to sob, Gillen grabbed Allaire's arm with his trembling hand and knelt down before her in the grass. Her eyes locked onto his and for an instant that radiated with pent up emotion, Gillen felt his body rebel at his lack of ecstasy. He had searched for his daughter across two planets and the length of a continent, yet could not allow for even a second of acknowledgement of all they had mutually endured.

Like the revving of an engine only to keep it in idle, Gillen felt his frame let out a small convulsive jerk as he took her in his hands and drained every fiber of his being for clarifying focus. "Allaire, listen to me," he pleaded.

"Oh good, a family reunion," Richard Kaine said while gazing down at Gillen on his knees. "Perhaps now I can get some answers. How the hell is she alive? Where's Cate? What kind of sorcery have you and Jack been up to with the Octagons?"

The dissonance of his intention for the moment and the reality of seeing Richard Kaine standing next to him left Gillen utterly speechless. His mind reeled as to what the man was doing here, if he had anything to do with Jack, and how many seconds remained before his window of opportunity would be nailed shut. Gillen blinked before turning back to Allaire. She stared at him blankly, without even an essence of relief.

"Allaire..." he whispered again, surprised at how much his voice had sounded like Jack's.

Too late, he thought to himself, *you're too late*.

A shadow overcame Gillen and Allaire as Jack DaLette marched up to them, his jaw set, his eyes bulging, and his right hand reaching out to manhandle Allaire away from Gillen's grasp. Without so much as a salutation, Jack twisted her arm toward him and slapped Allaire across the face.

"I told you to stay in the apartment!" he exclaimed, not noticing Kaine standing just behind her.

Gillen rose to his feet and felt the instinct to bodyslam Jack to the ground. But reason dictated that if he took that course of action, Jack would never again return to a standing position. *You have to calm down. For the sake of Allaire, you have to calm down. You're not that Gillen right now.* That was when he caught sight of a fist connected to a plaid blazer coming down hard against Jack's head.

A wheezing sound emitted from Jack's body as he slammed against the mound after absorbing Kaine's punch. Dazed and outraged, Jack took a moment to collect his bearings before pushing himself up to a sitting position and spitting a globule of blood from his mouth.

"You son of a bitch!"

Kaine stepped toward him. "Try that again and the only way you'll be getting to the moon is in a wheelchair."

Allaire looked over at Gillen with tearful eyes that refused to cry. Her expression transcended the red slap mark on her cheek, instead projecting a quiet defiance of everything that was happening for which she did not yet have an answer. Gillen gazed back with detached caution and wondered if he could suppress the urge to vomit.

Jack slowly arose and shifted his jaw with his hand. "Nice to see you again, Richard."

Kaine aimed his forefinger at Jack's throat as if wielding a switchblade. "An hour ago, I spotted Cate Iselin at the Plaza, who last I knew, was living in San Francisco. Now look who I find! Walter's little girl! For whom we all had a funeral after this stupid bastard drove her into an embankment. That must have been some crash too, because now she thinks Gillen is her father and that Cate is the one who died. So, you'll have to forgive my morbid and undoubtedly inconvenient curiosity as to what in the world is happening here, but I think you can understand my motivation in light of recent events in my own life." Kaine narrowed his focus in on Jack. "My little boy, Morley, has been missing for six days. The police are out of leads. I've been out non-stop searching for anyplace he might turn up. You wouldn't know anything as to his whereabouts... right?"

Dear God... Gillen thought, *Richard's son.*

"That's a tragedy," Jack said to Kaine. "I wish you every good fortune in finding him soon. Now if you don't mind, we're all going to be late for an import—"

"Is she not Walter's daughter?" Kaine demanded, pointing with agitated fervor at Allaire. "The one who supposedly died last year on the Bay Bridge? How is she here? And why does she think Cate is dead?"

Below the towering men, a question begging to be asked was being projected from a pair of mocha eyes. A shared glance between Jack and Gillen was imperceptible before Jack took a single sidestep away from Kaine and raised his arm deferentially. "You're obviously grief-stricken about Morley. That's understandable. But Gillen here can explain everything if you'd just give him a chance."

Gillen arched an eyebrow at Jack as Kaine turned toward him. "I... have no idea what happened to your son. But I'm sure... we can all work together to—"

The blunt metal object in Jack's hand and Allaire's scream occurred simultaneously, and before causality could be firmly established in Gillen's mind, he saw Richard Kaine stumble convulsively forward as Jack's arm completed a swing. With the kind of thud coming only from those rendered unconscious, Kaine's body landed face-first on the ground as a large welt formed along the base of his skull. Gillen stared at him for a moment, wondering if he was dead, and then contemplating if the other Gillen Rainer would actually be concerned. *Of course he would. He is still me, after all. Isn't he?*

Allaire breathed through her hand as she watched Gillen reach down to check Kaine's pulse. Gillen then looked back up at Jack and nodded. "He's alive." Jack didn't respond, and his chilling gaze suddenly drained Gillen of any confidence that he had made the correct assumption. Gillen then added, "To borrow the colloquialism... he never knew what hit him."

Jack cocked his head and took a scan of their surroundings. "Excuse me!" he called out to no one in particular. "This man has collapsed. He needs help." His vocal concern was inconsistent with his actions as he slipped the object back into his suit coat pocket and stepped away from Richard Kaine. Gillen began to do the same before realizing that Allaire remained motionless next to the man on the ground.

"*Allaire,*" Jack hissed. "Come along."

She refused to move, whether too stunned at the violence she had just witnessed or else too frightened of the people who had caused it, Gillen was uncertain. But he knew her instincts were correct, and his pride in her intuition was swallowed by his self-loathing in having to make her doubt it. "Allaire," Gillen ordered, grabbing her wrist. "We need to go right now."

Jack watched as Gillen forced Allaire forward, even as the crowd surrounding Richard Kaine began to grow. The tension of the seconds that followed waned with their increased distance from the center of the park and into the labyrinth layout of the exhibition booths.

He'll be fine, he'll be all right, Gillen assured himself. *That won't happen again. I won't let this go too far again.* As the thought faded from his attention, he looked down and noticed his stranglehold on Allaire's wrist. He immediately let go and gently pushed her ahead. "You stay with Jack," he gasped. "I'll meet you both at the intersection."

"Where are you going?" Jack barked.

But Gillen had already darted from the main thoroughfare and was cutting through a line of attendees standing along a side row of bas-relief bronze plaques. A turn brought him within sight of a drinking fountain next to a large trash bin. The fountain was being used by a man taking a quick sip, but that was irrelevant to Gillen, for his primary aim was still clear.

With his hands outstretched to make contact with the edges of the open receptacle, Gillen leaned forward into the trash bin and became physically ill.

CHAPTER 18

THE LIGHT FROM AFAR

High above the proscenium entryway of the Chrysler Building was an American flag. The pole on which it was draped leaned forward over Lexington Avenue, drawing any interested eye beyond the flapping and up to the breathtaking height of the tallest brick building in the world. On the street below, Gillen saw the colors of the flag billow in accordance with the same breeze that rushed along the contours of his face. The wind was warm and also fleeting, and just as the flag was gaining some momentum, the flapping altogether ceased.

"Do you need to eat something?" Jack asked Gillen as they marshaled toward the entrance with Allaire tagging along side.

"No, I'll be fine."

"An empty stomach and booze are not good bedfellows. I've told you that before."

Gillen nodded. "I'm sure you have."

The revolving door stood beneath an archway of plate glass. The decorative pane was in the shape of a capitalized *W* and etched into it were the numbers four-zero-five, notating the street address. Gillen tore his attention away from the grandeur of the building and instead stole a glance at Allaire in hopes of offering her even a hint of reassurance. However, her focus was elsewhere, absorbing the environment around her as if it had cosmic significance. When Gillen turned toward Jack, the man had the exact same expression on his face when looking at Allaire.

"Good evening, gentlemen," said the lobby attendant as the trio entered the building.

Jack acknowledged the man as they continued walking. Gillen kept in lockstep with his business partner while suppressing his wandering eye. It was hard to know where to gaze first, for everything within sight was competing for attention. The interwoven pattern on the waxed floor and the Moroccan marble of the walls made the interior seem alive, like the chromatophores of a creature intent on intimidation rather than concealment. Atop the creature was a marouflage ceiling mural drenched in rich colors and vivid depictions of industrialization.

"What's wrong?" asked Jack, suddenly concerned.

Forget the aesthetics. You've been here before. Gillen redirected his focus toward a flip clock above the elevator doors that had just changed to 6:50 pm. "Nothing, I was just wondering if we're late."

"What floor?" the operator more so announced than asked.

Jack removed his hat as they entered the car and placed it against his chest. "Sixty-eight. Silver Lining Club."

"I'm sorry, sir," the operator said. "But the Silver Lining Club is closed in the evenings."

Jack's smug reaction was as paternal as it was patronizing. "Not tonight."

The padded leather doors of the lounge waited at the end of an anteroom off the main corridor. Standing next to the entrance was the maître d' of the club. The aged man postured himself as if still in the army, his uniform a navy-blue suit which served as the only introduction the man required.

"Welcome back, Mr. DaLette, Mr. Rainer. Is this the guest of honor?"

Gillen instinctively extended his arm for Allaire to introduce herself before wondering just how fatherly the action might have seemed. She nodded gingerly at the manager. "Nice to meet you."

"She'll need to wait in the back room with the staff until I come to get her," Jack said, seemingly to both the manager and to set the expectation with Allaire. "Under no circumstances is she to enter the club room until then. I cannot stress this enough."

"Have no concerns, Mr. DaLette. We'll watch over her until you arrive."

Jack nodded while retrieving a cigarette from his pocket-sized metallic holder and placing it between his lips. Before he could reach for his lighter, the maître d' had a tiny flame at the tip of the cigarette and waited for the first puff of smoke before flipping the chrome top of the lighter shut.

"Thanks," Jack said. "Now, the three gentlemen we discussed should be here soon, but don't be surprised if they're late. Escort them inside the club and seat them opposite myself and Mr. Rainer at the far table. That will allow for the best lighting for our presentation." Jack continued speaking as a plume of smoke exited his nostrils. "Get their drink orders after they've been seated but before chitchat. I don't want any distractions once we dive into things. Oh, and just in case one of them has the gall to ask, we're not serving coffee or beer this evening. Hard liquor only. I'm here to collect a check not a damn referral."

The old man was unfazed. "Not a problem, sir."

Jack sighed heavily. "I guess that's everything. Allaire, go with this nice man and wait for me to come get you in a bit."

Allaire appeared as if she was holding out for something. Gillen knew what it was and why she wasn't requesting it. None of the events leading up to this moment had given her a reason for why she was here, why she hadn't been allowed to dress up for this party, or why she was suddenly being closeted away like an ironing board. No explanation had been offered as to who the man in the park was, why he had thought she was dead, and who the woman was whom he had mistaken for her mother. Yet the worst offense to her psyche remained the coldblooded way in which Jack DaLette had silenced the man's questions. The totality of his disregard, and the remorselessness of his actions afterward, left Allaire with a sickening sense of unease. This man was not to be trusted.

Was her father?

"Allaire," Jack reiterated, waving his hand toward her and causing her to wince. "Scram."

Her gaze locked onto Gillen's for only an instant before the arm of the manager guided her through the side door and out of the anteroom. Once again, she was gone, and Gillen felt his fingers tremble from a simmering rage.

"Shall we head in?"

Gillen followed Jack without reply as the double doors opened into the resplendent opulence of the Silver Lining Club room. A palette of mahogany-themed colors warmed everything from the velvet carpeting below to the wood grained window accents and the backdrop drapery that hugged them. The vaulted ceiling rested atop a series of rectangular marble columns that twinkled in the overhead lighting, fixtures devoted to the iconic Art Deco style of the building. Intimate tables were strategically placed throughout the floor, each covered in the finest white linen table cloths. As Gillen made his way deeper into the venue, his fingers gently slid across the fine wood finish of the hand-crafted chairs while he mused to himself about the powerful derrières who had graced these seats. *This is the room where it all ends.*

"You know how lucky you are to be here?" Jack said as he weaved around the various tables.

At first Gillen thought Jack was speaking to him, and the insinuation of his comment sent Gillen's heart racing. But as he followed Jack's line of sight, he noticed a person seated at the far table, the one next to the corner window.

"After all," Jack added, "it's not every day the Silver Lining Club allows a woman in this room."

Underneath the layered panels of lighting that cast a halo over everything in its reach, was a woman in a white dress suit. Her golden hair was thoughtfully set up in place behind her head by two rhinestone hair pins, the crystals in each shimmering within the halo. On her suit's lapel was a daffodil brooch, the stem of which seemed to vanish into the fabric. Coming out from the ends of her sleeves were the thin, naked wrists that never seemed to be able to maintain a bracelet, and on her left hand resting flat against the linen tablecloth, a marquise diamond in the center of a wedding ring.

Gillen gazed at the woman without reservation as she arose from her chair. With the light partially blocked, her face became less shrouded and the characteristics of her eyes, cheeks, and lips came into focus. It was her face, without a doubt, yet her cheeks were less gaunt, her lips more full, and her eyes generated a sparkle unmatched by the lights. She was identical in every way, except for one.

Despite a series of tragic events, this woman had discovered contentment.

"I'm gonna go grab the easel and posters from the back room," Jack said as he crushed his cigarette into an ashtray. "You two play nice."

No further time seemed to elapse before they were alone in the grand room. The privacy of the moment had little affect on Gillen's reaction, for he could not have quelled his emotions even if Jack had been standing in front of him. With tempestuous quivers, his chest rose and fell in ebbing waves, all while his eyes welled with tears, which he resisted, for they obstructed his view of the angel.

"I wasn't sure if you'd be here," the woman said softly, taking on the reservation that Gillen had abandoned. As she took a step forward, his countenance became clearer. Her eyes widened to see his condition. He was a man made witness to a death only to find a piece of himself as the thing resurrected. "Are you all right, Gillen?"

Hearing his name spoken by her was too much to bear. His eyes sank downward, overwhelmed by a flood. The red carpeting took on the form of ocean tides as the first tears rolled down his face. His tongue was rendered mute. His jaw was too heavy to open. So all encompassing was the sight of the woman that the imminent return of Jack DaLette made about as much difference to Gillen as one planet or another.

Fighting against the weight of gravity, he eventually found strength in his neck and lifted his head ever so slightly until she was once again within his eyeline. Not bothering to wipe the moisture from his cheeks, he stood as a marionette, barely clinging to frayed strings which could snap with any force.

With mounting pressure building up at the back of his throat, Gillen inhaled what little oxygen his lungs could endure and produced a sound intended to be a name, but that instead felt like a wail. "Cate."

The sound evoked a fear that her face could not conceal. It was the fear of a dawning realization. In contrast to her emotions, Cate progressed further toward Gillen until the only space between them was the width of a chair. Her lips parted in the way one would when about to form a question, yet she remained silent.

Gillen felt his muscles brace as her left hand gently reached toward him. The sensation of her soft skin making contact with his cheek sent an impulse throughout his body that momentarily convinced him this woman was otherworldly. At first, her intention was unclear, aside from physical contact. Yet his curiosity was assuaged when he felt the same kind of fingers that long ago had run through his hair, held his hand, massaged his shoulders, cared for their home, assisted with tinkering gizmos, shaken the hands of investors, penned thoughts on paper, pulled him into their bedroom, squeezed his hand in pleasure, squeezed his hand in pain, caressed the face of her newborn baby, placed the girl in his trembling arms, clenched the steering wheel, aligned it with destiny, pulled herself over the guardrail, and plunged into the bay. These were the kind of fingers now gently wiping the stream of tears from Gillen's face.

"I'm sorry," he whispered, "that there wasn't... more I could have done..."

He stopped, for he was addressing the wrong Cate.

"Someone wanna help me with these?" said Jack from the door.

The sudden removal of Cate's hand made Gillen gasp. As she swiftly moved around the maze of tables, he took advantage of the moment she had granted him to find his composure. *Oh my God...* he said to himself while walking over to the corner window. He dabbed his eyes repeatedly against his cuffs and tried to listen for any prompts from Cate over the pounding in his ears.

Pull yourself together. This isn't real. She is not the same woman. That person is not Cate. The effort to hold himself upright now seemed daunting. He pressed his palms against the mahogany window frame and felt his arms shiver. *Does Cate stand a chance? Once she sees Allaire... this thing, this experience is much too powerful.*

Gillen lifted his head. He saw through his own reflection in the pane of glass and zeroed in on the beacon which would be his signal to escape. Dusk had fallen over New York, and off in the distance, the Empire State Building was lit up like the console of the Hexagon, each office light an indicator on the panel board — but only one mattered. On the fiftieth floor of the spectacular tower was a window with a red hue.

"Attagirl," he whispered.

"You're not feeling woozy again, are you?" asked Jack from the easel.

Gillen remained facing the window and shook his head. "I'm fine. Just rehearsing my part of the pitch." He blinked and then squinted upon realizing just how far away three quarters of a mile was. The fiftieth floor of the Empire State Building would have been nearly impossible to identify without the visual aid of the red lighting. Even so, he knew his seating position would need to be ideal in order for him to have any hope of spotting the blinking signal upon Danielle's completion of the subversive task.

As Gillen turned to examine the seating arrangement, the club manager entered the double doors and announced that the gentlemen were on their way up the elevator. Jack snapped at Gillen to straighten his tie.

"Yeah," he replied, while eyeing the introduction on the first black poster board nested on the easel. The image was a logo with bold lettering encircled by what appeared to be a partially obscured hexagon. It read: *The Allaire Project.*

Gillen's vision slowly shifted over to the back of Jack's head. All too easily, he imagined himself bashing in the man's skull.

"Gentlemen," came the voice of the maître d'. "May I present Mr. Keath, Mr. Ledeen, and Mr. Van Kipp from the investment firms. Please, allow me," he added, taking their overcoats and hats.

Jack extended his hand to each investor like it was complimentary. "A pleasure, gentlemen," he said with vigor. "Thanks so much for joining us this evening. I'm Jack DaLette. This is my business partner, Gillen Rainer. And the lovely young lady in the corner is Cate Iselin."

The investors all nodded graciously yet without the level of enthusiasm projected by their host. "It's always nice to visit the Silver Lining Club," said Keath. "Especially after hours."

"Indeed," said Jack. "They only do this for important business people. But in my case they made an exception." The self-deprecating joke landed and evoked a mild chuckle from the men. "Please, make yourselves comfy."

As the investors sat down next to each other on the opposite side of the table and with their backs toward the windows, Gillen sidestepped Jack to ensure his seating next to Cate — and in direct view of the Empire State Building.

"So what are you boys drinking?" asked Jack as the server approached.

Keath smiled apologetically. "None for me, thank you."

"I'm fine for now," Ledeen added.

"Same for me," chimed Van Kipp.

Gillen caught Jack eyeing the server while digging his fingernails into his chair. "Very well. Come back in a bit, won't you?"

With the server having retreated into the kitchen, the room settled into the ambiguity of the moment. The three investors were all about the same height, had graying hair, and were dressed in the kind of couture suits that eliminated the need for references. Keath was portly and unsuccessfully hid his bulging chin underneath a trimmed patch of beard. Ledeen was slender and wore spectacles from a bygone era atop a face that appeared prepubescent. Van Kipp filled out his suit in a way that suggested he spent the hours away from his desk at a gym, the irony being that he was obviously a decade older than his contemporaries.

"Anyone?" Jack asked, holding out a small cedar box. "From Havana."

"No, thank you," said Van Kipp. "I gave up smoking years ago."

"Perhaps later," said Ledeen.

Jack's control over his faux smile was waning right before Keath nodded and withdrew a cellophane-wrapped cigar for himself. After removing the wrapping he slid the cigar under his nose and puckered his lips. "Quite nice."

"Mrs. Iselin was kind enough to bring them," said Jack as he lit Keath's cigar and then another for himself. "From her personal humidor, I should add."

The tip of Keath's cigar crackled as he rotated it between his thumb and forefinger. The engrafted blend of flavors permeated the table as he exhaled the smoke through several small puffs. "So you're Mrs. Iselin?" Keath inquired, turning his torso slightly sideways.

Cate shot a glance at Jack before addressing the man. "Yes, that's right."

"Walter Iselin's widow?"

"Yes."

Keath nodded remorsefully. "I'm terribly sorry for your loss."

Cate replied in kind. "Thank you."

"A tragedy," piped in Ledeen. "Walter was an astounding man. A true visionary. Plus a hell of a poker player."

"Yes, I believe I too lost some money to Dr. Iselin once," said Van Kipp. "It was many years ago, so who remembers? But after that meeting, I was convinced he would be the next great mind of our generation."

Cate again nodded graciously. "Your kind words mean so much."

"He was our mentor," Jack said solemnly. "He taught Gillen and I everything we know."

Gillen listened to Jack's tone vacillate between sorrowful and nostalgic and, unable to stomach the piece of theater, had to look away. Glancing over at the beacon in the sky, his squinting eyes confirmed that the office was still crimson.

"What was it like working with Walter?" came the question posed from Ledeen.

Gillen's vision darted back to the table. "It was life-changing. He... was like a father to me."

Van Kipp leaned forward and reached for a water pitcher sitting on a platinum serving tray. As he poured himself a glass, he said, "Wasn't Dr. Iselin also an actual father? I seem to recall hearing about a child. One who died."

Jack forced the rest of his inhaled smoke out prematurely before resting the edge of his cigar down on the ashtray. "Good memory. Yes, the Iselins lost a daughter about two years ago. Her name was Allaire."

Van Kipp's eyes shifted momentarily over toward Cate as he realized that it was a shared loss between the couple. "Of course. My apologies for bringing it up." Cate again nodded, but this time with less grace. Van Kipp said, "I mention it only as a corollary to the fact that Mr. Rainer is also sitting in this room right next to Mrs. Iselin. Seems remarkable to me."

For an instant, Gillen's mind whirled as to which part he was to play. *I'm the guilt-ridden idealist.* "I'm not afraid to broach the topic," he said humbly yet seasoned with a nonchalant attitude. "It's true. I was behind the wheel of the car in which my daughter died."

Ledeen blinked through his glasses. "I'm sorry... *your* daughter?"

A peripheral view of Jack proved that he had missed the slip-up entirely. Gillen swallowed the stale air in the back of his throat and smiled. "Forgive me, of course I meant... *Walter's* daughter. And yes. After the accident, Cate had every right to shut me out, to process what had happened, to grieve." His focus drifted away from the investors and sank down to the table. He thought about the Cate he had known, the fragile, detached, and at times overly ambitious woman who had never seemed to be in alignment with her own body. He then thought about the Cate sitting next to him, her resiliency, her poise, and about how she could have ever come to survive the loss of her family and still find a form of reconciliation with Gillen after the crash. "But in the end," he said, "Cate and I found common ground after Walter's passing. We found solace."

"You're an incredible woman, Mrs. Iselin," Keath mumbled through puffs. "What fortitude."

"Agreed," added Van Kipp. "Forgive me for raising the topic, but in doing my homework on you all, I needed to be sure that there was no bad blood betwixt the parties. You understand."

Gillen nodded in agreement but was caught off guard by the piercing stare gazing back at him, and only him, from Cate's green eyes. He heard Jack continue chatting about how difficult the situation had been on everyone involved. He spoke using only words from his pre-approved monologue yet in a way that sounded extemporaneous to the investors. But Cate had tuned him out entirely. The extent of her focus was locked in on the man seated next to her, and in that moment Gillen was certain that between his verbal misstep and his initial reaction when they first met, the gears in her mind were slowly beginning to work things out.

"Let's get down to business then, shall we?" said Ledeen, withdrawing from his suit pocket a small leather notepad and pen. "My understanding is that you and Mr. Rainer have been continuing the work started by Dr. Iselin. Is that correct?"

"You know it is," Jack said with a smirk. "Otherwise you'd have never accepted this meeting."

Ledeen flipped open the notepad and laid it on the table. "Too true. I can't speak for the other investors at this table, but I can say that I've rarely shied away from a speculative investment that involved a new type of technology. They seem to have a way of paying off for me. I suppose it's because I generally realize what the applications of the new technology could be even before the inventor does."

Arising from the table, Jack's face betrayed his inner glee. "I'm confident that this will meet your expectations."

Van Kipp also retrieved a pen and pocketbook from his suit. Keath leaned back in his chair and continued to smoke his cigar, relishing the benefits of having an eidetic memory.

"Gentlemen," Jack began, standing next to the easel, his shoulders back, his posture erect, aware that this was his imperative moment. "We've spoken of heartache and senseless pain here this evening. Of loss and regret. The emotions which go back to the dawn of man. We live in a world of brutal reality. And although the advancements of science, ethics, and industry have contributed to relieving man of the harshest of the daily horrors that once accompanied his waking moments, the preeminence of suffering persists."

Gillen quickly turned his head to peer out the window. The Empire State Building now seemed more aglow in the minutes that had passed. Yet the red light on the fiftieth floor remained.

"Dr. Iselin knew this," continued Jack, gesticulating with his hands, "for he experienced a level of suffering in this modern era which few of us will ever grasp. He reached a depth of despair brought on not by a natural disaster, or the consequences of time, but by the depraved actions of his fellow human beings. Walter Iselin's first family, his dear wife and young son, were both heinously murdered many decades ago."

The reaction from the investors was a mixture of surprise and disgust. They had known the man, but they had not really known the man. "The aftermath of this event was not only an assault on Walter himself, but on the basis of his values. Once faced with the reality that the innocent suffer along with the guilty—and suffer mercilessly, senselessly—Walter began to doubt the benevolence of providence."

Gillen suspected that the default position of the investors was to remain somewhat monolithic during a presentation, yet Ledeen and Van Kipp were struggling to suppress their shock, and Keath had all but forgotten about the cigar between his fingertips.

"That event changed Dr. Iselin's perception of the world. It forced him to acknowledge that only man is capable of making a difference through his intentional choices and actions."

Gillen looked down at the wood grain of the table and tried to center his kaleidoscopic thoughts. *There's nothing worse than loss.*

"All of this," continued Jack, "was the precursor to Dr. Iselin's realization that there could be a better way, a faster way, for man to jumpstart his evolution. So he built a team, and that team built a miracle."

With less flamboyance than Gillen was expecting, Jack turned to the easel and jabbed his finger at the logo on the poster board. "We are continuing the work started by Walter Iselin so many years ago, and we're calling it: The Allaire Project."

Keath again turned awkwardly toward Cate and flashed a modest grin. "What an appropriate homage."

Cate nodded appreciatively. Jack lifted the first panel off the easel and let it drop to the floor. Gillen stole a glance out the window. The light from afar still brightly burned.

As Jack proceeded in retelling the history of Iselin Amalgamate, the creation of the original Octagons, the death of Barry Sjöstrom on the first trip to the lunar surface, and Walter's subsequent abandonment of the project and ultimate personal demise, Gillen could tell that Jack was about to hand the next portion of the presentation over to him. The minute hand on his wristwatch confirmed his suspicion. Jack was running right on time and Danielle was falling behind.

"And now to explain our next steps, my friend and colleague, Gillen Rainer."

Gillen pushed himself up from his chair and stood on uncertain legs. It was then when he noticed that the easel's placement misaligned his line of sight from the Empire State Building. The sixty second window of opportunity could easily be missed. Biting down on his lower lip, Gillen gazed out at the investors who could no longer contain their intrigue. Jack sat down before him, smiling, sensing that all was going swimmingly. Cate was staring from the edge of the table in Gillen's general direction. It was the kind of stare not so much used in discussion as in interrogation.

"If you don't mind," Gillen began, fiddling with the hinges of the easel. "I'll need to move the presentation just a touch this direction."

"What are you doing?" Jack blurted, his nerves overcoming his charm.

"Just a little bit this way..." Gillen said, as he shifted the easel several inches to the right. The new position offered Gillen an almost perfect visual of the fiftieth floor, providing that he was willing to bend his knees ever so slightly.

Jack grimaced. "There's a bit of a shadow now across the—"

"So... the future of the company!" Gillen proclaimed. "Yes, Jack is absolutely correct. The only way to continue our trajectory toward a settlement on the moon is via a *stable* Alignment. That is what will allow for building materials, earthmoving equipment, power, and a host of other essentials necessary for a self-sustaining habitat." Gillen pulled at the next panel and let it fall to the floor.

"The Minreth-Hughes equation is the key to unlocking the reality of the Alignment here on earth." A hesitation interrupted his flow of speech as Gillen took a moment to examine the mathematical formula printed on the panel. The instance was fleeting yet powerful in its context, for the first person Gillen had ever shown the discovery to had not been Walter, but to a fascinated and bedridden Cate. "This... this is what we need to make work. Without this... there's... well... there can never be an Alignment."

His trail of words faded as he gazed helplessly at the panel. He tried to remember where his script was supposed to lead him next. Yet the totality of his thoughts were preoccupied with the awareness that Cate was sitting a few feet away from him; a woman for whom he had so many questions and who could provide not a single answer.

"Umm..." he whispered, suddenly appearing fatigued.

Jack looked back at the investors and nodded. "This is obviously a very emotional thing for him, for all of us. The Alignment represents more than just the ability for a man to walk on the moon. It goes beyond beating the Soviets, or expanding our real estate in this solar system. This is really about people. About connecting and reconnecting with them. About the chance for equilibrium. Isn't that right, Gillen?"

But Gillen had been staring out the window. A slight bend at his knees confirmed his dread. Danielle had run into problems.

"Apologies for interrupting," said Keath, "but I believe we're all wondering about this equation. How do you know this is the key to a stable Alignment?"

Jack looked up at Gillen. Gillen looked over at Keath. "Because we've seen it work."

Keath was baffled. "Then why in the hell aren't you using it?"

Gillen parted his lips. *Come on, Danielle, you can do this.* "Because we've seen it work... on a parallel earth at a parallel laboratory... operated by an alternate version of myself and Mr. DaLette."

With the decompressing power of a pinprick through the hull of a spacecraft, the atmosphere in the grand room was suddenly replaced by the suffocating pall of deafening silence. Gillen's intuition told him to ignore the looks of amused perplexity on the faces of Keath, Ledeen, and Van Kipp, for they were not at all amused.

Jack sat completely still, the sides of his mouth curled into a grin. Gillen could tell that each second of delayed explanation was ambrosia to Jack's palette. In any universe, the man was a provocateur.

"I hope that was the run-up to a punchline, Mr. Rainer," said Ledeen, "and not the punchline itself."

Gillen stole a glance at Cate, who now appeared more disjointed from the room than before. *I'm so very sorry about this.* "No, Mr. Ledeen, none of this is a joking matter. What will come as a surprise to you, as well as to Mr. Keath, Mr. Van Kipp, and undoubtedly as well—to Mrs. Iselin, is that while we were examining just what exactly the Octagons had allowed us to do, we realized that is was much more than just teleportation. The Octagons are also a gateway onto a duplicate planet earth. One with features, characteristics, history, culture, and people, all basically identical to you and me. Naturally, we inquired about ourselves. In doing so, we discovered that despite the similarities, minor variations existed in life choices, chronology, and even outcomes. One such distinction was this." Gillen lifted the next panel from off the easel. "Their team has a working, stable Alignment, using much of the same technology we have for our Octagons on this planet, and most interestingly, using the Minreth-Hughes equation."

Any jotting of notes or crackling of pages had ceased. The three gentlemen stared straight ahead without comment, as void of a tell as their former poker partner, Walter Iselin.

"Our team should have predicted that this was a possibility. Einstein talked about it. So did Schrödinger. Dabbling in the realm of quantum superposition made it only a matter of time. That's why your support will allow us to investigate why the Minreth-Hughes equation applies on their planet but not ours. It will shore up our capital and enable the construction of new laboratories in San Francisco as well as here in New York. And it will grant us more resources to further develop the teleportation technology we already have, providing an almost instantaneous return on your investment."

When Gillen dropped the next panel, a wave of nausea tugged at his abdomen. "Now," he said, pressing on with the presentation while at the same time sounding as if his words had been leashed.

"There... is... another possibility... we must... examine here. It would be a dereliction of discovery were we to not."

The image on the panel was of two clusters of people, mirror images of each other, straddling a line running the height of the board. A closer examination proved that the images were actually cutouts, from magazines no doubt, with a strip of adhesive on the back of each cutout. Gillen slowly lifted one of the cutouts from off the board, a teenage girl, and held it thoughtfully in his hand.

This is what Oppenheimer felt.

"The Manhattan Project," Gillen said, "changed the course of history forever. One night we all went to sleep in a world we knew, the next morning we awoke in a world drastically altered. What altered it was the knowledge of a new kind of weapon. One that could protect or threaten our way of life, depending on who possessed it. Well, we all now face the same reality."

Gillen placed the cutout back on the board. "The fact that an alternate earth exists, with alternate versions of ourselves, and possibly alternate outcomes for volitional actions taken, grants us both opportunity and peril. On the one hand, we could ignore the reality that they too have access to an Alignment and ways of reaching our planet, and simply write it off as the threat posed by asteroids in outer space—serious but not likely."

With the brush of his hand up against the side of his head, Gillen scratched an itch and then winced.

"But that would be as foolish as having not pursued atomic power in the name of morality. We knew the Soviets would eventually have it. The Manhattan Project offered us the peace in knowing that we could use that tremendous power... if we must. That, gentlemen, is what is on the second hand."

Returning his attention to the board, he said, "The alternative to complacency is preemptive action. A stable Alignment will give us just that. We know, because using our round-about approach to this concept, we've been able to prove it."

"Prove what?" Van Kipp asked, finally breaking the silence from the other side of the table.

Gillen hesitated before moving the teenage girl cutout from one side of the line to the other. "Man's newfound ability to correct the mistakes of fate."

Van Kipp leaned back in his chair, his renewed silence seeming to buy another few minutes for Gillen. Jack continued to bask in the delectable tension of the moment. Cate was horrified.

"If God can decide when an individual's time on this planet is through, why can't humanity decide to reverse that decision? Through the utilization of a fully functioning, fully stable Alignment, we will be the gatekeepers to this new frontier. A political leader assassinated? A replacement is most likely available in the other world. A woman dies in childbirth? Probably not in both realities. The subtle differences between the two earths will work in our favor thanks to free will — that pesky absolute we all know to be true yet love to deny. When a father of five chooses to leave for work one minute later than his alternate and narrowly misses the oncoming car, you now have something to work with. You now have an opportunity. You have, without putting it too mildly, an economy, for the transfer of parallel human beings. And the best part, we won't even have to fight a war. With the establishment of an embassy on each planet, both institutions will run available applicants through a tally of available alternates— creating incentives for individuals, societies, and governments in how to properly compensate the other planet for a single transfer. Via this system of orderly administration, with an ambassador from the alternate planet located at the other's embassy, and with limited access to the Alignments, it practically eliminates the threat of blackmarkets and corruption. They benefit. We benefit. And no one has to continue, I mean, *begin* trafficking humans from one earth to the other."

Gillen then again removed the teenage girl cutout from the board and placed it gently on the table. "We know this will work, because we've already tried it. With a teenage girl. One whose life ended too soon. And whose significance to the people in this room is almost immeasurable." At that moment, his eyes graced the reflection of Cate's image on the wooden table. As he followed the lines of grain over to the edge, the table gave way to the white dress suit leaning against it, and the woman within that suit — without verbalization, was pleading in every way for the cessation of what was coming next.

"Jack?" Gillen whispered, taking a step back.

"Well put," Jack said slowly, taking a second longer to stare at Gillen than seemed necessary. When he turned to address the investors, he was no longer grinning. "Like it or not, this is the future. And the physical evidence I'm about to show you will solidify that fact. The question is: Will you believe your own eyes?"

"I can answer that without the theatrics," said Van Kipp, pushing his chair back from the table. "I came here tonight to invest in teleportation technology. I almost walked out when you started babbling on about psionic nonsense. It seems I should have listened to my initial instincts."

"This...is... monstrous," added Ledeen. "Depraved beyond description. I had hoped you all were building upon the legacy Dr. Iselin devoted his latter years to. Teleportation could change the world. But this? Tampering with the natural order of time, of consequence, of destiny? If there is one man who deserves to be offered over to the sacrificial altars of the other world, it is you, Mr. DaLette."

Keath simply sat in his chair, smoking and through puffs muttering, "Unconscionable, absolutely unconscionable."

Gillen exchanged glances with Jack who had calculated the big reveal down to the exact reaction for which he had been waiting. Apparently that instant had arrived.

"In that case, I'm sorry to have wasted your time, gentlemen," Jack said slyly. "Please, allow me to go grab your coats." As he marshaled out of the club room, the investors remained indignant. Gillen however knew that the curtain had yet to close on this night of pageantry. For when Jack returned to the room with the young teenage girl under his arm, and Cate reacted to seeing her daughter resurrected from the dead, the power of that moment would be too overwhelming to write off.

With enough force to nearly topple him over, Gillen felt his arm wrangled sideways by the grasp of Cate's ring hand. "You have to tell me," she whispered, her eyes gripping him harder than her hand. "Jack... he isn't... tell me isn't coming back... with... Allaire."

Gillen strained his neck to glance back toward the galley door, then ducked a bit to peer the distance out the corner window. Across the city, on the fiftieth floor of the Empire State Building, the red light was finally gone. In its place, the amber glow of an office light madly blinked its coded message of victory.

"*Gillen,*" Cate stressed, pulling on his elbow as if to hoist herself up from quicksand. "Please tell me Allaire isn't about to emerge from that door!"

The edge of his lips brushed against the side of her cheek as they made their way to her ear. As he spoke, the scent of her perfume and the sensation of her hair nearly railroaded his thoughts. "It is Allaire..." he whispered back, "but I have a rescue plan. I just need you to—"

"Mr. Rainer?" came a voice.

Gillen and Cate turned to see the maître d' standing at the threshold. "Mr. DaLette has asked for some assistance. Do you mind?"

Nodding slowly, Gillen turned back to Cate and offered a gentle squeeze of her hand. "It's going to be all right. I have a plan that will fix all of this. Just remember, that girl is *not* your daughter."

The club seemed to have lost much of its luster as Gillen scurried around the tables and chairs en route to the galley door. The maître d' had gone back into the room but had left the door open for Gillen to enter. Once inside, he could see the coat rack, a series of stacked chairs, another door leading to the cloakroom, and a half-wall partition which seemed to serve no useful purpose. Behind him, the door suddenly closed.

"Allaire?"

The sucker punch landed centrally in his torso and sent Gillen doubled over onto the carpeted floor. Viewing the room from an oblique angle, he blinked repeatedly as the intense pain radiated up his ribcage. A pair of blue slacks stood before him, and even in his confused state, Gillen knew to push himself away from the wearer.

"Mr. DaLette wanted me to relay this message," the maître d' said graciously. "'Nice try, Gillen.'"

CHAPTER 19

CONTINENTAL DRIFT

The door to the stairwell swung open into the cinderblock wall as Gillen began his frantic descent. Coughing spastically, he leaned heavily on the railing as he scrambled down the flight, his shoes struggling to maintain purchase on the cement steps.

"What's going on?!" Cate exclaimed, following from behind in her white heels.

The stairwell was dimly lit from above, making it seem as if their elongated shadows were several paces ahead of their bodies. Around the next corner was a steel door marked sixty-seven. Gillen ignored it and continued descending.

"He set me up!"

"Who did?"

Gillen strained to formulate an answer while navigating the next landing. "I did. Me... from the other world. This world."

Their voices echoed down the stairwell into the bellows of the gargantuan tower. The sound reminded Gillen of being in a courtroom and hearing the judge remind the witness that failing to uphold the truth would result in perjury. "We have to get ahead of the elevator."

"What are you talking about?"

"Jack took Allaire in the elevator. If there's still enough people in the building at this hour, maybe we can catch it when it stops at a lower level."

The desperation of his words betrayed the inanity of his plan. Yet his feet continued alternating between steps as the number sixty-six passed by on an identical steel door.

"Why did Jack take that little girl away from her mother?" Cate demanded. "Away from... from me."

"He didn't," snapped Gillen. "He stole her from me. I'm the Gillen Rainer from the other world, only Jack didn't know it. I came here to rescue Allaire and destroy all his work so this can never happen again."

Cate suddenly found herself falling several steps behind as she processed the confirmation of what she had already suspected. "I knew something about you had changed..."

By the time they reached door sixty-five, Cate caught up to Gillen and placed her hand on his shoulder. "I'm fine," he wheezed, while pressing his arm against the wall.

"No, your head. It's bleeding."

Gillen dabbed at the scab near his temple and saw trace droplets of red on his fingertips. *The cut on my head. That's how Jack knew it was me.*

"Damn it!" he cursed, digging into his pocket for a handkerchief. "Well, then this wasn't a set up. I'm just an idiot."

Cate impulsively snatched the cloth from Gillen's hand and held it at his wound herself. "What do you mean Jack stole Allaire from you?"

"I don't have time to explain this."

"Gillen."

As the handkerchief smarted at his skin, he sighed with an anxious fury and said, "We must hurry or we'll lose them."

On the sixtieth floor they entered a hallway, which led to a corridor, which led to the elevator. As Gillen had feared, the indicator dial above the doors showed the car ascending back toward their floor. "They already made it to the lobby."

"Where would he be taking her?"

Gillen snatched up Cate's hand as the elevator doors opened. Her question amplified the terror already manifesting in his tensing limbs. There were several plausible options. Jack's apartment. The Empire State Building. The Octagon on Welfare Island. Each in different directions. And that was assuming this wasn't a diversion to some unknown lair. One in which Allaire could not be found without police assistance — and would therefore not be found — for no one of sound mind would issue an all-points bulletin for an already deceased girl.

He shook his head as the elevator came to a stop at the mezzanine. *We can't let them out of our sight.*

A darkened sky was no match for the ambient city light enveloping the downtown streets. As Gillen and Cate raced out of the Chrysler Building and slowed to a stop along Lexington Avenue, the artificial lights popped and twinkled off the chrome fixtures of the steadily moving traffic. With eyes darting rhythmically from one car to the next, from one pedestrian to the next, the endless flow of movement made his heart palpitate.

"Are we looking for a taxi?" Cate asked.

Gillen's eyes widened. Unless they had just missed them, it was likely that Jack was also trying to hail a cab. He peered toward Forty-Third Street and saw cars making left turns from that direction. Hand in hand, Gillen and Cate ran the remaining length of the block while being careful not to get separated. The signpost at the corner seemed unsure of itself. One panel stretched toward Lexington Avenue, the other, East Forty-Third Street, while a third was slightly lower on the pole and simply read: One Way.

"Over there," pointed Cate, drawing Gillen's focus to an amber-colored car with an illuminated rooftop box. The side door of the vehicle gleamed under the streetlamp next to which it was parked. The lettering sparkled — TAXI.

"Perfect!" Gillen blurted out, knowing that he was a little too relieved. For just as they closed in on the vehicle, the taxicab began pulling away from the curb in a less than courteous manner. No more than a few steps removed from the metal handle of the rear door had Gillen and Cate spotted the occupants of the back seat. Similar in pose but flashing a very different expression, Allaire looked back at them through the rear windshield as the cab accelerated around the corner. Gillen's frame pivoted with the car, as if tethered not to the vehicle itself, but to someone within it, all the while recognizing that in seconds the tether would be riven, leaving behind only a certainty that the girl yet again vanishing before his eyes now knew who he was.

At least... who she thinks I am.

Another taxi filled the empty parking spot. Cate opened the rear door and looked back at Gillen who was suspended within the mosaic of industrial shapes and light. She called out to him with a pleading urgency. The back of his head moved as if recognizing a voice from the past and not the present. Seeming to peel his psyche from a hypnotic daze, Gillen willed one foot in front of the other and lurched into the back seat next to Cate.

"An amber-colored cab just turned onto Lexington Avenue," directed Gillen to the driver. "Your only objective is to not let it out of your sight."

The driver exchanged glances with Gillen through the rearview mirror. It was the kind of solidarity that expressed a familiarity with the situation even without the salient details. "Can do," he said calmly, and wheeled the taxi left onto the one-way street.

The lampposts blurred as the vehicle accelerated, pulling Gillen and Cate into their seats. Taking advantage of every opening within the traffic pattern, the driver merged around a box truck and weaved back into the central lane. The amber cab was well ahead of them but still visible through the windshield. A tap of its taillights suggested it would attempt a rapid merge yet within its lane the cab remained.

"Yeah, that's them," Gillen confirmed to the driver.

Cate suddenly placed her hand on Gillen's wrist. "Please, I must know," she whispered, with an abundance of caution. "What do you mean Jack stole Allaire from you?"

The driver cocked his head as the amber cab suddenly swerved into a slower moving lane. As other cars tried escaping it, he stuck his arm out the window to indicate a right merge. The maneuver closed some distance between the two taxis as the endless city block stretched on. Gillen exchanged glances between the pursuit outside the windshield and the impossibility of Cate seated next to him. *Why did she come along?* he suddenly wondered.

"I mean that in my world, Allaire is my daughter," he said forcefully, yet with a twinge of regret.

"So... you and I... were—"

"Married, yes."

Cate nodded nervously. "And... we had a daughter together, who was also named Allaire?"

The taxi completed a turn onto another street as the amber cab led the way. Gillen said, "Not also. Only. Because despite the fact that you and I were married, Allaire is the biological offspring of you and Walter Iselin, not you and me. That's why she looks the same. That's why she seems the same. That's why my alternate thought he could offer her up as some sort of penance for his guilt—to you, in exchange for eternal forgiveness or something."

Despite the cacophony of city noises competing for airtime within the cabin of the taxi, a conspicuous silence suddenly permeated the backseats. Cate's face was a visage of shifting expressions, ranging from shock, to disgust, to embarrassment, to finally a resigned sort of surrender. It was the face of one who both acknowledged a transgression and had also come to terms with it. With little more than a mutter she said, "I see."

Gillen exhaled and returned to staring out the window. The neighborhood was rapidly changing, and off in the distance, the silhouette of a bridge could be seen levitating over water. An amber glow pulsed under each suspended light the cab passed, making the vehicle seem sentient. It was almost as if human beings had formed an alliance with machinery and now even forged steel was determined to keep him and Allaire apart.

Cate pursed her lips to speak but was caught by Gillen's periphery. He shook his head slowly and her words retreated. No further explanation was offered for none would have served any purpose. After all, making apologies for the actions of her other self would have been just as immoral as the infidelity. Not in this world nor in any other would Gillen allow for what had destroyed so much already — the idea and practice of imputed guilt.

"Looks like they're taking the bridge," the driver announced. "And they ain't too determined to lose us either. If that cabbie is trying, he's about the worst I've ever seen at it."

The statement pulled at the corners of Gillen's mouth. "In other words, we're not chasing them, they're leading us."

"Exactly."

Over the East River, the Queensboro Bridge appeared like a bad omen. The possibilities of where the amber cab was heading had substantially narrowed. Familiar as the locale now seemed to Gillen, he had witnessed it earlier in the day from the opposite direction, heading into New York, with Danielle Hoyne by his side, after having just left Welfare Island. Now, as the two vehicles traveled across the massive bridge, and the trusses whipped past the windows at tremendous speed, two inseparable bouts of awareness unified Gillen's mind.

I wonder... he thought to himself as he stole a glance at the woman to his right, *if she looked something like this... that day... on the other bridge... when she ended her life?* The question then gave immediate birth to an obvious and sobering answer. *Of course not. This woman looks alive.*

The thought dissipated as the trusses gave way to open sky. Constellations relayed the stories of old around a waning gibbous moon and the disconcerting shadow threatening to overtake it. All too clear were the indicators of destination, and as if silently acknowledging a message from Artemis herself, Gillen nodded calmly and then whispered to Cate, "Jack is taking Allaire back to the moon."

"What? Why?"

"Because she's his only bargaining chip, and the embassy on Ortelius was built to bargain."

The taxi continued following the amber cab into Astoria and then across the Welfare Island Bridge. All other traffic had vanished along the stretch, leaving little to compete with the splendor of dotted lights pinpointing the outline of midtown Manhattan's skyline. Gillen squinted as his eyes gravitated from the curtain wall of the recently constructed United Nations Building at the crest of the East River, to where they had just been minutes earlier at the sixty-eighth floor of the Chrysler Building, which now seemed eternally distant.

"Looks like they're heading there," the driver said, tapping his finger on the windshield. "That funny looking place."

"Agreed."

"We should settle up now, seeing as how I expect you folks will need to be bolting after them double quick."

Gillen removed several denominations from his billfold and stuffed them into the driver's hand without looking. "Will that cover it?"

The driver glanced at the money and then chuckled. "Just so we're clear, the only services I offer are taxiing."

The taillights of the amber cab turned solid red as the vehicle slowed to a stop. The rear curbside door was then not so much opened as kicked by a man struggling to do two things at once. With aggressive spasms of movement, Jack had almost worked his way out of the vehicle but was still pulling against some invisible force that was rocking the chrome fender of the cab.

"You can stop here," Gillen said to the driver as the taxi halted several yards back from the other cab. Cate proceeded to open their door while watching through her window as Jack manhandled a recalcitrant Allaire onto the sidewalk. Her arm twisted and bent in resistance to his inescapable grasp of her wrist, all the while pulling her away from the amber cab with progressive steps.

Cate gripped the top of her door and hoisted herself to a standing position. "Jack! You end this madness right now!" she ordered.

The speed at which Jack had spun on his heels, pulled the pistol from his suit pocket, and fired a round at Cate was hard to compartmentalize within the confines of the moment. Only the ricocheting clank, the spiderwebbing of the glass window, and the amount of force with which her door had pushed back, could confirm what had been too instantaneous to see. Cate jerked away from the window and clenched her teeth, preparing to feel the worst of scenarios.

"Are you all right?" Gillen gasped, his hands on her hips, his eyes searching for any emergence of crimson from her white outfit.

"I... I think... I'm all right," she said, dazed.

He held onto her as he gazed through the splintered window pane and saw Jack continue to wrestle Allaire up the entryway steps toward the Octagon. It was then that Gillen and Cate's eyes met for the exchange of a nonverbal discussion. They were both shaken and they were both furious.

Exiting the taxi, Gillen stood to embrace Cate before slamming the door closed. A series of methodical steps forward offered proof that Jack and Allaire had already entered the structure. Feeling like they could be used for target practice in the open walkway, they quickly shuffled up the steps and then stood on either side of the double-entry doors.

"What's the plan?" Cate whispered while pressing her back up against the brick wall.

Gillen's hand reached out gradually until his fingertips made contact with the metal handle of the left door. As he crouched underneath the sidelight, his arm rose above his head to such a degree that maintaining the awkward pose caused his dress shoe's heel to scrape several inches along the porch's surface. The sound elicited a wince from both Gillen and Cate. He gave the handle a moderate tug, but his relative distance made it difficult to know if he was simply too far to properly pull or if the doors had been latched from the inside. Another step forward would expose him completely within the frame of the sidelight, and unable to balance his stance on a twisted leg, Gillen retreated back against his end of the wall and let out a frustrated sigh.

"I can't reach the handle from here," he said, while adjusting his sock and shoe. "There's an exit door around back. Let's see if it's unlocked."

Making their way around the brick walls of the Octagon led to unkempt shrubbery and rocky terrain. Fallen stones from the deteriorating upper-level balcony littered what was left of the lawn and threatened to beleaguer their progress.

"Careful," Gillen whispered to Cate after watching her nearly trip over a chunk of gneiss. The final steps along the southern wall of the Octagon revealed a solitary door which appeared as if it had remained unopened for years. Gillen bolted up the steps and wrenched the handle with one hand while pressing against the jamb with his other.

"It's locked?" asked Cate.

Gillen shook his head. "No, just *really* obstinate. I think the building settled a bit over the years."

The small metal handle groaned under the stress, yet the amount of give the door was willing to offer was infinitesimal. Removing his hand from the jamb, Gillen pressed the heel of his shoe along the wooden frame to attain greater force with which to pull. The muscles in his arm burned against the tension. His hand felt as if it would slip from the handle and never again resume the ability to grasp. And suddenly, as if raptured into the night by some phantom of the former insane asylum, Gillen realized that Cate was no longer standing at his side.

"Cate!" he called out into the thick void of crepuscular atmosphere surrounding the Octagon.

The vacancy remained undisturbed by movement, and the only sound came from the muffled fancy of nightlife emitting from Manhattan, serving only to further highlight his isolation on the island. He let go of the handle and crept along the angular wall of the building, peering behind him for good measure. The ground beneath his feet rumbled menacingly. It felt as if someone had left a generator running below the structure. Kneeling down to the grass, Gillen placed his hand to the earth and sensed the vibrations throbbing into his wrist. Even the weatherworn bricks of the Octagon appeared to be shivering.

"We must hurry," Cate announced as she appeared from around one of the many corners of the building. Startled, Gillen bolted upright and caught his breath upon seeing Cate carrying the massive gneiss stone between her delicate hands.

"You scared me to... why didn't you tell me where you were going?"

"I did."

Gillen reached for the rock, and as his hands joined hers in the support of the weight, a piercing blast tore through the evening air. In wide-eyed terror they gazed at the Octagon, knowing full well the origin of the noise that had pulsed into their ears with unforgiving pitch, for it was the same as what they heard a second after the attempt on Cate's life.

"Oh my God," she whispered. "Allaire."

Jostling the rock between them as they ran, Gillen's mind ran equally wild with images of a struggle between Allaire and Jack, an attempted escape, the firing of his pistol. *Could have been an accident... fired a warning shot and instead hit her directly... if she's wounded, what do I do? Take her to a hospital here or risk transporting her back to earth?*

"You pull and I'll ram," said Cate as they reached the door.

Gillen nodded and cracked his knuckles. "I'm ready."

With all the strength she could muster, Cate lifted the stone and slammed it repeatedly against the upper part of the door while Gillen resumed pulling on the handle below. Each impact from the rock set the door flush in the frame, yet Gillen could now sense improvement during his intervals of pulling. The slightly askew jamb began to buckle under the merciless pounding from the stone. Indentations pockmarked the door as Cate stepped back and then threw her body into the ramming, the reverberations of which threatened to break Gillen's clasping hand. Small splinters of wood fell to the ground, and after a final go from the rock at both the door and the jamb, Gillen felt the handle separate completely as the whole frame fractured open.

Cate dropped the stone and leaned against the wall for a moment, catching her breath and looking at Gillen. Gillen stared back at her in grateful acknowledgement before tossing the fragmented handle to the ground and reaching his hand out toward Cate. As his fingers gently tucked an unruly strand of blonde hair back behind her ear, he whispered, "Stay close to me."

The inside of the Octagon was nearly pitch black, yet the outlines of corridors and stairways could be faintly discerned by the sliver of light coming from down the hall. The air left an astringent taste on Gillen's tongue as he drew in his first breath. Dust particles drifted hauntingly across the gossamer light, reminding Cate of the kind of snowfall that kills instead of enchants. Each of their steps clapped effortlessly from off the tiled floor, and as Gillen set the pace, he was torn between subversion and rampage.

"Jack!" Gillen called out into the veiled space. "Let's talk about this."

Their eyes darted expectantly from side to side, half hoping to finally see someone, half hoping they wouldn't. As Cate pressed her hand to the wall, she noticed something along the floor begin to move. In a zigzag manner it scurried away from them and vanished into the dark. Gillen leaned cautiously into an open doorway and scanned a small room. From what little he could see, it was empty.

"Allaire!"

They walked further into the corridor, the dim light ahead of them coming from the main rotunda. Gillen quickened his pace despite the sensation that his legs were about to give out. It was the walk of a man assured of the valor of his mission without the guarantee of salvation at the end. He sensed Cate in lockstep behind him. She too seemed fearless in the moment, yet in the way one acts when hoping choice will usurp fate.

"Jack!" Gillen demanded. "This has gone too far. None of this is what Walter would have wanted, and you know it."

A distant moan echoed within the rotunda. Cate instinctively grabbed Gillen's hand and met it sooner than anticipated as he had been motioning the same direction for hers. The guttural sound was met with a cough and then followed by what they could only discern was the noise of fabric scraping along the ground. Gillen glanced back at Cate whose eyes he could now see and betrayed a sudden horror at the image his mind had manufactured.

Someone had been shot.

Without reservation, they closed the distance across the dingy corridor and entered the main lobby entrance of the Octagon. Gillen spun around in panic, remembering the spiraling staircases, rotting wood, and circular vaulted ceiling that seemed to serve no other purpose than to marginalize those entering the insane asylum.

"Oh God," Cate whispered, pointing toward the floor.

Off to the corner, with a trail of blood smeared behind him, was Gillen Rainer.

Gillen and Cate rushed over to him and knelt down to gaze upon a face as ashen as the twilight moon. His shirt was partially unbuttoned and could no longer be classified as white. His hand shook with the will to survive, covered in his own blood,

blood still seeping out of a gaping gunshot wound to his abdomen.

"In case... you're wondering... who did this..." he whispered hoarsely. "It wasn't Allaire."

Gillen and Cate struggled to laugh. Then instead of struggling to laugh they struggled not to cry. "You're gonna be okay," Gillen said, wholly lost in what to do or where to turn.

Cate repeated the sentiment while removing her suit blazer and gently pressing it against his torso. "This will help slow the blood loss."

The other Gillen shook his head. "Don't worry about me," he choked, before grabbing Gillen's arm with his bloodied hand. "Jack took Allaire through... before... before I could stop him. Everything... is all set. Both locations. Just hit the button and... *oh*" — he winced— "and you'll have him trapped in the... in the other world."

Cate eased up on the pressure even as the bleeding returned. She looked at Gillen who nodded down at his other self with reluctant understanding. "Thank you."

"I'm sorry, Gillen... so very... sorry for what I put you through. And Cate..." he said, now holding back tears of his own. "Whatever happens, please know..."

Cate ran her fingers through the other Gillen's hair and slowly shook her head. For nothing he could say would be something she hadn't already heard. The endless apologies. Living in a perpetual state of self-immolation. Seeking something she could not offer, eternal forgiveness, for what had been a temporal offense. There were no words or actions that could bring back her daughter, or remove the history of a man obsessed with winning her affection, only to allow that obsession to chart a collision course with disaster. What was done was done. And no replacement Allaire could ever serve as a suitable tribute.

"Gillen," Cate whispered softly, in a tone wooing in its tenderness, emerging not from pain, but from the nascent inklings of resilient wisdom. "You... can... never... bring... Allaire... back... and I have chosen to forgive you anyway."

The words left her lips and the moment passed, acknowledged by other lips too weak to respond. Without the swell of emotion or the circumstance of setting, the statement landed as it could, and momentarily unified two people destined by spacetime to be forever misaligned.

Gillen stared at himself in wonder, and wondered at who he had become. A sudden gasp from the dark corridor wrenched his attention from the scene. As he stood to obtain a clearer view of the person who had entered the giant room, his instincts confirmed what his eyes saw later.

"Danielle," he breathed.

"Oh no," she whimpered, taking infantile steps forward. "Gillen..."

She never looked at the standing man once, for she never broke concentration from the man on the ground. Her movements propelled her onto the floor and into his trail of blood. She cupped his head between her hands and sobbed at the state of reality. Her shoulders shook, her neck bent, her back heaving in bursts of agony.

"I'm not gonna let you die," she wept. "My cab is waiting outside. I'll get you to a hospital. I'm not gonna let you die."

The other Gillen smiled as he bled and reached his non-bloodied hand out to caress Danielle's cheek. "I'll live," he muttered. "For you... I'll try... to live."

Cate nodded and motioned for Gillen to come assist in getting the other Gillen upright, but the man on the ground protested. "You two don't have time. Gillen... it's all primed. Hit the button and get the hell out of here. We'll make sure... make sure the Octagons are destroyed. Go! Go get Allaire!"

As Danielle worked on getting him to a semi-standing position, Cate joined Gillen at the control box in the corner as he flipped a switch and activated what felt like an aftershock. The floor rumbled into the rafters shaking loose more particles of dust, and the spiraling staircase surrounding the interior of the Octagon seemed to twist all the more under the mounting pressure.

Gillen embraced Cate as they stood in the center of the Octagon and watched as Danielle moved a hobbling Gillen closer to the door. With his arm hanging precipitously around Danielle's shoulders, he appeared determined to make it to the cab, if not for his own survival, then to at least have made an effort to believe in her plan to save his life. Compression bore down upon Gillen and Cate as the machine neared its critical mass. The sensation in his eyes made him wish to close them, yet he knew that was not an option.

I love you, Danielle...

I love you, Gillen...

Her words lived on even as the woman had died, and for the first time, Gillen understood that. He understood it as he stood holding Cate within his arms. He understood it as Danielle opened the entryway door, bathing her face in evening light. He understood it as she glanced back at him for the longest of brief moments. And he expressed it with a subtle nod toward her as she and the other Gillen left the Octagon.

He had hoped to see her signature smirk one last time. The one indelibly etched onto her face no matter the situation. But he had not. He wondered if he had actually ever seen it on this woman — on this version of Danielle. He pondered that question as the Octagon transformed into the Palace of Fine Arts in San Francisco, and then as the monument morphed into its replica on the original planet earth, settling Gillen and Cate safely underneath the rotunda while wrapped in each other's embrace.

CHAPTER 20

TO THE MOON AND BACK

Gillen Rainer and Cate Iselin approached the steel doors of the laboratory. Even from down the hallway, he could tell that the locking mechanism had been tampered with as a narrow beam of fluorescent light shined through the partially opened doors. It served as an invitation. A personal welcome into the final portal before confronting the mastermind of a nightmare. Gillen pulled back the door without trepidation, for Jack's motive was now abundantly clear. The plan to wipe every trace of his research on the Alignment from off the face of his earth had succeeded, and in exchange for Allaire, Jack intended to get it all back.

The laboratory looked the same, with indicator lights blinking at random intervals on the workstation console, the Hexagon's amniotic field rippling with energy, and over in the corner, the drafting table still littered with schematics and cups of coffee. The familiar hum of the lab brought with it a newfound sense of fatigue for Gillen as he surveyed the surroundings. He had helped build something spectacular here, and like so many other inventors before him had experienced, felt the crushing disappointment in human nature at the desecration of it.

"Are we all here now?" came Jack's voice from behind the blackened fabric of the console speakers. For an instant, Gillen didn't recognize it. At first he suspected the audio transmission was the cause of Jack's phonetic interference. But as Gillen and Cate slowly walked up to the black-and-white monitor at the workstation panel, and saw Jack's haggard visage staring back at them, Gillen realized his assumption was wrong.

Jack is as tired of this as we are.

"Where's Allaire?" Gillen's taciturn voice asked.

The question needed no response as her image appeared in the left side edge of the monitor. Allaire was back on the moon. She sat at the lunar workstation console while Jack stood gazing up at the ceiling camera with his fists planted firmly on his hips. His body language reminded Gillen of the dictators of his youth who had tried to project authority even after the writing was on the wall.

Jack spoke morosely, as if the effort to utter words was barely worth the intended outcome. "Can we begin now? Can we stop playing these insipid games of one-upmanship? Are you ready to come to the table and act like adults? Because that's where

I am, Gillen. On Ortelius, right next to the embassy you built. I am a man with a grievance and this is my forum. What was rightfully mine was destroyed by plebeians too daft to comprehend what they burned.

"That's right, burned. I know what Danielle was doing at the Empire State Building this evening because the manager there called the Silver Lining Club to tell me that my office had been ransacked. My safe opened. My files burned in a wastepaper bin as if they were so much kindle. As soon as I heard that I grabbed Allaire and bolted. The investors be damned. Not a brain among them. No concept of vision. No stomach for innovation. Lecture me on morality? In due time, they all can be replaced, and I do mean that literally.

"It's a grotesque thing to see an alternate version of yourself, isn't it Gillen? Whether that version is a madman or a saint, it's a terrible thing to gaze upon what might have been. I used to believe that there was nothing worse than loss. Then I discovered regret. Walter knew that better than any of us. He escaped one torture chamber only to find himself hopelessly encased in another. At least his regret was tied to an ideology which he later found to be fraudulent. Regret tied to a belief that is sound is much worse. It's irreconcilable. It's a voice in your head that never goes away. Night and day accusing you of betraying a principle you were too weak to hold.

"Anyway, I've said more than enough. Are we all here now? Can we stop with the charade? Here's what's going to happen. You're gonna hand over every page your company ever wrote about the Alignment, and in exchange, I will hand over a child who belongs to neither of you."

The torrent of words came to an end leaving Gillen and Cate speechless. At no point in Jack's diatribe had they interrupted him for there was no counterargument to make. Debating fine points of philosophy or the details of a timeline wouldn't bring Allaire safely through the Hexagon. Jack was sitting on the moon, with Allaire, and despite its reduced mass and weight, in their current situation, the moon held considerable leverage over the earth.

Gillen silently looked over at Cate. She returned the stare with eyes that he remembered from years back. Eyes which never seemed capable of guiding him through any dilemma, yet were filled with empathy for his having to be the decision-maker. He had cursed himself at the time for recoiling from that glance, unaware of the reason for his impulse. Yet now it all made sense. For those eyes had not been gazing in empathy after all. Cate had always transferred the burden of difficult decisions to him in every scenario, and now, as they stood together on the brink of losing everything, it finally dawned on Gillen just what was wrong with the expression in those emerald irises.

It was never empathy... it was always pity. Gillen looked down at the laboratory floor and felt a simmering anger start to build before something from the recesses of his memory extinguished it. This woman wasn't Cate.

"Well?" Jack interjected. "I believe you're both smart enough to see when the goose is cooked. Unless you can think of something I forgot, let's see some hustle. I want the binders, schematics, codes, all of it—everything that comprises the Hexagons and Alignment."

In the corner of the screen, Allaire shifted uneasily in her chair. In one sense it seemed as if she was trying to calm herself in a terrifying situation, in another sense, it seemed as if she was trying to get Gillen's attention.

Without comment, Gillen walked away from the console and began gathering the three-ring binders, rolled-up blueprints, and file folders cluttering the desks and cabinets surrounding the lab. As he stacked them together, Cate suddenly appeared with a few large cardboard boxes and began piling the contents accordingly. Gillen would flip open a binder cover, take a peek at the first page, and either hand it over to Cate or else toss it onto the drafting table. His eyes would stop short of viewing the bottom line of the title pages, as otherwise he would be forced to see a row of signatures, including his own, verifying the brilliant work for which so many minds had strived and which was now to be handed over to the lowest common denominator of men.

Gillen hucked the last folder into the box with a flick of hostility and said, "That should be everything."

Jack nodded into the screen. "Good work. Now how should we do this?"

Gillen shrugged and was about to look over at Cate but decided against it. Instead he looked into the monitor and noticed that Allaire had moved closer to Jack. "I have an idea," she said gingerly.

"What's that?" asked Jack, as if addressing an adult.

Allaire's words came methodically. "Dad can put it all on a chair and roll it into the Hexagon, and you can stand there and catch it when it arrives."

A vacuous silence filled the room before affirming nods came from Jack and Cate. Their reactions seemed expected to Allaire, and also unimportant, for her eyes were fixed solely on her target audience. Gillen stared into the monitor, a lost man. He stood dumbfounded, horrified, like one who only a second ago had a firm grasp on the sequence of events that were set to occur, and who now had completely lost track of the mission. The countenance of his face was inexplicable to everyone else involved, save for one — his daughter, who as if nonchalantly suggesting a restaurant along the Embarcadero, had just handed him the means to end Jack DaLette's life.

He knew he needed to speak without stammering. Rebut without endangering. Suggest an alternative to Allaire's plan which didn't involve killing a man. Yet at the moment he finally wedged his lips apart with his tongue, Gillen's mind drew a comprehensive blank.

Allaire...

"You can use the one from your workstation," she added, pointing back toward her own for reference. "Right, Dad?"

Gillen swallowed his response only to regurgitate it back up into a hollowed reply of, "What?"

"Works for me," said Jack while slapping his hands together. "Let's get a move on. And you better not be holding out on me, Gillen."

Still frozen in spacetime, his eyes searched the screen for any indicators that Allaire had been replaced by an alternate. Her idea pummeled the corridors of his mind without cushion, unable to find a logical place to land. The abduction from the moon, the physical violence against Allaire, the assault on Richard Kaine in the park and the kidnapping of his son, the shooting of Gillen's alternate, and the attempted murder of Cate, all could be directly blamed on the man staring back at him through the grainy lines on the screen. Yet now, once again holding Allaire hostage on the moon of a foreign universe, the troubled man who was Jack DaLette had unwittingly stepped into his own web.

That doesn't justify us ending his life.

Gillen heard the sound of tiny wheels rolling across linoleum and felt desperately sick. As Cate stacked the boxes precariously between the chair's two arms, Gillen looked back and wondered how he could warn her of the action in which she was about to participate. He knew instantly that no subterfuge would be possible without words, and any attempt at explanation would not only eliminate this chance, but most likely threaten Allaire's life.

The realization lingered long after Cate rolled the chair back from the drafting table and placed it next to Gillen. "That should be everything. Now what?"

Gillen's fingers dug into the back of the chair in hopes that either of them would break and create a diversion from what they were about to do. The shock of Allaire's idea, and that she had placed the responsibility of executing it squarely on his shoulders, left him vacillating. His eyes darted left and right, refusing to see the panel on which a pair of protective clips guarded two siloed switches. One of the two switches would purge the Alignment.

She's not insinuating this! Allaire is not suggesting I kill this man!

A single look at her expression through the monitor contradicted that premise.

"Jack," Gillen said, his voice faltering. "Are you... are you sure you want to... do this?" He had hoped the statement would grant him some clemency from his searing conscience.

"Send it through."

It did not.

Even as his mind rebelled against the use of his right hand, Gillen watched as his fingers made contact with the protective clip and then with the lifelessly cold metal of the failsafe switch. The sound of its single click was deafening.

"All set," he whispered, barely vocal enough for even Cate to hear.

The chair rolled easily along the laboratory floor, and all too soon Gillen was standing in front of the Hexagon staring at himself in its reflective field. *You can't do this. Just hand the files over and you'll get Allaire back. No need to kill this man.*

"I'm ready," Jack said, his hands outstretched, his legs poised, his body in direct alignment with the opening of the Hexagon.

You can't do this. It's not self-defense. It's unnecessary.

"Perhaps... we could talk about this first—"

"Hey!" Jack barked. "It's not my fault you chose to destroy my work. Choices have consequences in the real world. This is the price you pay. Now roll the goddamn chair!"

This isn't about Jack. This is about you. You can't live with this. It will destroy you.

The chair rolled back an inch, and then forward an inch, and then back an inch again, his trembling fingers unwilling to release. Cate glanced over at him suspiciously, as if his delay tactic was a signal meant for her. Gillen's eyes remained straight ahead, into the Hexagon, into himself.

"Now!" Jack exclaimed.

Gillen... don't do this.

"Gillen?"

The voice was accompanied by a firm hand on his right shoulder. Turning suddenly to absorb the man standing next to him, Gillen blinked repeatedly while trying to determine which version the man was and what his reaction was supposed to be.

Walter Iselin then said soothingly, "If you can't do this, I will."

Mystified, Gillen stumbled back a step and nearly walked into Cate who was equally bewildered at seeing her husband back from the dead. The old man had a small notebook in his hand and waved it in front of the camera. "Gillen failed to offer up this," Walter said, and tossed it into the pile. "My personal notebook."

Jack tilted his head appreciatively. "Well done, Walter. I can understand your personal desire to expunge all of this and move forward with your life."

Walter shifted his gaze toward Gillen, who stared back at his friend and mentor with eyes still searching for a recognizable face. There was no time to process the onslaught of volatile emotions and dwindling energy left to try. Gillen was wholly lost as to the nature of the man standing before him, yet he was absolutely certain as to his own. Through a shameless exhaustion he surrendered to the words, "I can't do it."

Walter gazed up at the camera as his hands took control of the chair. "That's all right, Gillen," he said gently. "I can."

"Perfect," Jack said to Walter. "For the record, I always thought of you with the utmost respect."

Digging his fingers into the fabric, Walter replied, "Funny, I never thought of you at all." Without an instant of hesitation, Walter launched the chair into the Hexagon and watched it disappear into a flash of reflective light.

"Jack..." Gillen whispered, as they all turned toward the console and heard an unnervingly familiar, high-pitched rattling sound echo through the speakers. He shut his eyes and lowered his head as the Alignment purged the chair out through the lunar Hexagon and directly into Jack DaLette. Gillen could identify the sounds in order, from bones breaking, to blood splattering, to the impact of a human body slamming into a metal wall. The final noise was the cacophony of binders and pages exploding into the laboratory as the chair broke open and landed in pieces on the floor. Silence followed, and it was in the silence that Gillen knew the one sound he had not heard.

Allaire. She stood motionless next to the console, her hand over her mouth, her eyes transfixed on the carnage. She had not screamed prior to the moment, and she would not scream in the aftermath.

"Allaire," Walter spoke into the microphone, having been the first to rush up to the workstation. "Don't look at it. There's nothing to learn from that image." With a simple flick of his wrist, the failsafe switch closed and the mechanical whirling of the Alignment ceased. "Please, just come down. You're safe now."

Compliantly, Allaire focused her attention instead on the glut of papers strewn across the open floor space of the laboratory. Calculations, sketches, and hand-scribbled notes littered the walkway leading right up to the base of the Hexagon. Above the apparatus, the green bulb shone solidly, indicating all was aligned between the two worlds. She turned to the monitor. "But... what's happening?"

Walter paused as he weighed both the inquiry and his response. Cate had not been able to look away from him. She gazed in wonder at the wrinkles on his face, the silver of his hair, the baritone of his voice, and the mannerisms known only of Walter. Her chest heaved against the pressure of simultaneously wanting to laugh and cry. Unable to choose between the two, Cate simply wrapped her arms gently around his shoulders and buried her face into his neck. "Is it really you?" she whispered.

Walter shut his eyes as his hands found their way around her torso and up the length of the back of her white blouse. As his fingers stopped short of her blonde hair, the rough stubble of his cheek smiled against her soft skin as he answered, "Not exactly."

The two melted into each other, and for a moment, they were alone in the lab. Only the need to acknowledge the next miracle on the docket caused Cate to reluctantly pull away from Walter, and as she wiped the tears from her eyes and turned to address the screen, the waterworks began again without warning.

"Allaire..." Cate breathed. "I can't believe I'm saying your name."

The monitor crackled as the girl's image came into view. Much the same as Walter, she appeared no different from the daughter whom she had tragically lost. The auburn hair, the cherubic expression, and those eyes. Allaire had Walter's mocha eyes. Cate pressed her finger against the glass and smiled warmly. "How I missed them."

Allaire remained silent, processing a volley of observations in the span of a few blinks. Everything Jack and the other Gillen had said was starting to make sense. Alternate worlds. Being on the wrong planet. Other versions of ourselves. And now Cate, her mother, no longer mangled from a car accident, or a bridge barrier, or a suicide attempt, but standing before her, more alive than Allaire had ever witnessed.

"And you?" Allaire asked, seeming to now look toward Gillen, her voice maintaining an enormity of caution. "Are you my real father, or was that man on the moon?"

If Gillen had been three thousand miles away by land and another Alignment's distance from planet earth, he still could not have felt more isolated from what was happening. The crushing shock of what they had all just done was not as easily discarded for him as it seemed to be for them. Without reply, he slowly turned away from the workstation and walked over to the laboratory window overlooking the Golden Gate Bridge.

"Oh," Allaire suddenly said, her voice brimming with certainty as she addressed the only other man in the room. "Then it's you."

Walter glanced at Cate before turning his head partially toward Gillen's direction. He stopped short of actually seeing the back of Gillen, who was still looking out the window, and somehow, Walter felt that Gillen had just made a similar half-hearted attempt to gaze back at him too. The words Walter had prepared to say were gone, words he had cultivated since the day she was born. They had been genuine and thoughtfully chosen, and Walter couldn't remember a single one.

As the old man pressed his hands against the workstation desk, he shut his eyes and nodded slowly, confirming a truth meant for himself. When he finally spoke, only Gillen knew that Walter was not just addressing Allaire. "Your father is Gillen Rainer, but you are *my* daughter. You were a gift from your mother to me, a man who did not deserve the gift or the love she bestowed upon me. I was distant from you because it needed to be that way. If you forget everything else—remember that fact, Allaire. Nothing I did after the day you were born mattered that much. The Alignment, Ortelius, the embassy, all of it was a distraction. A grand, ostentatious curtain with which I pulled over my eyes to blind me from an ever-present reality. When you were born, it seemed like my life had finally begun anew. But as seems to be my hallmark trait, I ruin everything I touch. Everything except you. You are the sole survivor of my existence. Born impervious to imposed guilt and shame. And nothing on this planet or any other could subvert this single truth. The truth that I regret everything I have ever done... but there isn't a horror yet conceived which could make me recant my pride in creating you.

"I love you now even as I loved you then, back when you were too young to recall, back when I used to sing to you a lullaby I had written on the night of your birth. I wrote it to the music of my favorite cantata, but only had enough lyrics for the first section of the instrumental since I'm not much of a songwriter. I wouldn't expect you to remember it now, but just know that—"

The first nine notes of the lullaby drifted like a dream from Allaire's lips, through the console speakers, and into the ears of a mesmerized Walter. Overwhelmed by the sensations of reminiscence, he bowed his head for a moment to allow his faculties time to catch up to the present. "How," he whispered, "can you possibly remember that?"

When his eyes returned to the monitor, Allaire was gone, and only the sound of a breach in the amniotic field of the Hexagon had the power to tear his vision from the screen.

"Oh my God," Cate mouthed through her fingers as Allaire emerged from the Alignment and stepped foot onto planet earth. The girl's face was flushed with raw, unprocessed emotion as her eyes shifted between the occupants in the room. If there had been an iota of indecision in her mind, her reflexive jolt forward put any lingering questions to rest. With the force of several lifetimes, Allaire closed the distance of the laboratory and buried herself into the torsos and arms of Walter and Cate Iselin.

"Because..." Allaire wept, her words coming as an answer to a question that Walter had already forgotten. "You still sing it to me every night."

With that confession, Walter was back in her first bedroom.

"She's getting to be much too old for this," Cate had said.

"I only stop by when Gillen is working late."

"Usually on a project you gave him. Besides, Allaire is going to start remembering this soon. She's going to remember you in this room and it will confuse her in the future."

Walter had chuckled nervously, his hat still in his hand. "She's still so young. And she loves it. She loves when I sing to her. Puts her right to sleep."

"She can talk now," Cate said, putting an abrupt end to his narrative. "And some night she's going to ask for you instead of Gillen. She's going to ask Gillen to sing the song you wrote. This is a serious problem with an easy solution."

"Not yet," Walter had said, a sudden desperation growing in his eyes. "Just... a little more time is all—"

"This has to be the last time."

Cate's words tolled inside Walter's head as he felt the fingers of his past placing the tonearm of the phonograph onto the black vinyl. The horn sprouting from the machine had been painted to look like a blossoming flower, but that night it was a giant mouth opening wide to swallow him into its gullet. The soft features of the nursery faded into just Allaire laying serenely under the sheets of her small bed. Her piercing eyes, those eyes that were unmistakably his, gazed back at him in childlike wonder.

The music had started before Walter had been ready, for although he knew the lyrics, he did not know how to savor the final moment. The first nine notes lilted from his voice as he hummed the introduction of the cantata. When it became time to sing the words, the music continued without him as his tongue atrophied into silence.

'*Allaire's Song*', he had said to himself, *she must forget it and now so must I.*

Placing his hat back onto his graying head, Walter had kissed Cate goodbye and left the bedroom. It was the last time he would interact with Allaire as a father, and it was the last evening spent with Cate as a lover.

"You used to be so happy," Allaire said to Cate as she squeezed her tighter. "I remember you used to smile so much. I remember it now so clearly. I knew it wasn't just a dream."

Cate nodded and understood a little of what Allaire was saying. Walter nodded and understood all of it. Nothing else was uttered as she moved her face between the woman who wasn't her mother and the man who wasn't her father. Tufts of auburn hair muffled her whimper as drops of relief cascaded down her cheeks. Walter and Cate absorbed the moment, in some ways fully aware of what was transpiring, and in other ways only maintaining a tenuous grasp. Each pushed back the encroachments of their individual pasts and reserved room for just the happiness of what was pulling them into harmony.

A harmony existing as a trio instead of a quartet.

"Dad," Allaire suddenly whispered, and pulled away from Walter and Cate. Circling around them, she bolted past the workstation and drafting table and came up to where Gillen's back had been turned from the whole progression.

"Dad?" she repeated, speaking to an empty window, for he was gone.

◂ ◆ ● ● ● ● ● ◆ ▸

Gillen bristled as he staggered up the front steps of his house. Upon entering the foyer, he hung his hat on the rack but left his overcoat on. He passed the wainscoting along the wall on his way toward the den, never before more grateful to hear the familiar creaking of the wooden floors beneath his shoes. The top of the crystal decanter popped off and was dropped carelessly on the platter, rolling precipitously to the edge while he filled a tumbler with ice and scotch. As the drink jangled in his hand, he marched over to the telephone and stabbed his finger into the holes of the rotary dial.

"May I speak with the nurse on duty, please?"

"She's currently occupied," the woman said. "Perhaps I can be of assistance?"

"I'm calling to speak with one of your patients. Mr. Jack DaLette."

"I'm afraid Mr. DaLette has just finished a round of treatments and is resting. The doctor said he is not to be disturbed."

Gillen nodded into the receiver before taking a sip from his glass. "I see."

"Is there anything else I can help you with?"

"Is he well?"

"I'm sorry?"

Gillen cleared his throat. "With his treatments. Is Jack doing well?"

The woman on the other end of the line hesitated. "May I ask who is calling?"

"Just a friend."

"In that case, I can only take down a message and have the doctor call you back. At what number may you be reached?"

The receiver slid back onto the cradle silently as he felt his physical frame decompress. Jack DaLette was still alive. Gillen set the glass down as he acknowledged both the relief and how perverse that relief actually was. Assuaging one emotion with the next, he then retraced his steps back down the hallway before grabbing hold of the newel post and propelling his body up the stairwell. As he opened the door to his bedroom, he reached for the knob of his nightstand's drawer and quickly identified a solitary key amongst the clutter. His thumb gently ran along the teeth of the key, as if absorbing something that was more than tactile.

Outside the house, the streets of San Francisco were awash in early evening light, the kind that slowed the pace of pedestrians and thinned out the traffic. The graded roads peaked and valleyed against the backdrop of grassy knolls on top and the glistening water below. Residential homes interspersed the scenery giving way to buildings and towers, the plaza and the piers, all seeming to serve as the signposts one would need in order to determine their next activity. Running parallel to the water was the Embarcadero, with its historical Ferry Building and imposing clocktower, and nearing the end of the stretch was a pavilion and a park which overlooked a bridge crossing the bay.

Pulling up to the curb, Gillen applied the parking brake to his vehicle and gazed out over the panoramic. The sun was steadily slipping behind the Bay Bridge, casting a gradient of pink and orange rays through the steel cables of the cantilevered structure. Waves crashed against the shoreline and seemed to be trying to expand the boundaries of the estuary into the park. At the edge of the park was a bench. Seated on the bench was a woman.

"I went to your house, but you'd already left," Gillen said as he approached.

Samantha arose from the bench and restrained a burgeoning smile. "We must have missed each other."

"Yes, we must have."

The hem of her overcoat flapped with the breeze as she stood against the backdrop of the bridge, the water, and the moonrise. "Where's Allaire?" she asked, her voice a mixture of expectation and caution.

"Allaire's safe," Gillen replied, closing the distance between them. "She's... back here on earth... with Walter."

Samantha sighed heavily and nodded. "So, everything's okay?"

Gillen mirrored her nod.

Samantha said, "Let me put it another way. Are you okay?"

There were not sufficient words in Gillen's vernacular to answer her question. So he simply reached his arms around her waist and gently pulled her into the same full-bodied embrace they had shared near the Palace of Fine Arts. Impervious to the passage of time, they held one another against the occasional gusts of wind or lingering passerby. The scent of lilac became his air, and left Gillen with the tactile memory of how hugging Cate had always felt like she was holding onto him for dear life. Or Danielle, and how her fingers had pressed into his back as if trying to mold him into another.

By contrast, Samantha simply stood on her own, embracing Gillen without pretense. The steadfastness of her friendship, the commitment of her values, the limitless interest she maintained in his life, all converged upon the actualization of a truth so astounding, that he gasped in awe at its sophisticated simplicity.

Closure is the bridge to new love.

Free from fantasies and phantoms, he touched the side of Samantha's face and placed a tender kiss on her cheekbone. The moment was neither magical nor celestial. It was not otherworldly at all. Instead, it was the culmination of a series of moments so grounded in the makings of the earth, that no phenomena could ever root it out of reality.

He then smiled and said, "I should check in on Allaire."

"I'll wait for you."

Gillen marched across the pavement and into a dimly lit telephone booth next to the pavilion's entrance. After maneuvering the bifold door closed, he lifted the receiver from off the box and slipped a dime into the receptacle.

"Hello?" came a soft voice on the other end of the line.

Gillen shut his eyes and pressed his free hand against the glass of the booth. "Hey, champ."

"Hey, Dad," she responded, sounding relieved. "Are you all right?"

"Yes, I am. Sorry I left so suddenly, but I thought I should let Samantha know that you're safe."

"Where are you?"

"I'm... at the Bay Bridge."

Allaire breathed into the mouthpiece. After a long pause, she said, "I'm over at Grandpa Walt's apartment. But then I guess you knew that since you called here. Mom... Cate... is here too."

Gillen nodded. "I appreciate Walter watching out for you. I'll be by to pick you up in a little while."

"Dad," she said, on the tail end of his statement. "Is... do you think that... is Cate going to stay?"

The telephone booth seemed to shrink as the gravity of her words replaced the oxygen in the tiny space with wonder. Gillen continued to keep his eyes shut as he felt his fingers sliding slowly down the pane. "She'll stay. Even if Walter has to justify it by making her the first lunar ambassador. In fact, if he mentions that, tell him I thought of it first. She'll certainly have her work cut out for her. There's still a little boy who needs to be reunited with his real father. But... I guess in answer to your question... yes... he'll find a reason for her to stay."

Allaire sighed. "But, I mean... do you think she'll choose to stay? What if she chooses to stay... and then decides later... that she wants to leave?"

Gillen felt his shoulders slump down against his outstretched arm as it pressed against the inside of the booth for greater support. "You mean... are you asking—"

"How do I know she won't leave us again?" Allaire blurted, her voice raw with emotion.

A few yards away from the telephone booth, Samantha stood casually in the foreground of Gillen's vision while the Bay Bridge stretched out across the water behind her. She smiled in his direction before reaching into her purse. Seconds later, the amber pulse from a freshly lit cigarette blazed into the darkness, seeming to try and compete with the strobe lights in the harbor.

"How do I know?" Allaire repeated. "How do I know she won't leave?"

Gillen gazed upon Samantha as she smoked, as she smiled at him, and as the compressing weight of the walls surrounding him no longer seemed as insurmountable as they had been a moment earlier. Straightening his posture within the booth, he removed his hand from the glass leaving behind his handprint as a signature. Allaire's question had not escaped his mind, and before she had a chance to ask it again, the answer dawned upon Gillen as he stared at Samantha through the handprint he had just made.

"Because she loves him."

CPSIA information can be obtained
at www.ICGtesting.com
Printed in the USA
LVHW111456141022
730656LV00003B/75